Mentally Healthy: Mind over Matter

A Comprehensive Companion Guide to Achieving Mental Wellness

Innovative Products

J.E. LaSure Jr.

COPYRIGHT INFORMATION

Dedication

To our legacy, which lives on through our children and their children – I dedicate this book to them, for the wisdom and mental health they will carry into countless years to come. To my son, JT, for his unwavering commitment, and my daughter, Ashley, for her hard work and steadfastness. April, Isaac, Ethan, and Eli, you are the future, and the torch of well-being is passed on to you.

Foreword
Foreword by J.E.LaSure Jr.

Today, mental health has assumed a position of utmost importance. With tension, anxiety, and emotional imbalance affecting innumerable lives, there has never been a greater need for practical, evidence-based advice. With great enthusiasm, I present "Mentally Healthy: Mind over Matter - A Comprehensive Companion Guide to Achieving Mental Wellness," an indispensable resource for anyone wishing to improve their mental health and quality of life as a whole.

This exhaustive guide is a valuable compilation of expert advice, research, and real-world examples that will motivate and equip readers to take charge of their mental health journey. Our devoted team of licensed therapists and exhaustive research have skillfully distilled their collective knowledge into a highly accessible format, ensuring that every reader, regardless of background or experience, can benefit from the insights contained in these pages.

From self-care and mindfulness to stress management and relationship building, "Mentally Healthy: Mind over Matter" provides a plethora of strategies for navigating the complexities of mental health and cultivating resilience. In addition, the book provides an in-depth examination of prevalent mental health disorders, equipping readers with the tools they need to effectively manage their own well-being and seek professional assistance when necessary.

While this exhaustive guide is an excellent resource, it is essential to keep in mind that it is not a substitute for consulting a licensed therapist. Each individual's mental health journey is unique, and individualized professional guidance can be invaluable.

As a manager of numerous cross-functional teams, I can attest to the transformative force of the techniques and practices described in this book. I am confident that "Mentally Healthy: Mind over Matter" will be an invaluable resource for those wishing to enhance their mental health and well-being. As you embark on your own journey towards greater mental health, I encourage you to explore the plethora of information contained in these pages, but do not forget to seek professional assistance when necessary.

Table of Contents

Section I.
Welcome to Mentally Healthy –
Mind Over Matter

Introduction:
Welcome Message

Welcome to "Mentally Healthy: Mind over Matter - A Comprehensive Companion Guide for Achieving Mental Wellness."

We are ecstatic that you have decided to join us on this voyage toward improved mental health and wellbeing. If you are a subscriber to our YouTube channel, https://youtube.com/MentallyHealthy IPP , you are aware of our mission to provide actionable ideas and advice for enhancing mental health and happiness. In this book, we've compiled some of our most popular and influential topics into one comprehensive guide, designed to be a helpful companion on your path to improved mental health.

Mental health is a vital component of our overall wellbeing, and its significance is greater than ever before. Many of us struggle to maintain a healthy balance and keep our minds and emotions under control due to the ongoing stressors of the contemporary world. The good news is that we can take basic, effective measures to enhance our mental health and cultivate resilience. This book is designed to help you reduce tension, enhance your relationships, or simply find more serenity and contentment in your life.

MentallyHealthy is committed to delivering high-quality, evidence-based information and resources to promote mental health and well-being. Our team of licensed staff therapists spends innumerable hours researching the most recent developments and best practices in the field of mental health so that we can provide you with the knowledge you need to make educated decisions regarding your own well-being.

In the following pages, we will examine topics such as self-care, mindfulness and meditation, contending with tension and anxiety, and developing healthy relationships. Also covered will be the fundamentals of mental health, including information on common mental health conditions and how to manage them. And for those who may require additional assistance, we will provide information on how to pursue professional assistance and locate the appropriate resources to meet your particular requirements.

Whether you are an experienced mental health practitioner or just beginning your voyage, we hope you find this book to be a useful and informative resource.

If you're ready, let's get started!

Section II.
Mental Health Fundamentals

Chapter 1:
Definition of Mental Health and What it Means to Have Good Mental Health

Introduction: What it Means

Mental health, which is frequently overshadowed by its physical counterpart, is a vital component of overall health and plays a significant role in the quality of a person's existence. As society becomes more aware of the significance of mental health, it is essential to comprehend its definition, implications, and means of promotion and maintenance. Good mental health enables individuals to manage life's challenges, cultivate healthy relationships, and pursue personal development, which ultimately contributes to a more satisfying and balanced existence. In this chapter, we will examine the meaning of mental health, its significance, and the factors that contribute to maintaining mental health. In addition, potential obstacles to attaining positive mental health will be discussed, along with suggestions for overcoming these obstacles and cultivating a healthy mental state.

Good mental health has far-reaching effects on multiple aspects of our lives, so its significance cannot be exaggerated. It affects our ability to perform daily tasks, form and maintain relationships, attain personal objectives, and even our physical health. By comprehending and prioritizing mental health, we can create a society in which individuals have access to the resources necessary for their mental and emotional well-being.

The purpose of this chapter is to provide a comprehensive comprehension of mental health and its significance, as well as insights and strategies for promoting mental health. By emphasizing the significance of mental health, we hope to stimulate a broader dialogue about mental health and encourage a more holistic approach to overall wellness.

Defining Mental Health

Mental health is a multifaceted concept that incorporates the emotional, psychological, and social well-being of an individual. To comprehend the significance of mental health and to foster a more comprehensive approach to well-being, it is essential to acknowledge its complexity and the numerous factors that contribute to it.

The World Health Organization defines

WHO defines mental health as "a state of well-being in which the individual realizes his or her own abilities, can cope with the normal stresses of life, can work productively and fruitfully, and is able to make a contribution to his or her community." This definition highlights the significance of mental health not only for individual functioning, but also for societal contributions and quality of life as a whole.

Elements of Psychological Health

Mental health consists of three essential components that collectively contribute to a holistic view of well-being:

This aspect of mental health refers to an individual's capacity to experience, comprehend, and regulate a broad spectrum of emotions in a healthy and balanced manner. Emotional health entails being aware of one's emotions, expressing them appropriately, and using them as a guide for decision-making and personal development. It also encompasses the capacity to experience positive emotions such as pleasure, contentment, and satisfaction, while managing effectively with negative emotions such as sorrow, wrath, and anxiety.

Psychological Well-Being: Psychological well-being is concerned with an individual's cognitive functioning and includes self-awareness, adaptability, resiliency, and self-esteem. It entails the capacity to manage duress and adversity, adapt to change, and engage in self-reflection and introspection. The pursuance of personal objectives, the development of autonomy, and the capacity to establish a sense of purpose and significance in life are also components of psychological well-being.

Social Well-Being: The focus of social well-being is a person's relationships and interactions with others, as well as their sense of belonging to the larger community. It requires the ability to establish and maintain healthy relationships, communicate effectively, and have empathy for others. Social well-being also involves a sense of belonging, social support, and the capacity to contribute to and participate in one's community.

Together, these three components constitute a comprehensive understanding of mental health, emphasizing the contribution of emotional, psychological, and social well-being to overall health and pleasure. By recognizing the complexity of mental health and its many influencing factors, we can cultivate a more informed and empathetic approach to well-being.

The Importance of Good Mental Health

Good mental health is a cornerstone of overall well-being, as it influences numerous aspects of life, such as physical health, daily functioning, relationships, and personal development. By comprehending the significance of mental health, we can better appreciate its role in promoting a satisfying and balanced existence.

Relationship with Physical Health: Mental and physical health are inextricably linked, with each having a profound effect on the other. Inadequate mental health can increase the likelihood of developing heart disease, diabetes, and a compromised immune system. Inversely, poor physical health can result in a decline in mental health, which may contribute to melancholy, anxiety, and other psychological issues. Good mental health can motivate people to adopt healthier lifestyles and make better decisions regarding their physical health, thereby generating a positive feedback cycle between the two aspects of health.

Effects on Daily Functioning: Good mental health enables individuals to effectively manage daily tasks, make sensible decisions, and solve problems. It allows for enhanced concentration, increased productivity, and the capacity to deal with everyday stresses. In contrast, poor mental health can impede an individual's ability to complete daily tasks, maintain focus, and make rational decisions, ultimately diminishing their quality of life.

Influence on Relationships and Social Interactions: Emotional and social health facilitates positive interactions with others and meaningful, supportive relationships. Good mental health enables people to effectively express their emotions, empathize with others, and resolve conflicts constructively. In contrast, poor mental health can strain relationships, impede effective communication, and lead to feelings of isolation or loneliness.

Role in Personal Growth and Self-Actualization: Psychological well-being enables individuals to pursue personal objectives, build resiliency, and progress through self-reflection and introspection, thereby contributing to personal development and self-actualization. Good mental health encourages individuals to pursue personal fulfillment and self-actualization by fostering a sense of life's purpose and meaning. Moreover, sustaining mental health fosters the growth of self-esteem, self-confidence, and a healthy sense of autonomy.

Good mental health is crucial for many aspects of an individual's existence, including physical health, daily functioning, relationships, and personal development. Individuals can enhance their overall well-being and live more fulfilling, balanced lives by recognizing the significance of mental health and striving to promote it. Moreover, a society that prioritizes mental health can foster an emotionally, psychologically, and socially healthy environment for individuals.

Factors Contributing to Good Mental Health

A complex interplay of biological, psychological, social, and environmental factors influences the attainment and maintenance of excellent mental health. Understanding these contributing factors can assist individuals and communities in fostering conditions conducive to mental health.

Biological Factors

Genetics: Hereditary factors can influence a person's susceptibility to mental health disorders or their resilience. The presence of a family history of mental health disorders may increase the likelihood of developing comparable issues, whereas protective genetic factors may contribute to increased mental resilience. Environmental factors can frequently alter genetic predispositions.

Brain Chemistry: The balance of neurotransmitters and hormones in the brain plays an essential role in mood regulation and mental health. These chemical mediators can contribute to mental health disorders such as depression and anxiety when they are out of balance. A healthy lifestyle, which includes proper nutrition, exercise, and rest, can help regulate brain chemistry and promote mental health.

Psychological Elements

Resilience: The capacity to overcome adversity and adapt to new situations is an important factor in promoting mental health. Various strategies, such as cultivating a positive outlook, practicing self-compassion, and developing effective coping skills, can be used to develop and strengthen resilience.

Coping Skills: Effective coping strategies, such as problem-solving, emotional regulation, and seeking support from others, can aid in stress management and mental health maintenance. Individuals can navigate life's challenges more effectively and safeguard their mental health by developing a toolbox of healthy coping mechanisms.

Social Aspects

Supportive Relationships: Strong connections with family, colleagues, and loved ones provide emotional support and contribute to mental health. Supportive relationships can provide encouragement, understanding, and a sense of belonging, thereby assisting individuals in overcoming obstacles and preserving their emotional health.

Sense of Belonging and Community: Participating in social activities, connecting with others who share similar interests, and feeling connected to a community all contribute to a sense of belonging and social well-being. Participation in community events, volunteer work, or social groups can provide individuals with opportunities to strengthen their mental health and develop relationships.

Environmental Factors

Access to Healthcare: The availability of mental health resources, including therapy and medication, is crucial for promoting positive mental health outcomes. Providing access to mental health care to all individuals, regardless of socioeconomic status, can help address and prevent mental health issues.

Safe Living Conditions: A stable, secure, and nurturing living environment promotes emotional and psychological well-being. Access to fundamental necessities, such as shelter, sustenance, and protection, is essential for maintaining mental health. Moreover, fostering a supportive and inclusive community can promote a sense of belonging and improve mental health.

Individuals and communities can create the conditions and resources necessary to support mental health if they have a thorough comprehension of the factors that contribute to mental health. Taking a comprehensive and holistic approach to addressing these factors can help enhance mental health and overall well-being.

Barriers to Good Mental Health

Despite the significance of mental health, numerous obstacles can prevent individuals from attaining and maintaining mental health. Recognizing these barriers can inform strategies for overcoming them and nurturing a mental health-supportive environment.

Stigma and Lack of Knowledge

Stigma Surrounding Mental Health: Mental health issues are frequently stigmatized and misconstrued, leading to feelings of humiliation, remorse, and reluctance to seek assistance. This stigma can exacerbate mental health problems by isolating individuals and preventing them from gaining access to the necessary resources and support.

Lack of Awareness and Education: Insufficient awareness and comprehension of mental health issues can lead to misunderstandings and perpetuate stigma. A lack of education about mental health can also prevent individuals from recognizing the signs and symptoms of mental health disorders, thereby delaying the provision of appropriate treatment and intervention.

Access to Mental Health Care is Limited

Financial Barriers: The cost of mental health care, such as therapy or medication, can be prohibitive for many people, particularly those without insurance or with deficient coverage. This financial barrier can prevent individuals from gaining access to the treatment they require to address and manage their mental health issues.

Geographic Barriers: Access to mental health professionals and resources may be limited or nonexistent in some regions, particularly rural and remote areas. This dearth of availability can make it difficult for individuals with mental health concerns to receive timely and appropriate care.

In some instances, mental health care systems may be overburdened, leading to lengthy wait times and restricted access to services. This can delay necessary care and exacerbate the mental health issues of those in need of assistance.

Socio-Economic Factors

Poverty and Income Inequality: Socioeconomic disparities can have a negative effect on mental health, as financial stress and restricted access to resources can exacerbate mental health problems. In addition, individuals experiencing poverty may encounter additional obstacles, such as hazardous living conditions or limited employment opportunities, which can lead to increased stress and diminished mental health.

Discrimination and Marginalization: Members of marginalized communities, such as racial and ethnic minorities, LGBTQ+ individuals, and people with disabilities, may encounter unique obstacles that affect their mental health. Discrimination, prejudice, and systemic barriers can result in feelings of isolation, stress, and a heightened risk for mental health problems.

Stressors and Adversities in Life

Trauma and Deleterious Life Experiences: Exposure to traumatic events, such as violence, abuse, or loss, can have a significant impact on mental health and result in long-term psychological problems. Often, coping with trauma requires specialized support and resources that are not readily available to all individuals.

Chronic Stress: Prolonged exposure to stress, whether from work, family, or other life circumstances, can have detrimental effects on mental health. Chronic stress can result in exhaustion, fatigue, and an increased risk of developing mental health conditions such as depression and anxiety.

Individuals, communities, and policymakers can work toward establishing a more inclusive and supportive environment for mental health by recognizing and addressing these obstacles. This may involve raising awareness and reducing stigma, enhancing access to mental health care, and addressing broader socioeconomic and systemic issues that affect mental health.

Methods for Achieving and Sustaining Optimal Mental Health

Adopting healthy routines, developing effective coping mechanisms, and gaining access to the necessary resources and support are essential for promoting and maintaining mental health. The following strategies can assist individuals in attaining and maintaining mental health:

Personal Maintenance and Lifestyle Practices

- o **Regular Exercise:** Regular exercise has been shown to enhance mood, reduce tension, and ameliorate anxiety and depression symptoms. Aim to include a variety of aerobic and strength-training exercises in your routine to improve both your physical and mental health.

- o **Balanced Diet:** A healthy, balanced diet can positively affect cognitive function and mood. Concentrate on consuming a variety of whole foods, such as fruits, vegetables, lean proteins, and whole carbohydrates, while limiting your consumption of processed and sweetened foods.

- o **Adequate Sleep:** A substantial quantity of high-quality sleep is essential for mental health. Establish a regular sleep schedule and develop a soothing twilight routine to promote restful sleep.

- o **Mindfulness and Relaxation Techniques:** Practicing mindfulness, meditation, or relaxation techniques, such as deep breathing or progressive muscle relaxation, can aid in stress management and enhance mental health.

Social Ties and Assistance

Cultivate Supportive Relationships: Invest time and effort in establishing and sustaining supportive relationships with friends, family, and loved ones. To cultivate a sense of belonging and support, seek out social activities and have meaningful conversations.

Seek Professional Help When Needed: When experiencing mental health challenges, do not hesitate to seek the aid of mental health professionals, such as therapists or counselors. Early intervention can aid in more effective problem-solving and prevent symptoms from worsening.

Creating Coping Skills and Resiliency

Develop Problem-Solving Skills: Enhance your ability to address challenges and solve problems by dividing them down into manageable steps. This can help you feel more in control and better equipped to face the challenges of life.

Cultivate Emotional Intelligence: Develop emotional intelligence by learning to recognize, comprehend, and constructively manage your emotions. This can enhance your capacity to deal with tension, communicate effectively, and form solid relationships.

Practice Self-Compassion and Self-Care: Be kind and understanding to yourself, and prioritize activities that promote relaxation and well-being as forms of self-care. This can contribute to the development of resilience and a healthy sense of self-worth.

Engage in Productive Endeavors

Pursue Personal Passions and Pastimes: Participate in activities that bring you happiness and a sense of accomplishment. This can help improve mood, reduce tension, and boost mental health overall.

Set Attainable Goals and Recognize Accomplishments: Establish personal goals that are attainable and work towards them incrementally. Celebrate your accomplishments, both large and minor, to reinforce your sense of purpose and sense of self-worth.

Volunteer and Contribute to Your Community: Participating in volunteer work or community-based initiatives can provide a sense of purpose, connection, and belonging. Volunteering can also improve mental health and promote a positive outlook.

Individuals can work toward attaining and maintaining good mental health by implementing these strategies and concentrating on the various aspects of mental health. It is essential to remember that mental health is a continuous process that may require ongoing effort and assistance. Individuals can improve their overall quality of life and nurture a more fulfilling, balanced existence by prioritizing mental health and employing a holistic approach to well-being.

Summary and Conclusion

Mental health, which encompasses emotional, psychological, and social aspects of an individual's existence, is a vital component of overall health. Good mental health promotes physical health, daily functioning, relationships, and personal development. It is essential for nurturing a comprehensive comprehension of well-being to recognize the complexity of mental health and the numerous factors that contribute to it.

Biological, psychological, social, and environmental factors, among others, can contribute to mental health. However, numerous obstacles, such as stigma, limited access to mental health care, socioeconomic factors, and life stressors, can prevent people from attaining and sustaining mental health. By acknowledging these obstacles, we can strive to overcome them and create a more supportive environment for mental health.

Good mental health is achieved and maintained through a combination of self-care, social connection building, resilience and coping skill development, and engagement in meaningful activities. Individuals can improve their overall quality of life and nurture a more fulfilling, balanced existence by prioritizing mental health and employing a holistic approach to well-being.

Ultimately, promoting mental health awareness and removing obstacles to good mental health should be a group effort involving individuals, communities, and policymakers. We can ensure that mental health is a priority and accessible to all by collaborating to create a more inclusive and supportive environment.

Chapter 2:
Overview of Common Mental Health Conditions and Their Symptoms

Introduction: Mental Health Conditions

Mental health encompasses our emotional, psychological, and social well-being and is a vital component of overall health. It influences how we think, feel, and act, shaping our capacity to manage tension, interact with others, and make decisions in life. Mental health conditions, also known as mental disorders or psychiatric disorders, are a diverse group of maladies characterized by alterations in thinking, emotion, or behavior that result in distress or functional impairment. These conditions can affect individuals of all ages, genders, races, and socioeconomic classes.

According to the World Health Organization (WHO), approximately one in four individuals will experience a mental health condition at some stage in their lives. These conditions can range in severity from mild to severe and can be either temporary or permanent. The development of mental health disorders is influenced by genetics, brain chemistry, personality traits, and environmental factors, such as exposure to stress or trauma.

Mental health disorders are frequently misconstrued and stigmatized, resulting in discrimination and exclusion of those affected. This stigma can create barriers to seeking help and receiving appropriate treatment, which can worsen symptoms and prolong recovery. As public awareness and comprehension of mental health conditions continue to increase, it is essential to promote early intervention, destigmatize these disorders, and ensure that individuals receive the necessary support and treatment.

In this chapter, we will examine several prevalent mental health disorders, such as anxiety disorders, mood disorders, obsessive-compulsive disorder and related disorders, trauma and stress-related disorders, eating disorders, personality disorders, schizophrenia, and other psychotic disorders. We will discuss their symptoms, causes, prevalence, and potential treatments in order to provide a comprehensive understanding of these complex conditions and their impact on individuals' daily lives and health.

Anxiety Disorders

Anxiety disorders are characterized by excessive anxiety, dread, and agitation that can impair daily functioning. Common anxiety disorders include the following:

Generalized Anxiety Disorder (GAD)

GAD is characterized by excessive, chronic anxiety about daily events and situations. Restlessness, fatigue, difficulty concentrating, irritability, muscle tension, and sleep disturbances are all symptoms of insomnia. Psychotherapy, medication, or a combination of the two may be utilized in the treatment of schizophrenia.

Panic Disorder

Panic disorder is characterized by recurring panic attacks, which are abrupt episodes of intense dread accompanied by physical symptoms like shortness of breath, vertigo, and heart palpitations. Common treatments for panic disorder include cognitive-behavioral therapy (CBT) and medications like antidepressants and benzodiazepines.

Social Anxiety Syndrome

Social anxiety disorder is characterized by a persistent dread of social situations that results in social avoidance or extreme discomfort. Symptoms include excessive self-consciousness, fear of being judged, and social avoidance. CBT, exposure therapy, and medications such as selective serotonin reuptake inhibitors (SSRIs) may be used to treat anxiety disorders.

Specific Phobias

Specific phobias are irrational fears of specific objects or situations. Common phobias include fear of flying, heights, or certain animals. Exposure therapy and CBT are commonly used treatments.

Mood Disorders

Mood disorders are characterized by mood or emotional disturbances that result in periods of despondency or agitation. Two frequent psychological disorders include:

Major Depressive Disorder
Major depressive disorder is characterized by persistent feelings of melancholy, despondency, and loss of interest in previously enjoyable activities. Symptoms include fatigue, changes in appetite, sleep disturbances, and suicidal ideation. Typically, antidepressant medications, psychotherapy, or a combination of both are used to treat depression.

Bipolar Disorder
Bipolar disorder is characterized by alternating depressive and manic episodes (elevated mood, increased energy, and impulsive behavior). In addition to psychotherapy, treatment may include mood stabilizers, antipsychotics, and/or antidepressants.

Obsessive-Compulsive and Related Disorders

These disorders involve obsessive and/or compulsive thoughts and/or behaviors.

OCD is Obsessive-Compulsive Disorder
OCD is characterized by persistent, intrusive thoughts (obsessions) and time-consuming and disruptive repetitive behaviors (compulsions). CBT, specifically exposure and response prevention (ERP), and medications such as SSRIs may be used for treatment.

Body Dysmorphic Disorder

This disorder is characterized by an inordinate fixation on perceived defects in one's appearance. Frequently, CBT and medications such as SSRIs are utilized in treatment.

Hoarding Disorder
Hoarding disorder is characterized by the excessive accumulation of items and the inability to discard them, resulting in chaos and distress. CBT, medications, and professional organizing assistance may be used in treatment.

Trauma and Stress-Related Disorders

These conditions are frequently precipitated by traumatic or distressing events.

Post-Traumatic Stress Disorder (PTSD)

Following a traumatic event, PTSD symptoms include flashbacks, nightmares, and avoidance of trauma reminders. The treatment may include trauma-focused cognitive behavioral therapy (CBT), eye movement desensitization and reprocessing (EMDR), and SSRIs.

Acute Stress Disorder

Acute stress disorder develops within a month of a traumatic event and shares many symptoms with post-traumatic stress disorder. Nevertheless, it usually resolves within a month. Acute symptoms may be managed with short-term psychotherapy and medication.

Adjustment Disorder

Adjustment disorder is a stress-related condition triggered by major life changes or stressors. Depression, anxiety, and behavioral disturbances can be symptoms. Typically, treatment involves brief psychotherapy with an emphasis on coping skills and emotional support.

Eating Disorders

Eating disorders involve abnormal eating habits and significant distress or concern about body weight or shape.

Anorexia Nervosa

Anorexia nervosa is characterized by self-imposed deprivation and an intense dread of acquiring weight, resulting in a severe loss of weight. The treatment may consist of medical stabilization, nutritional therapy, and psychotherapy such as family-based therapy (FBT) or cognitive behavioral therapy (CBT).

Bulimia Nervosa

Bulimia nervosa is characterized by recurrent compulsive eating episodes followed by compensatory behaviors such as self-induced regurgitation or excessive exercise. CBT, nutritional counseling, and medications such as SSRIs may be used in treatment.

Binge Eating Disorder

Frequent episodes of binge eating devoid of compensatory behaviors characterize binge eating disorder. The treatment may include cognitive behavioral therapy, interpersonal psychotherapy, and medications such as selective serotonin reuptake inhibitors or appetite suppressants.

Personality Disorders

Personality disorders involve long-standing patterns of thought and behavior that deviate from cultural expectations and cause distress or impaired functioning.

Borderline Personality Disorder (BPD)

Impulsive behavior and unstable relationships, self-image, and mood are hallmarks of borderline personality disorder. Dialectical behavior therapy (DBT), mentalization-based therapy (MBT), and schema-focused therapy may all be utilized in treatment.

Disorder of Narcissistic Personality

This disorder is characterized by a persistent pattern of grandiosity, admiration-seeking, and lack of empathy. Psychodynamic or cognitive-behavioral psychotherapy may be used in treatment.

Disorder of Antisocial Personality

Antisocial personality disorder is characterized by a pattern of persistent disregard for and violation of others' rights. To manage co-occurring issues like substance abuse, treatment may include CBT, psychodynamic therapy, and medication.

Schizophrenia and Other Psychotic Disorders

Schizophrenia is a severe mental disorder characterized by distorted perceptions, ideas, feelings, and behaviors. Hallucinations, delusions, disorganized speech, and social withdrawal may be symptoms. Antipsychotic medications and psychosocial interventions, such as psychotherapy, social skills training, and vocational rehabilitation, are typically used to treat psychosis.

Summary & Conclusion

Mental health conditions are an essential component of public health because they can have a significant impact on an individual's daily life, relationships, and well-being as a whole. As discussed throughout this chapter, mental health conditions appear in a variety of forms and can manifest in a variety of ways. By comprehending the complexities of these conditions, we can better identify, assist, and treat those who are afflicted, thereby nurturing healthier communities and reducing the burden on individuals and society.

Reducing the stigma associated with mental health conditions is essential for encouraging individuals to seek assistance and obtain appropriate treatment. By facilitating open dialogue, promoting education, and raising awareness, we can create more inclusive and empowering environments for those on the path to recovery.

Collaboration among mental health professionals, individuals, families, and communities is crucial for effectively addressing mental health conditions. Providing mental health condition sufferers with psychoeducation, support groups, and access to evidence-based treatments can make a significant difference in their lives. In addition, ongoing research in the field of mental health can assist in refining existing treatments, developing novel therapies, and increasing our understanding of the underlying causes and mechanisms of these disorders.

In conclusion, mental health conditions are a vital aspect of human health and well-being that require our care and attention. By recognizing the signs and symptoms of these conditions, understanding their causes and potential treatments, and nurturing a supportive and empathetic environment, we can assist those afflicted in overcoming obstacles, enhancing their quality of life, and thriving in the face of adversity.

Chapter 3:
Factors that Contribute to Good Mental Health

Introduction:
Factors that Contribute

Our mental health encompasses our emotional, psychological, and social well-being; it is an essential and multifaceted aspect of our existence. It is the basis for our ability to think, feel, and interact with others, as well as our capacity to adapt to change, deal with adversity, and bounce back from setbacks. Good mental health is not solely defined by the absence of mental disorders, but rather by a state of overall well-being that enables individuals to actualize their potential, cope with everyday challenges, and make a significant contribution to their communities.

It is impossible to exaggerate the significance of maintaining good mental health, as it influences every aspect of our lives, from personal relationships and professional success to physical health and overall life satisfaction. Poor mental health can have serious repercussions, including decreased productivity, strained relationships, and an increased risk of developing physical health issues. Therefore, it is of the utmost importance to comprehend the factors that contribute to good mental health and to implement strategies to promote well-being.

Examining the role of social connections, regular physical activity, balanced nutrition, quality sleep, stress management, and emotional regulation in promoting mental health, this chapter examines the main factors that contribute to mental health. This chapter seeks to equip readers with the knowledge required to make informed decisions regarding their mental health by providing evidence-based explanations for the significance of each factor. In addition, the chapter provides readers with strategies and suggestions for incorporating these factors into their lives, empowering them to take command of their mental health and enhance their overall well-being. By comprehending and addressing these factors, individuals can take strides toward attaining and maintaining optimal mental health, leading to a life that is more fulfilling, balanced, and resilient.

Social Connections
It is impossible to exaggerate the significance of social connections in promoting mental health. As social creatures, humans have an inherent need to establish

connections with others and to feel a sense of belonging. Strong and supportive relationships with family, friends, and colleagues give us a sense of belonging, contribute to our sense of self-worth, and make us feel valued and understood. These relationships can serve as a protective factor against mental health issues and are vital to recovery and resiliency.

Research indicates that individuals with stronger social ties have lower rates of depression, anxiety, and other mental health problems. On the other hand, social isolation and loneliness have been associated with an increased risk of developing mental health issues and a worsening of existing ones.

This highlights the importance of cultivating and maintaining strong social connections in order to support our mental well-being.

Social connections can be nurtured and strengthened through various means:

Active Engagement
Participate in social activities, such as community events, clubs, or interest groups, that align with your hobbies and passions. This can help you meet like-minded individuals and form lasting connections.

Open and Honest Communication
Building strong relationships requires open and honest communication. Share your thoughts, feelings, and experiences with those you trust, and make an effort to listen empathetically to their needs and concerns as well.

Emotional Support

Offer emotional support to your friends and family when they need it, and don't hesitate to ask for help when you're struggling. Remember that giving and receiving support is a key aspect of building strong relationships.

Quality Time

Spend quality time with the people you care about. This can be as simple as having a meal together, going for a walk, or enjoying a shared activity. By investing time in your relationships, you can deepen your connections and foster a sense of belonging.

Conflict Resolution

Disagreements and conflicts are a natural part of any relationship. Learning to address and resolve conflicts in a healthy and respectful manner can help to strengthen your relationships and maintain your mental well-being.

By actively cultivating and maintaining healthy social connections, we can create a strong foundation for good mental health and enhance our overall well-being.

Practical Tip: Cultivate and maintain healthy relationships by actively engaging with others, whether it's through participating in social activities, joining clubs or groups, or volunteering. Additionally, make an effort to communicate openly and honestly, and listen empathetically to the needs of others.

Regular Physical Activity

Physical activity has consistently been associated with improved mental health outcomes. Exercise can reduce depressive and anxious symptoms, increase mood, and boost cognitive function. Additionally, regular physical activity promotes improved sleep and tension management.

Numerous studies have demonstrated the positive effects of exercise on various aspects of mental health, establishing the link between regular physical activity and mental health. Regular physical activity can reduce depressive and anxious symptoms, improve mood, and enhance cognitive function. In addition, exercise has been shown to improve self-esteem, sleep quality, and stress management.

The mental health benefits of physical activity can be attributed to several factors:

- o **Neurotransmitter Release:** Exercise stimulates the release of endorphins, serotonin, and dopamine, neurotransmitters responsible for regulating mood, motivation, and feelings of pleasure. This helps to reduce feelings of anxiety and depression while enhancing mood and overall well-being.

- o **Stress Reduction:** Physical activity has been shown to lower cortisol levels, the body's primary stress hormone. By reducing cortisol levels, exercise can help alleviate stress and its negative impact on mental health.
- o **Cognitive Function:** Exercise has been linked to improved cognitive function, including enhanced memory, attention, and executive function. Regular physical activity can promote the growth of new neurons and improve overall brain health, protecting against age-related cognitive decline.
- o **Social Interaction:** Participating in group exercises or sports can foster social connections and provide opportunities for interaction and support. The social aspect of physical activity can contribute to improved mental health and overall well-being.

Practical Tips for Incorporating Regular Physical Activity:

- **Set Realistic Goals:** Start with achievable goals that match your current fitness level, and gradually increase the intensity and duration of your exercise routine as you build strength and endurance.
- **Choose Enjoyable Activities:** Select physical activities that you enjoy and look forward to doing, as this will increase the likelihood of maintaining a regular exercise routine. Options could include walking, swimming, dancing, or participating in team sports.
- **Establish a Routine:** Develop a consistent exercise schedule and incorporate physical activity into your daily routine. Aim for at least 150 minutes of moderate-intensity aerobic activity or 75 minutes of vigorous-intensity aerobic activity per week, spread across multiple days.
- **Mix It Up:** Vary your exercise routine to prevent boredom and maintain motivation. Include a mix of aerobic exercises, strength training, and flexibility exercises to promote overall fitness and mental health benefits.
- **Seek Support:** Enlist the help of friends, family, or exercise groups to provide encouragement, accountability, and companionship during your physical activities. This can improve your motivation and make exercise more enjoyable.

By incorporating regular physical activity into our daily lives, we can support our mental health and enhance our overall well-being, benefiting from the numerous mental health advantages exercise has to offer.

Balance Nutrition

A well-balanced and nutritious diet is essential for maintaining mental health. The food we eat provides the essential nutrients necessary for optimal brain function, and a well-balanced diet can help improve mood, enhance cognitive function, and reduce the risk of developing mental health problems. On the other hand, poor dietary habits, such as excessive consumption of processed foods, refined sugars, and toxic lipids, have been associated with an increased risk of mental health issues.

The following components of a balanced diet are particularly important for promoting good mental health:

- **Complex Carbohydrates:** Whole grains, fruits, and vegetables provide a steady source of energy and help maintain stable blood sugar levels, contributing to improved mood and cognitive function.
- **Lean Proteins:** Sources of lean protein, such as fish, poultry, beans, and legumes, provide essential amino acids required for the synthesis of neurotransmitters, which play a vital role in regulating mood and brain function.

- **Healthy Fats:** Omega-3 fatty acids, found in fatty fish, nuts, and seeds, are essential for maintaining brain health and have been linked to reduced symptoms of depression and anxiety.
- **Vitamins and Minerals:** A diet rich in vitamins and minerals, such as B vitamins, vitamin D, magnesium, and zinc, supports optimal brain function and can help alleviate symptoms of mental health issues.
- **Practical Tips for Incorporating Balanced Nutrition:**
- Focus on Whole Foods: Prioritize the consumption of whole, unprocessed foods, such as fruits, vegetables, whole grains, lean proteins, and healthy fats. These nutrient-dense foods provide the essential nutrients required for good mental health.
- **Limit Processed Foods and Refined Sugars: Reduce** your intake of processed foods, which often contain high levels of unhealthy fats, sugars, and additives. Excessive consumption of refined sugars can lead to fluctuations in blood sugar levels, negatively impacting mood and cognitive function.
- **Stay Hydrated:** Ensure that you drink enough water throughout the day, as dehydration can lead to feelings of fatigue, irritability, and difficulty concentrating.
- **Practice Mindful Eating:** Pay attention to your hunger and satiety cues, and eat slowly to fully savor and enjoy your meals. Mindful eating can help prevent overeating and promote a healthier relationship with food.
- **Seek Professional Guidance:** If you're unsure about how to create a balanced and nutritious meal plan, consider consulting with a registered dietitian or nutritionist who can provide personalized guidance based on your specific needs and preferences.

By focusing on consuming a balanced and nutritious diet, we can provide our bodies and minds with the essential nutrients required to support good mental health, paving the way for improved well-being and resilience.

Quality Sleep

Sleep is essential for sustaining good mental health because it enables the brain to restore itself and consolidate memories. Quality sleep is necessary for emotional balance, cognitive function, and overall health. Insufficient sleep can have significant effects on mental health, contributing to the development of mental health problems such as depression, anxiety, and cognitive impairments and exacerbating existing issues.

The following factors highlight the importance of quality sleep for mental health:

Emotional Regulation: During sleep, the brain processes and regulates emotions experienced throughout the day. Adequate sleep allows for more effective emotional regulation, reducing the risk of mood disturbances and emotional reactivity.

Cognitive Function: Sleep is essential for optimal cognitive function, including memory consolidation, learning, problem-solving, and decision-making. Poor sleep can impair cognitive abilities, leading to difficulties in concentration, memory, and overall mental performance.

Stress Reduction: Quality sleep can help reduce stress levels and lower the production of stress hormones, such as cortisol. This contributes to better mental health by promoting relaxation and emotional resilience.

Immune Function: Sleep plays a crucial role in maintaining a healthy immune system, which is essential for overall health and well-being. A weakened immune system can increase susceptibility to illness and negatively impact mental health.

Practical Tips for Prioritizing Quality Sleep

Establish a Consistent Sleep Schedule: Aim to go to bed and wake up at the same time every day, even on weekends. This helps to regulate your body's internal clock and improve sleep quality.

Create a Relaxing Bedtime Routine: Develop a calming pre-sleep routine to signal to your body that it's time to wind down. This may include activities such as reading, taking a warm bath, or practicing relaxation techniques.

Optimize Your Sleep Environment: Ensure your bedroom is conducive to sleep by keeping it dark, cool, and quiet. Consider investing in a comfortable mattress, supportive pillows, and blackout curtains to create an optimal sleep setting.

Limit Screen Time Before Bed: Exposure to blue light from electronic devices can interfere with your body's production of melatonin, the hormone responsible for regulating sleep. Try to avoid using electronic devices for at least an hour before bedtime to promote better sleep.

Manage Stress and Anxiety: Addressing stress and anxiety through relaxation techniques, such as mindfulness meditation or deep breathing exercises, can help promote better sleep by calming the mind and body.

Avoid Stimulants and Heavy Meals Before Bed: Limit your intake of caffeine, nicotine, and alcohol in the hours leading up to bedtime, as these substances can interfere with sleep. Additionally, avoid consuming large or heavy meals close to bedtime, as this can cause discomfort and disrupt sleep.

By prioritizing quality sleep and implementing healthy sleep habits, we can support our mental health and enhance overall well-being, providing our minds and bodies with the restorative rest they need to function optimally.

Stress Management

Chronic tension can have a negative effect on mental health, leading to issues such as anxiety, melancholy, and concentration difficulties. Learning to effectively manage tension is crucial for maintaining mental health.

Stress is an unavoidable aspect of life, and the ability to effectively manage it is crucial for maintaining mental health. Chronic stress can have detrimental effects on mental health, resulting in increased anxiety, depression, and cognitive impairments. Effective stress management is essential for fostering emotional resilience, enhancing our ability to face daily challenges, and preserving our mental health as a whole.

The following strategies can help individuals manage stress more effectively:

a. Mindfulness and Relaxation Techniques: Practicing mindfulness meditation, deep breathing exercises, or progressive muscle relaxation can help calm the mind and reduce stress levels. These techniques promote relaxation by shifting focus away from stressors and bringing attention to the present moment.

b. Time Management: Developing effective time management skills can reduce stress by helping individuals prioritize tasks, set realistic goals, and create a more balanced schedule. This can help prevent feelings of overwhelm and reduce the stress associated with unmanageable workloads.

c. Physical Activity: As previously discussed, regular exercise can help lower stress levels by promoting the release of mood-enhancing neurotransmitters and reducing cortisol levels. Engaging in physical activities that you enjoy can act as a healthy coping mechanism to manage stress.

d. Social Support: Reaching out to friends, family, or support groups to share your feelings and concerns can help alleviate stress. Connecting with others can provide emotional support, practical advice, and a sense of belonging, which can contribute to better stress management.

e. Setting Boundaries: Learning to set boundaries in both personal and professional life can help reduce stress by preventing over commitment and enabling individuals to allocate time for self-care and relaxation.
f. Cultivate a Positive Mindset: Adopting a positive mindset, which includes practicing gratitude, reframing negative thoughts, and focusing on problem-solving rather than dwelling on stressors, can help individuals manage stress more effectively and enhance overall well-being.

Practical Tips for Implementing Stress Management Techniques:

Identify Stressors: Recognize the specific sources of stress in your life and determine which factors are within your control to change or manage.

Develop a Stress Management Plan: Create a personalized stress management plan that incorporates a combination of the strategies mentioned above. This plan should be tailored to your unique needs, preferences, and lifestyle.

Prioritize Self-Care: Ensure that you allocate time for self-care activities, such as engaging in hobbies, spending time with loved ones, and practicing relaxation techniques, as a part of your daily routine.

Seek Professional Help: If you find that your stress levels are unmanageable or negatively impacting your mental health, consider seeking professional help from a mental health professional, such as a psychologist or counselor, who can provide guidance and support.

By implementing effective stress management techniques and prioritizing self-care, individuals can build emotional resilience, reduce the negative impact of stress on their mental health, and enhance their overall well-being.

Emotional Regulation

Emotional regulation is the capacity to effectively manage and respond to positive and negative emotions. Developing effective emotional regulation skills is essential for sustaining mental health because it enables individuals to navigate challenging situations, manage with stress, and develop stronger relationships. Ineffective emotional regulation can result in increased anxiety, depression, and interpersonal difficulties.

The following strategies can help individuals improve their emotional regulation skills:

Self-awareness: Developing self-awareness is the first step towards effective emotional regulation. By recognizing and understanding your emotions, you can better identify triggers and implement strategies to manage them appropriately.

Mindfulness: Practicing mindfulness meditation can help individuals become more aware of their emotions and develop a non-judgmental approach towards them. This can lead to better emotional regulation by promoting acceptance and reducing emotional reactivity.

Cognitive Reframing: Cognitive reframing involves altering negative thought patterns and shifting perspectives to view situations more positively. This can help individuals manage their emotions more effectively, reducing the intensity and duration of negative emotional experiences.

Coping Strategies: Identifying and implementing healthy coping strategies, such as engaging in physical activity, seeking social support, or practicing relaxation techniques, can help individuals manage their emotions more effectively and reduce the negative impact of stress.

Emotional Expression: Encouraging open and honest communication about emotions, both with oneself and with others, can contribute to better emotional regulation. This can involve journaling, discussing feelings with trusted friends or family members, or seeking professional support from a mental health professional.

Practical Tips for Developing Emotional Regulation Skills:

Practice Self-Reflection: Regularly engage in self-reflection to identify your emotional patterns, triggers, and the effectiveness of your current emotional regulation strategies. This can help you develop a better understanding of your emotions and implement changes as needed.

Prioritize Self-Care: Ensure that you allocate time for self-care activities, such as engaging in hobbies, spending time with loved ones, and practicing relaxation techniques, to promote emotional well-being and resilience.

Develop a Support Network: Cultivate strong social connections and build a support network of trusted individuals who can provide guidance, encouragement, and empathy when you are experiencing strong emotions.

Seek Professional Help: If you find that your emotional regulation skills are insufficient or negatively impacting your mental health, consider seeking professional help from a mental health professional, such as a psychologist or counselor, who can provide guidance and support.

By working on improving emotional regulation skills, individuals can better navigate the complexities of their emotional experiences, build resilience, and enhance their overall mental health and well-being.

Summary & Conclusion

Promoting mental health is a continuous endeavor that requires addressing the various factors that affect our emotional, psychological, and social wellbeing. As discussed in this chapter, cultivating strong social connections, engaging in regular physical activity, eating a well-balanced diet, prioritizing quality sleep, effectively managing stress, and modulating emotions are all essential components of mental health. By comprehending the significance of each of these factors and implementing evidence-based strategies, individuals can proactively work toward attaining and maintaining optimal mental health, thereby improving their quality of life as a whole.

Mental health is a dynamic and ever-changing aspect of our existence that is influenced by a complex interplay of biological, psychological, and environmental factors. This means that our mental health can fluctuate over time, and strategies that work for one individual may not necessarily work for another. Consequently, it is essential to adopt a personalized and adaptable approach to mental health, perpetually evaluating and modifying our habits and practices to suit our specific needs and circumstances.

In addition to the guidelines and recommendations provided in this chapter, it is essential to seek support from friends, family, and mental health professionals whenever necessary. Having a strong support network and being willing to seek assistance can make a substantial difference in our ability to navigate life's challenges and maintain good mental health.

Investing in mental health is ultimately an investment in ourselves and our future. By prioritizing and nurturing our mental health, we not only enhance our own lives but also have a positive effect on the lives of those around us. The path to optimal mental health may be difficult, but the rewards of increased resiliency, enhanced relationships, and a more satisfying life make it a worthwhile pursuit.

Chapter 4:
The Impact of Genetics and Environment on Mental Health

Introduction:
Genetics and the Environment

Mental health, which encompasses our emotional, psychological, and social states, is a vital component of overall wellbeing. It has a profound effect on how we think, feel, and act, influencing our daily lives, relationships, and stress tolerance. The complexity of mental health is a result of the intricate interaction between a person's inherited composition and the numerous environmental factors they encounter throughout their lifetime.

Understanding the functions of genetics and the environment in mental health is essential for both the prevention and treatment of mental disorders. As our knowledge in these areas grows, it provides new insights into the underlying mechanisms of mental health disorders and facilitates the development of targeted interventions for those at risk. This chapter will provide a comprehensive examination of the roles of genetics and environment in mental health, discussing specific mental health disorders, gene-environment interactions, epigenetics, and the ethical, social, and policy implications of our expanding understanding of these influences.

This chapter seeks to provide a comprehensive comprehension of the topic by examining the complex relationships between genetics, environment, and mental health, highlighting the importance of both genetic and environmental factors in determining an individual's mental health trajectory. This knowledge can ultimately contribute to more personalized and effective approaches to mental health care, empowering individuals to take charge of their own well-being and live healthier, more fulfilling lives.

Genetics and Heredity in Mental Health

Behavioral Genetics: An Overview
The discipline of behavioral genetics investigates the genetic basis for individual differences in behavior, including mental health. Researchers have been able to estimate the heritability of various mental health disorders by analyzing patterns of inheritance and genetic similarities among family members. Heritability refers to the

proportion of variance in a trait that can be attributed to genetic factors. Behavioral genetics primarily employs twin studies, adoption studies, and family studies as its primary research methodologies.

Twin Studies

Twin studies compare the concordance rates of mental health disorders between identical (monozygotic) and fraternal (dizygotic) twins, who share approximately 50% of their genes. If the concordance rate for a disorder is higher in monozygotic twins than in dizygotic twins, this indicates that genetic factors play a role in the disorder's development. Multiple mental health disorders, including depression, anxiety, schizophrenia, and bipolar disorder, have been shown to be heritable through twin studies.

Family and Adoption Research

Comparing the prevalence of mental health disorders among the biological relatives of affected individuals, family studies provide additional evidence for the heritability of these conditions. Adoption studies, on the other hand, examine the prevalence of mental health disorders among adopted children and their biological and adoptive families in order to disentangle the effects of genetic and environmental factors. Consistently, these studies have demonstrated that mental health disorders tend to run in families, bolstering the importance of genetic factors in their development.

Genome-wide Association Studies (GWAS)

With advances in genomics, researchers have been able to conduct genome-wide association studies (GWAS) to identify specific genetic variants associated with mental health disorders. These studies have revealed that mental health conditions are polygenic, meaning they involve the combined effects of many genes, each contributing a small effect. Although no single gene is responsible for causing a mental health disorder, the cumulative effect of numerous genetic variants can significantly influence an individual's susceptibility to developing a condition.

The Complexity of Psychological Disorders

Notably, although genetic factors play a substantial influence in the development of mental health disorders, the relationship between heredity and mental health is complex. Environmental factors can influence genetic predispositions, and the etiology of many mental health disorders is multifactorial, involving both genetic and environmental factors. In the following section, we will investigate the role of environmental factors in mental health and how they interact with genetic predispositions to determine mental health outcomes.

The Role of Environmental Factors in Mental Health
Early Life Experiences

A person's mental health can be profoundly and permanently affected by early life experiences. Adverse childhood experiences (ACEs), such as trauma, abuse, neglect, or parental loss, can disrupt healthy brain development and increase the risk of developing mental health disorders in adulthood. Positive early life experiences, such as secure attachment, supportive relationships, and learning and development opportunities, can contribute to resilience and mental health.

Social and Economic Circumstances
Social and economic circumstances can also play a substantial role in determining mental health outcomes. Poverty, lack of access to education, unemployment, and social isolation can contribute to the development of mental health problems by increasing stress exposure, decreasing access to resources and support, and limiting opportunities for personal growth and fulfillment. In contrast, social networks, employment stability, and access to resources can function as protective factors that promote mental health.

Impact of Stressors
Stressors are events or conditions that disrupt a person's equilibrium and necessitate adaptation or coping. Acute stressors, such as deleterious life events (e.g., job loss, divorce, or death of a loved one), can induce or exacerbate mental health disorders in individuals with genetic susceptibilities. Chronic stress, caused by ongoing difficulties or challenges (e.g., financial duress, caregiving responsibilities, or discrimination), can also have a cumulative effect on mental health, thereby increasing the risk of developing mental health disorders over time.

Environmental Pollution and Toxins
Environmental contaminants and pollution have been associated with a variety of mental health disorders. For example, childhood lead exposure has been linked to an increased risk of attention deficit hyperactivity disorder (ADHD) and cognitive impairments. Similarly, there has been a correlation between air pollution and increased rates of melancholy and anxiety. Understanding these environmental risk factors can aid in guiding prevention efforts and policy interventions aimed at reducing exposure to hazardous substances.

Interactions between Genes and Environment
Environmental factors can interact with genetic predispositions to either increase or decrease an individual's risk of developing mental health disorders. For instance, individuals with particular genetic variants may be more prone to the negative effects of stress or more receptive to the positive effects of social support. Recognizing these gene-environment interactions can aid in identifying at-risk individuals and improving intervention targeting.

In the following section, we will examine the interaction between genetics and environment in the development and progression of specific mental health disorders.

Specific Mental Health Disorders and the Interplay of Genetics and Environment

In this section, we will discuss the contributions of genetics and environment to the development and progression of specific mental health disorders, including:

Depression

Depression, a prevalent mood disorder characterized by persistent feelings of melancholy, loss of interest, and a spectrum of emotional and physical symptoms, has a complex etiology involving genetic and environmental factors. According to twin studies, the heritability of depression is between 30 and 40 percent, indicating a substantial genetic component. However, environmental factors, such as negative life events, chronic stress, and developmental adversity, play a significant role in the development of depression. Particularly essential are gene-environment interactions, as some individuals are more susceptible to the effects of stress due to their genetic composition.

Anxiety

Anxiety disorders, such as generalized anxiety disorder, panic disorder, and social anxiety disorder, are characterized by excessive fear and concern that impair daily functioning. According to twin studies, the heritability of anxiety disorders ranges between 30 and 50 percent, indicating a substantial genetic influence. The development of anxiety disorders is also influenced by environmental factors such as childhood adversity, trauma, and stress. Certain genetic variants moderate the effects of environmental stressors on anxiety symptoms, demonstrating the existence of gene-environment interactions in anxiety disorders.

Schizophrenia

Schizophrenia is a severe mental disorder marked by disorganized thought processes, delusions, hallucinations, and cognitive deficits. The estimated heritability of schizophrenia is approximately 80%, indicating a significant genetic component. However, environmental factors including prenatal complications, childhood adversity, and substance abuse have also been linked to the onset of schizophrenia. Certain genetic variants can increase a person's susceptibility to environmental risk factors, such as cannabis use or urban living, making gene-environment interactions particularly important in this disorder.

Bipolar Disorder

Bipolar disorder is a mood disorder characterized by manic and depressive episodes that alternate. According to twin studies, the heritability of bipolar disorder is approximately 70%, indicating a significant genetic influence. However, ambient factors, such as negative life events, stress, and disruption of circadian rhythms, may also contribute to the onset and progression of the disorder. In bipolar disorder, gene-environment interactions are complex, with certain genetic variants modifying the effect of environmental stressors on mood symptoms.

For each of these disorders, it is essential to recognize the complex interaction between genetic and environmental factors in determining a person's mental health. Understanding these connections can help inform targeted mental health prevention and intervention strategies and promote personalized approaches to mental health care. In the following section, we will examine the significance of gene-environment interactions and epigenetics in mental health by providing examples of how these processes can influence the mental health trajectory of an individual.

Gene-Environment Interactions and Epigenetics

Gene-Environment Interactions

Gene-environment interactions refer to the influence of a person's genetic composition on their susceptibility to environmental factors. These interactions can help explain why some individuals are more susceptible to developing mental health disorders in response to particular environmental stressors, whereas others are more resilient. Individuals with particular genetic variants in the serotonin transporter gene (5-HTTLPR), for instance, have been found to be more prone to depression in the face of adversity than those without these variants. By identifying these gene-environment interactions, researchers can gain a deeper understanding of the complex mechanisms underlying mental health disorders and devise more effective preventative and therapeutic measures.

Epigenetics: An Overview

Epigenetics is the study of changes in gene expression that are inherited but do not entail changes to the DNA sequence. Environmental factors, such as stress, nutrition, or exposure to pollutants, can influence these alterations, which can have significant effects on an individual's mental health. DNA methylation, histone modification, and non-coding RNA molecules are all epigenetic modifications that can regulate gene expression and contribute to mental health outcomes.

Changes in the Epigenome Caused by Environmental Factors

Environmental factors can induce epigenetic alterations, which have the potential to influence mental health outcomes. For instance, research has demonstrated that early-life stress can alter the DNA methylation patterns of genes implicated in the stress response, thereby increasing the risk of developing anxiety and depression later in life. In contrast, interventions such as exercise, mindfulness, and social support can promote positive epigenetic modifications that improve mental health.

Intergenerational and Transgenerational Effects of Epigenetics

Furthermore, epigenetic modifications can have intergenerational and transgenerational effects, meaning they can be transmitted from one generation to the next. For example, maternal stress during pregnancy can result in epigenetic alterations in the fetus, which may increase the child's susceptibility to mental health disorders. In addition, there is evidence that epigenetic changes induced by environmental factors can be transmitted across multiple generations, though more research is required to fully comprehend these complex processes.

The Fields of Epigenetics and Personalized Medicine

Understanding the function of epigenetics in mental health creates new opportunities for personalized medicine, in which treatments are tailored to the genetic and epigenetic profile of each individual. By identifying specific epigenetic markers associated with mental health disorders, researchers may be able to devise more targeted interventions and preventive strategies that account for the genetic and environmental background of each individual.

In the following section, we will discuss recent developments in the fields of genetics and mental health, including new techniques for studying gene-environment interactions, breakthroughs in understanding the genetic basis of mental health disorders, and potential applications of this knowledge in the prevention and treatment of mental health disorders.

Current Research and Developments

New Techniques for Studying Gene-Environment Interactions
The development of molecular genetics, bioinformatics, and statistical methods has enabled researchers to investigate gene-environment interactions with greater precision and accuracy. GWIS and Mendelian randomization enable for the identification of novel genetic variants that interact with specific environmental factors to influence mental health outcomes. These findings can aid in the elucidation of the intricate mechanisms underlying mental health disorders and inform the development of targeted prevention and intervention strategies.

Advances in the Knowledge of the Genetic Basis of Mental Health Disorders
Numerous genetic loci associated with mental health disorders have been identified by large-scale genomic studies, including genome-wide association studies (GWAS) and whole-genome sequencing. Researchers are currently characterizing the biological pathways and mechanisms by which these genetic variants contribute to the development and progression of mental health disorders. This information may facilitate the development of novel therapeutic targets and personalized treatment approaches.

Recognizing Endophenotypes
Endophenotypes are quantifiable characteristics that exist between genetic risk factors and the clinical manifestations of mental health disorders. Identifying endophenotypes can aid researchers in determining the underlying biological mechanisms that link genetic risk factors to specific mental health disorders. For instance, studies have identified endophenotypes associated with neurocognitive functioning, neural connectivity, and stress reactivity, which can aid in elucidating the pathways through which genetic and environmental factors influence mental health outcomes.

Precision Medication and Individualized Treatment Strategies
As our knowledge of the genetic and environmental factors influencing mental health continues to expand, there is a growing interest in developing personalized treatment approaches based on the genetic and environmental profile of each individual. This

may involve customizing pharmacological treatments based on a person's genetic composition or developing interventions that target specific gene-environment interactions. Precision medicine promises more effective and targeted remedies for mental health disorders, with fewer adverse effects and improved outcomes.

Strategies for Prevention and Early Intervention

Researchers can develop preventative strategies and early interventions aimed at mitigating risk and promoting mental health by identifying the genetic and environmental factors that contribute to mental health disorders. For instance, public health initiatives that address environmental risk factors, such as poverty, access to education, and social support, can contribute to a reduction in the prevalence of mental health disorders. Similarly, early interventions that target populations at risk, such as those with a family history of mental health disorders or exposure to deleterious childhood experiences, can aid in preventing or mitigating the development of mental health conditions.

In the final section, we will discuss the ethical, social, and policy implications of our expanding knowledge of the genetic and environmental influences on mental health, including privacy, genetic testing, and access to mental health care.

Ethical, Social, and Policy Implications

Several ethical, social, and policy implications must be considered as our understanding of the genetic and environmental factors that influence mental health continues to advance. In this section, we will examine some of the most prevalent issues, such as:

Confidentiality and Individuality

The growing availability of genetic information raises privacy and confidentiality concerns. Protecting individuals' genetic information is essential for preventing potential abuse or discrimination by employers, insurers, or other parties. To maintain public confidence and encourage participation in research studies that advance our comprehension of mental health disorders, it is crucial to protect the confidentiality and security of genetic information.

Genetic Counseling and Testing

Individuals and families may pursue information regarding their genetic susceptibility to mental health disorders as genetic testing becomes more accessible. This raises considerations regarding the appropriate application of genetic testing, the necessity of informed consent, and the function of genetic counseling in assisting individuals to comprehend the implications of their genetic information. Genetic counseling can assist individuals in making informed testing decisions and interpreting and managing their genetic risk for mental health disorders.

Discrimination and Stigmatization

Greater awareness of the genetic and environmental factors influencing mental health may result in increased stigmatization and discrimination against those with mental health disorders or those at risk of developing these conditions. It is crucial to educate the public about the complex interaction between genetics and environment in mental health and to foster understanding and compassion for those with mental health disorders.

Availability to Mental Health Care

As novel interventions and treatments are developed based on our expanding knowledge of the genetic and environmental influences on mental health, it is essential that all individuals have equal access to these resources. Particularly for underserved and marginalized populations, disparities in access to mental health care can exacerbate existing inequalities and perpetuate the cycle of mental health disparities. Policymakers and healthcare providers must collaborate to develop strategies for expanding access to mental health care and guaranteeing that all individuals can reap the benefits of the most recent research developments.

Ethical Considerations in Clinical Practice and Research

As researchers continue to investigate the genetic and environmental influences on mental health, ethical considerations must be taken into account to ensure that studies are conducted with respect for the rights and dignity of study participants. Consent of the subject, preservation of the subject's privacy, and consideration of the potential risks and benefits of research findings are essential elements of responsible research practice. Similarly, clinicians must navigate the ethical challenges posed by the incorporation of genetic information into their practice and ensure that their patients are treated with dignity, respect, and sensitivity.

The complex interaction between genetics and environment has substantial implications for our understanding of mental health disorders and their treatment. By addressing the ethical, social, and policy implications of this knowledge, we can ensure that the benefits of our expanding understanding of the genetic and environmental influences on mental health are realized responsibly and equitably.

Summary & Conclusion

This chapter examined the complex relationships between genetics, environment, and mental health, discussing how both genetic and environmental factors contribute to the development and progression of various mental health disorders. By analyzing specific conditions such as depression, anxiety, schizophrenia, and bipolar disorder, we have emphasized the significance of recognizing the complex interaction between these factors in determining an individual's mental health.

In addition, we have explored the intriguing world of gene-environment interactions and epigenetics, demonstrating how these processes can help us understand why some individuals are more prone to developing mental health disorders in response to certain environmental stressors. In addition, we have reviewed recent research and advancements in the disciplines of genetics and mental health, with an emphasis on the potential for the development of novel treatment and prevention strategies.

Nonetheless, as our understanding of the genetic and environmental influences on mental health continues to expand, it is essential to address the resulting ethical, social, and policy implications. A responsible and equitable approach to mental health research and practice requires the protection of privacy and confidentiality, the provision of access to mental health care, and the promotion of understanding and empathy for those affected by mental health disorders.

Understanding the impact of genetics and environment on mental health has the potential to transform our approach to mental health care, paving the way for personalized interventions, targeted prevention strategies, and a deeper understanding of the complex mechanisms underlying mental health disorders. We can work toward a future in which mental health care is more effective, accessible, and tailored to the specific requirements of each individual by embracing this knowledge and addressing the associated challenges.

Chapter 5:
The Role of Lifestyle in Maintaining Mental Health

Introduction:
Role of Lifestyle in Maintaining

Mental health is an essential component of our well-being, influencing our daily thoughts, emotions, and behaviors. It influences how we view ourselves, our relationships, and our ability to deal with challenges and stressors. As awareness of the significance of mental health has increased, so has the desire to comprehend how various lifestyle factors affect our psychological health. Adopting a healthy lifestyle can be a proactive approach to promoting overall well-being, as it is now widely acknowledged that our daily behaviors and decisions can either support or hinder our mental health.

This chapter will examine the role of lifestyle in maintaining mental health, concentrating on key factors such as sleep, nutrition, physical activity, social connections, and stress management. Each of these factors has a significant impact on our mental health, and comprehending their significance can help us make deliberate decisions to enhance our mental health. We will provide evidence-based explanations for the significance of each factor, relying on pertinent research and expert opinion to show how these areas contribute to mental health.

In addition to examining the relationship between these lifestyle factors and mental health, this chapter will provide actionable advice and recommendations to help readers improve their mental health by incorporating these lifestyle factors into their daily lives. This chapter seeks to equip readers with the knowledge and skills necessary to make informed decisions and embrace healthier behaviors for a happier, more balanced life by presenting an exhaustive overview of the role of lifestyle in maintaining mental health.

Sleep and Mental Health

The Science of Sleep and Psychological Health
The Restorative Effects of Sleep on the Brain

- o Sleep is necessary for maintaining optimal cognitive and emotional health. During slumber, the brain endures essential restorative processes that are necessary for maintaining mental health. These processes include detritus elimination, memory consolidation, and the strengthening of neural connections. These mechanisms allow the brain to function effectively during conscious hours and help us to remain vigilant, focused, and emotionally stable.

o Different stages of sleep, such as rapid eye movement (REM) sleep and non-REM sleep, serve distinct functions in sustaining cognitive and affective processes, according to research. REM sleep, for instance, is associated with the processing of affective experiences, whereas non-REM sleep contributes to the consolidation of memories and learning.

The Effects of Sleep Deprivation on Mood and Cognition

o Chronic sleep deprivation can have negative effects on mental health, resulting in memory impairment, concentration difficulties, and mood disturbances. According to research, sleep-deprived people are more susceptible to negative emotions such as irritability, anxiety, and depression. In addition, sleep deprivation can exacerbate the symptoms of pre-existing mental health disorders and increase the likelihood of developing new ones.

o Sleep deprivation can also impair decision-making, problem-solving, and impulse control, which can have negative effects on personal and professional relationships, as well as the quality of life overall.

The Importance of Sleep Hygiene
Sleep hygiene refers to the habits and practices that contribute to good sleep quality and daytime alertness. Maintaining good sleep hygiene is essential for promoting mental health, as it helps ensure that the brain can undergo the necessary restorative processes during sleep.

Tips for Improving Sleep Quality

Establishing a Consistent Sleep Schedule
Going to bed and waking up at the same time every day, even on weekends, helps regulate the body's internal clock, or circadian rhythm, and improve sleep quality. Consistency in sleep patterns can lead to a more restful sleep, increased daytime alertness, and improved mood.

Creating a Relaxing Bedtime Routine
Engaging in calming activities before bedtime, such as reading, listening to soft music, or practicing relaxation techniques, can signal the body that it's time to wind down and prepare for sleep. Avoiding stimulating activities, such as watching television, using electronic devices, or engaging in intense discussions, can also help create a more conducive environment for sleep.

Optimizing the Sleep Environment

Creating a sleep-friendly environment is crucial for promoting better sleep. This includes a comfortable mattress and pillows, dark curtains or blackout shades to block external light, and a comfortable room temperature. Minimizing noise and disruptions, as well as removing electronic devices from the bedroom, can also contribute to a more restful sleep.

Limiting Caffeine and Alcohol Intake

Caffeine is a stimulant that can interfere with sleep, so it is essential to limit its intake, particularly in the afternoon and evening. Alcohol, although initially sedating, can disrupt sleep later in the night and lead to fragmented sleep. Reducing alcohol consumption, especially close to bedtime, can improve sleep quality.

Addressing Sleep Disorders

If sleep problems persist despite implementing these strategies, it may be necessary to consult a healthcare professional to determine whether an underlying sleep disorder, such as insomnia or sleep apnea, is contributing to poor sleep quality.

By prioritizing sleep and incorporating healthy sleep habits, individuals can experience significant improvements in their mental health and overall well-being.

Diet and Mental Health

The Connection Between Nutrition and Brain Function

Nutrients That Support Mental Health

Our diet plays a crucial role in maintaining brain health, as certain nutrients are essential for proper brain function and mental well-being. Some key nutrients that support mental health include:

Omega-3 fatty Acids: These essential fats are crucial for brain function, and deficiencies have been linked to mood disorders such as depression. They help maintain the structure of brain cells, support neuron communication, and reduce inflammation. Sources of omega-3 fatty acids include fatty fish, walnuts, flaxseeds, and chia seeds.

B Vitamins: B vitamins, such as B6, B9 (folate), and B12, help produce neurotransmitters, which are essential for mood regulation and cognitive function. Deficiencies in these vitamins have been associated with depression and cognitive decline. Sources of B vitamins include whole grains, legumes, leafy greens, and animal products.

Antioxidants: Antioxidants, such as vitamin C, vitamin E, and selenium, help protect brain cells from damage caused by free radicals and oxidative stress. Diets rich in antioxidants have been linked to improved mental health and cognitive function. Sources of antioxidants include fruits, vegetables, nuts, and seeds.

The Impact of Poor Nutrition on Mood and Cognition

A diet high in processed foods, unhealthy fats, and sugar can lead to inflammation, which can negatively affect brain function. Research suggests that individuals who consume a diet high in sugar and processed foods are more likely to experience mood disorders and cognitive decline. Additionally, deficiencies in essential nutrients can impair neurotransmitter production and function, leading to imbalances that affect mental health.

The Role of the Gut-Brain Axis

The gut-brain axis is a bidirectional communication system between the gastrointestinal tract and the central nervous system. This connection suggests that the composition of our gut microbiota can influence our mental health. A healthy gut microbiome, which can be supported through a nutrient-rich diet, has been associated with reduced risk of mood disorders and improved cognitive function.

Tips for Adopting a Mentally Healthy Diet

Incorporating Whole, Nutrient-Dense Foods

Eating a balanced diet that includes a variety of whole, nutrient-dense foods can support optimal brain function and mental health. This includes incorporating a wide range of fruits, vegetables, whole grains, lean proteins, and healthy fats into daily meals.

Moderating Sugar and Processed Food Intake

Reducing the consumption of added sugars and processed foods can help minimize inflammation and promote overall brain health. This may involve limiting sugary beverages, snacks, and fast food, while focusing on more natural, whole-food sources of nutrition.

Staying Hydrated

Drinking enough water throughout the day is essential for maintaining proper brain function and overall well-being. Dehydration can impair cognitive function, mood, and energy levels, so it is important to prioritize hydration for optimal mental health.

Implementing a Balanced, Mindful Approach to Eating

Adopting a mindful approach to eating can help promote healthier food choices and foster a positive relationship with food. This involves paying attention to hunger and satiety cues, eating slowly, and savoring each bite. Additionally, focusing on balance and moderation, rather than adhering to restrictive diets, can support long-term mental health and well-being.

By making intentional dietary choices that prioritize nutrient-dense foods, individuals can support their mental health and promote overall brain function. A balanced, healthy diet can serve as a powerful tool in maintaining and enhancing mental well-being

Exercise and Mental Health

The Mental Health Benefits of Exercise

The Impact of Exercise on Mood and Emotional Well-being

Exercise has been shown to have a positive effect on mood and emotional well-being. Physical activity stimulates the release of endorphins, which are natural mood enhancers that can help reduce stress, anxiety, and depression. Regular exercise has been linked to increased self-esteem, improved mood stability, and a greater sense of overall happiness.

Exercise as a Stress-Reducer and Coping Mechanism

Exercise can be an effective way to cope with stress and reduce the impact of stressors on mental health. By engaging in physical activity, the body's stress response is tempered, leading to a reduction in stress hormones such as cortisol. Exercise can also improve mental resilience by promoting the growth of new neurons and enhancing the brain's ability to adapt to stress.

Cognitive Benefits of Exercise

In addition to its mood-enhancing effects, exercise has been shown to have positive effects on cognitive function. Physical activity can improve memory, attention, and problem-solving skills by increasing blood flow to the brain and promoting the growth of new brain cells. Regular exercise has also been associated with a reduced risk of cognitive decline and the development of neurodegenerative diseases, such as Alzheimer's and Parkinson's.

Exercise and its Effects on Sleep

Regular physical activity can improve sleep quality by helping to regulate the body's circadian rhythm and promoting deeper, more restorative sleep. Exercise can also help alleviate sleep disturbances, such as insomnia, by reducing stress and anxiety levels. In turn, better sleep quality can contribute to improved mental health and emotional well-being.

Exercise as a Protective Factor Against Mental Health Disorders

Engaging in regular physical activity can serve as a protective factor against the development of mental health disorders. Studies have shown that individuals who maintain consistent exercise routines have a lower risk of developing depression, anxiety, and other mood disorders. Exercise can also help alleviate the symptoms of existing mental health conditions and improve overall quality of life.

Tips for Incorporating Exercise into Daily Life

Finding Enjoyable and Sustainable Physical Activities

Selecting physical activities that are enjoyable and sustainable will increase the likelihood of maintaining a consistent exercise routine. This may include activities such as swimming, dancing, hiking, or yoga. The key is to find activities that are enjoyable and can be easily integrated into one's lifestyle.

Setting Realistic Goals and Tracking Progress

Establishing achievable fitness goals and tracking progress can help motivate individuals to maintain a regular exercise routine and experience the mental health benefits of physical activity. Setting small, attainable goals and celebrating milestones can lead to long-term adherence and success.

Prioritizing Consistency and Balance

Aiming for consistency and balance in exercise routines is key to achieving long-term mental health benefits. This may involve incorporating various types of activities, such as aerobic exercise, strength training, and flexibility exercises, throughout the week. Consistency is more important than the intensity or duration of each workout, so finding a routine that can be maintained over time is crucial.

Making Exercise a Social Activity

Incorporating social aspects into exercise routines can increase motivation and adherence, as well as provide additional mental health benefits through social connection. This can be achieved by participating in group fitness classes, joining a sports team or club, or simply exercising with friends or family members.

By making exercise a regular part of daily life, individuals can experience numerous mental health benefits, including improved mood, reduced stress, and enhanced cognitive function. Physical activity can serve as a powerful tool for promoting mental health and overall well-being.

Social Connections and Mental Health

The Importance of Social Connections for Mental Health

Function of Social Support

Strong social connections provide an essential support system that can have a substantial effect on mental health. According to research, people with robust social networks tend to experience less tension, reduced rates of depression, and a greater sense of well-being overall. Social support can take the form of emotional support, practical assistance, or simply a sense of community belonging.

Social Interactions and Cognitive Performance

Positive social interactions are associated with improved cognitive function and a lower risk of cognitive decline. Engaging in mentally stimulating social activities can help preserve and enhance memory, focus, and problem-solving abilities. Moreover, social interactions can stimulate the release of neurotransmitters that support brain function and mental health as a whole.

Mental Health Implications of Loneliness and Social Isolation

In contrast, loneliness and social isolation have been identified as significant mental health risk factors. Chronically lonely or socially isolated individuals are more likely to develop depression, anxiety, and other mental health disorders. Additionally, prolonged social isolation can result in increased tension, diminished cognitive function, and weakened immunity.

Guidelines for Establishing and Sustaining Social Connections

Developing Current Relationships

Maintaining a robust social support network requires strengthening existing relationships with friends, family members, and coworkers. This may involve reaching out to loved ones on a regular basis, offering assistance when required, and engaging in meaningful dialogues.

Developing New Relationships

Developing new social connections can expand a person's support network and provide more opportunities for social engagement. This may entail joining organizations, attending community events, or engaging in social activities that correspond with one's interests.

Conducting Group Activities

Group activities, such as sports teams, specialty societies, and volunteer organizations, can facilitate social interaction and the formation of new friendships. These activities also provide a sense of shared purpose and belonging, which can promote mental health.

Acceptance of Digital Connections

Despite the importance of face-to-face interactions, digital connections can play a role in maintaining social relationships, particularly when physical distance is a barrier. Using technology, such as video calls, social media, and online forums, can facilitate the maintenance and expansion of social networks.

The Promotion of a Sense of Community

Developing a sense of community in one's neighborhood, workplace, or among peers can foster a sense of belonging and provide emotional support. This may involve coordinating social events, providing assistance to neighbors, or simply making an effort to become acquainted with those in your immediate vicinity.

Individuals can substantially improve their mental health and well-being by actively cultivating social relationships and a strong support network. Social connections provide a crucial barrier against stress, loneliness, and the onset of mental health disorders, making them an indispensable component of a mentally healthy lifestyle.

Stress Management and Mental Health

Understanding the Impact of Stress on Mental Health - The Body's Stress Response

The release of hormones such as adrenaline and cortisol, which prepare the body for action, is a natural response to challenging or hazardous situations, causing stress. In certain circumstances, short-term stress can be beneficial, but chronic stress can be detrimental to mental health, leading to anxiety, depression, and other mood disorders.

Stress Chronicity and Mental Disorders

As chronic stress impairs the brain's ability to modulate emotions and manage with adversity, it can contribute to the development or exacerbation of mental health disorders. Additionally, prolonged exposure to stress can have detrimental effects on cognitive function, sleep, and physical health, thereby diminishing overall health.

Effective Stress Management Techniques

Identifying and Addressing Stressors

An essential component of stress management is recognizing the sources of tension in one's life and taking measures to eliminate or reduce them. This may involve reevaluating priorities, delegating tasks, or seeking professional assistance to manage onerous circumstances.

Developing Effective Coping Strategies

Developing healthy coping mechanisms can assist individuals in managing stress more effectively and mitigating its negative psychological effects. The following are examples of effective coping strategies:

a. Mindfulness and relaxation techniques, including meditation, deep breathing exercises, and progressive muscle relaxation, which can help soothe the mind and reduce tension.
b. Participating in enjoyable and fulfilling pastimes or activities, such as gardening, painting, or playing an instrument.
c. Maintaining a robust social support network, as discussed in the preceding section, in order to express emotions and obtain advice or assistance when necessary.
d. Practicing self-compassion and self-care, including setting realistic expectations, recognizing personal limitations, and taking time to rest and recharge.

Including Physical Exercise

As described in the section on exercise, regular physical activity is an effective stress management tool. Physical activity can reduce stress hormones, enhance mood, and increase stress resistance.

Prioritizing Sleep

As discussed in the section on sleep, prioritizing slumber can help individuals better manage stress and mitigate its negative effects on mental health. Good sleep quality is essential for maintaining mental and emotional equilibrium.

Seeking Professional Assistance

Seeking professional assistance from a mental health professional, such as a psychologist or counselor, can provide valuable guidance and support in managing stress and enhancing overall mental health if it becomes overwhelming or persistent.

Individuals can mitigate the negative effects of stress on their mental health and maintain a more balanced, resilient mindset by implementing effective stress management strategies. Managing stress is essential for maintaining mental health and overall well-being, and adopting a proactive stance can result in long-term enhancements to one's quality of life.

Summary & Conclusion

It is impossible to exaggerate the significance of lifestyle in preserving mental health. Individuals can substantially enhance their mental health and overall quality of life through the adoption of healthful behaviors and routines. This chapter has emphasized the main lifestyle factors that can impact mental health, such as sleep, diet, exercise, social connections, and stress management, including sleep, diet, exercise, and social connections. Individuals can establish a solid foundation for optimal mental health and resilience by addressing these factors.

In conclusion, implementing the following behaviors can promote mental health and well-being:

- Establishing a consistent sleep routine that promotes restorative sleep by prioritizing sleep.
- Eating a nutrient-dense, well-balanced diet that promotes cognitive health and a healthy intestinal microbiome.
- Engaging in regular, pleasurable, and sustainable physical activity.
- Fostering social relationships and a sense of community and belonging.
- Managing stress by developing healthy coping mechanisms, prioritizing self-care, and when necessary, seeking professional assistance.

In spite of the fact that the path to enhanced mental health may appear different for each individual, adopting these evidence-based lifestyle adjustments can serve as an effective starting point. It is essential to keep in mind that sustained improvements in mental health demand consistency and dedication, and that progress may be gradual. Individuals can experience significant and long-lasting benefits to their mental health and well-being by taking minor, deliberate measures towards a healthier lifestyle.

Chapter 6:
The Connection Between Physical and Mental Health

Introduction: How our Physical Health Connects

The relationship between physical and mental health is multifaceted and dynamic, and it has gained increasing significance in the fields of medicine, psychology, and public health. As our knowledge of the human body and mind continues to expand, it has become evident that physical and mental health are not distinct entities, but rather intertwined facets of overall health. This chapter seeks to provide an exhaustive overview of the various ways in which physical and mental health are interconnected, delving into their bidirectional relationship and the role of lifestyle factors that influence both. Moreover, this chapter will present practical strategies for individuals seeking to enhance their well-being, emphasizing an integrated mental and physical approach to health.

In recent years, the emphasis has shifted from merely treating physical maladies to contemplating psychological aspects of health and wellness, due to the increasing recognition of the significance of mental health. This integrated perspective has prompted an abundance of research into the numerous linkages between physical and mental health, as well as the development of interventions based on scientific evidence that address both aspects simultaneously. By investigating these relationships and gaining an understanding of the factors that influence our overall health, we can empower individuals to take charge of their health and make well-informed decisions that promote a healthy, balanced lifestyle.

The Bi-Directional Relationship Between Physical and Mental Health

The relationship between physical and mental health is complex and bidirectional, which means that each aspect can have a significant effect on the other. This interdependence can manifest in a variety of ways, emphasizing the significance of considering both dimensions when addressing health concerns.

Mental Health Influenced by Physical Health: Mental health can be significantly affected by a person's physical health. Chronic physical conditions, such as cardiovascular disease, diabetes, or obesity, can increase the likelihood of developing mental health issues such as depression or anxiety. The physical distress, limitations, or changes in lifestyle that accompany these conditions can contribute to feelings of stress, helplessness, and social isolation, thereby aggravating mental health issues. Additionally, the tension of contending with a chronic illness can contribute to elevated cortisol levels, which, when sustained, can have a negative impact on mood and cognitive function.

Inversely, mental health problems can impact physical health and increase the risk of developing chronic diseases. Depression and anxiety can result in physiological alterations in the body, including increased inflammation, altered immune function, and hormonal imbalances. These alterations can contribute to the development of cardiac disease, diabetes, and autoimmune diseases. Additionally, people with mental health disorders may be more likely to engage in behaviors that negatively impact physical health, such as poor diet, lack of exercise, substance misuse, and inadequate sleep. These behaviors can increase the likelihood of developing physical health problems even further.

Physical and Psychological Health Interactions:
The reciprocal relationship between physical and mental health can lead to a downward spiral in which one aspect exacerbates the other, resulting in a decline in overall health. Due to their physical limitations and distress, a person with chronic pain may experience increased anxiety and depression, for instance. This elevated anxiety and depression can then result in altered sleep patterns, decreased motivation to engage in physical activity, and social withdrawal, all of which can deteriorate the individual's physical health. Recognizing and addressing the interaction between physical and mental health is essential for breaking this cycle and promoting overall health.

Understanding the intricate relationship between physical and mental health is crucial for healthcare professionals, as it informs the development of treatments that take both dimensions into account. Incorporating mental health care into the administration of physical health conditions can improve outcomes and enhance the overall quality of life for those with chronic diseases. Similarly, resolving physical health concerns within the context of mental health treatment can result in more effective and long-lasting outcomes. By recognizing and addressing the bidirectional relationship between physical and mental health, healthcare providers can offer a more holistic approach to patient care, thereby promoting enhanced well-being across multiple dimensions.

Lifestyle Factors Affecting Physical and Mental Health

Numerous lifestyle factors can have a significant impact on both physical and mental health, making it imperative to consider how daily behaviors and decisions contribute to overall health. Individuals can make decisions that promote a healthier and more balanced lifestyle if they comprehend the function of these variables. Here, we will delve deeper into the lifestyle factors of diet, exercise, sleep, and stress management, examining their impact on physical and mental health and offering improvement strategies.

Diet: A balanced and nutrient-dense diet is essential for maintaining overall health and can have a substantial effect on mental health. Poor dietary choices, such as menus high in processed foods and low in essential nutrients, can result in physical health problems such as obesity, heart disease, and diabetes, which can have a negative impact on mental health. In addition, nutrients such as omega-3 fatty acids, antioxidants, and B vitamins play a crucial role in supporting cognitive function and mood regulation. A diet rich in these nutrients can aid in alleviating anxiety and depression symptoms and bolstering cognitive function.

Practical Tip: Prioritize a variety of whole, minimally processed foods, including fruits, vegetables, lean proteins, whole cereals, and healthy lipids, in your daily diet. Experiment with new recipes and ingredients to create nourishing and delicious meals that promote physical and mental health.

Exercise: Regular physical activity has numerous positive effects on both physical and mental health. Exercise can enhance cardiovascular health, lower the risk of chronic diseases, and aid in weight control. In addition, physical activity has been shown to reduce depressive and anxious symptoms, enhance cognitive function, and promote self-esteem. Exercise promotes neuroplasticity, which is essential for sustaining a healthy brain, as well as the release of endorphins, which are natural mood-enhancing compounds.

Practical Tip: Find a form of physical activity that you appreciate and can easily incorporate into your daily regimen, such as walking, swimming, or group fitness classes. Aim for at least 150 minutes of moderate- or vigorous-intensity aerobic exercise per week, combined with muscle-strengthening activities on at least two days per week.

Sleep: Sleep is necessary for both physical recuperation and mental health. Insufficient sleep or poor sleep quality can exacerbate mental health issues, contribute to the onset of chronic physical conditions, and impair cognitive function. Sleep deprivation can result in increased inflammation, hormonal imbalances, and diminished immune function, all of which are detrimental to overall health.

Practical Tip: Even on weekends, develop a consistent sleep schedule by going to bed and rising up at the same time every day. To signal to your body that it is time to shut down, establish a bedtime routine that may include reading, mild stretching, or meditation. For restorative sleep, ensure that your sleeping environment is comfortable, silent, and dark.

Stress Management: Chronic stress can negatively impact both physical and mental health. Chronic stress can result in increased inflammation, diminished immune function, and hormonal imbalances, all of which can contribute to the onset of chronic diseases. In addition, stress can exacerbate anxiety and depression symptoms and impair cognitive function. Developing effective stress management skills is crucial for mitigating the negative effects of stress on overall health.

Practical Tip: Incorporate stress-relieving activities, such as deep breathing exercises, meditation, yoga, or mindfulness practices, into your daily routine. Consider engaging in hobbies or pastimes that bring you pleasure and relaxation, such as painting, gardening, or spending time in nature. In addition to mitigating the effects of stress and improving mental health, a strong social support network can also serve as a buffer.

Individuals can promote a healthier balance between physical and mental health by addressing these lifestyle factors and implementing strategies to enhance diet, exercise, sleep, and stress management. Establishing and maintaining healthy behaviors can serve as a foundation for overall health, bolstering resilience and decreasing the risk of developing chronic physical and mental health conditions. It is essential to keep in mind that each individual's requirements and preferences may vary; consequently, it is essential to investigate a variety of strategies to identify the most effective and long-lasting ones for your specific circumstances.

Social Connections: Developing and sustaining strong social connections is another important lifestyle factor that can have a significant effect on both physical and mental health. Positive social interactions can provide emotional support, reduce feelings of isolation and loneliness, and foster a sense of belonging. Research indicates that people with strong social support networks tend to have better mental health, are more stress-resistant, and have a reduced risk of developing chronic physical conditions.

Practical Tip: Make an effort to connect with friends, family, and community members on a regular basis, whether in person or online. Participate in group activities that correspond to your interests, such as joining a sports team, attending community events, or volunteering with local organizations. By engaging in open and supportive communication and providing assistance to those in need, you can foster meaningful connections.

Mindfulness and Emotional Well-Being: Cultivating mindfulness and emotional well-being is an additional essential component of a healthy lifestyle that can benefit both physical and mental health. Mindfulness involves being aware of your thoughts, emotions, and bodily sensations in the present moment and embracing them without judgment. Developing mindfulness skills can aid in tension reduction, emotional regulation, and resilience.

Practical Tip: Incorporate mindfulness practices, such as meditation, deep breathing exercises, and body assessments, into your daily routine. You can also practice mindfulness informally by observing your thoughts, emotions, and bodily sensations throughout the day with an attitude of openness and nonjudgment. Engaging in emotional well-being-promoting activities, such as journaling, therapy, and support groups, can also enhance mental health and contribute to overall wellness.

By comprehending the numerous lifestyle factors that influence physical and mental health, individuals can take a proactive approach to their well-being and make choices that promote a balanced and healthy way of life. Individuals can accomplish a holistic approach to health by implementing practical strategies to resolve these factors and seeking professional guidance when necessary, thereby fostering enhanced well-being across multiple dimensions.

Practical Strategies to Improve Physical and Mental Health

To enhance both physical and mental health, it is necessary to establish an all-encompassing strategy that addresses multiple facets of well-being. This section will focus on strategies that can assist individuals in establishing and maintaining a balanced and healthful lifestyle.

Set Realistic Goals: Establishing health objectives that are attainable and quantifiable can provide motivation and direction on the path to better health. Break down your larger goals into smaller, more manageable stages, and celebrate your progress along the way. This strategy can help you maintain concentration and motivation, as well as prevent feelings of overload and despondency.

Develop a Personalized Routine: Create a daily routine that includes healthful behaviors, such as regular exercise, balanced meals, and sufficient rest. A routine can provide stability and predictability, making it simpler to maintain a healthy lifestyle. Personalizing your routine according to your preferences, requirements, and schedule will increase your chances of long-term success.

Seek Professional Help: Consult a healthcare professional, such as a primary care physician, a psychologist, or a dietitian, if you are struggling with your physical or mental health, in order to develop a plan that is tailored to your specific requirements. Professional guidance can help you navigate the complexities of managing your health by providing valuable insight, support, and resources.

Social Support: Participating in social activities and maintaining strong relationships with family and friends can provide emotional support and enhance mental health. Attend social events, join organizations or groups, and engage in shared activities to foster connections. Having a strong support network can improve your resilience and help you remain motivated and accountable throughout your health journey.

Prioritize Self-Care: Make time for activities that offer you pleasure, relaxation, and rejuvenation, such as interests, time spent in nature, and creative pursuits. Self-care is crucial for preserving mental health and avoiding exhaustion. By routinely engaging in mind- and body-nourishing activities, you can enhance your overall health and stress management.

Monitor Your Progress and Make Necessary Adjustments: Regularly evaluate your progress toward your health objectives and make any necessary adjustments. This may involve modifying your exercise regimen, experimenting with new stress management techniques, or seeking additional medical assistance. Regular self-evaluation can help you stay on course and ensure that your approach to health remains sustainable and effective.

Inform Yourself: Keep abreast of the latest physical and mental health research and developments. This information enables you to make informed decisions about your health and to advocate for your requirements. Participate in seminars, read books or articles, and converse with healthcare professionals in order to perpetually expand your knowledge of health and wellness.

Maintain a Growth Mindset: Adopt a growth mindset, which involves viewing obstacles as learning and development opportunities. This perspective can aid in the development of resilience, adaptation to change, and motivation in the face of adversity. Recognize that your health journey is an ongoing process of learning, and be patient and compassionate with yourself as you strive to achieve your objectives.

By implementing these strategies, individuals can develop a holistic approach to health that encompasses both the physical and mental aspects. This holistic approach can result in enhanced well-being, enhanced resilience, and enhanced life quality. Keep in mind that each individual's requirements and preferences may vary, and that it is essential to investigate various approaches to identify the most effective and long-lasting solutions for your specific circumstances.

Summary & Conclusion

In conclusion, the relationship between physical and mental health is a crucial aspect of overall health that merits more attention and comprehension. The reciprocal relationship between these two dimensions emphasizes the significance of addressing both aspects in healthcare, research, and individual lifestyle decisions. By recognizing the interdependence of physical and mental health, we can devise more effective and comprehensive wellness promotion strategies.

Diet, exercise, sleep, stress management, social connections, and mindfulness play a crucial role in determining both physical and mental health. Individuals can take control of their well-being and make decisions that support a balanced and healthy lifestyle by comprehending the impact of these factors and implementing practical strategies to resolve them.

This chapter has provided an exhaustive overview of the relationship between physical and mental health, highlighting the significance of a holistic approach to well-being that takes into account both dimensions. Through the incorporation of pertinent theories and research, as well as the presentation of practical tips and recommendations, readers can better comprehend the complex interplay between physical and mental health and take steps to improve their overall health. As our knowledge of the human body and mind continues to expand, it is essential to maintain an integrated perspective on health that recognizes the potent influence of both physical and mental dimensions on our well-being.

Section II. Self-Care and Wellness

Chapter 7:
Explanation of what self-care is and why it's important

Introduction:
Why is Self-Care Important

Mental health and well-being have assumed center stage as essential components of a healthy, balanced existence in today's fast-paced, high-pressure society. The increasing demands of contemporary life and the prevalence of mental health issues such as anxiety and depression have made self-care more crucial than ever. Self-care is more than occasional self-indulgence or self-pampering; it involves taking consistent, deliberate measures to maintain and enhance one's overall health and well-being.

This chapter examines the significance of self-care for mental health and well-being, delving into the concept of self-care. It seeks to provide a comprehensive comprehension of self-care by describing the various aspects and categories of self-care practices that are geared specifically toward mental health and well-being. The chapter will also provide practical advice on how individuals can integrate these practices into their daily lives, thereby nurturing a more balanced and fulfilling way of life.

By comprehending and prioritizing self-care, individuals can develop resilience, manage with life's challenges more effectively, and ultimately improve their mental health. As a result, they can not only enhance their own well-being, but also positively impact their relationships, careers, and communities.

Understanding Self-Care

Self-care is a multifaceted concept that incorporates the conscious and intentional actions individuals take to maintain and improve their overall health. It involves recognizing and actively addressing one's physical, emotional, mental, and spiritual requirements through a variety of practices and activities. Self-care is fundamentally about nurturing self-awareness and accepting responsibility for one's own well-being, thereby guaranteeing a balanced and satisfying existence.

Each person's self-care is unique, as individual requirements and preferences vary. In order to establish a personalized approach to self-care, it is essential to assess and identify one's individual needs. Some people may find consolation in physical activities such as yoga or running, while others may find solace in artistic pursuits or spending precious time with companions.

Self-care is distinct from narcissism and self-indulgence. Self-care practices may occasionally involve engaging in pleasurable activities or treating oneself, but their ultimate purpose is to promote overall well-being, which includes fostering mental health. In addition, self-care is not a one-time activity or a fast remedy; it is an ongoing process that requires commitment and perseverance.

Individuals can develop resilience, manage stress, and cultivate a positive mindset by recognizing the significance of self-care and employing a proactive approach. In turn, these benefits can contribute to improved mental health and well-being, enabling individuals to navigate life's challenges more effectively and live a more balanced, fulfilling existence.

The Relationship Between Self-Care and Mental Health

Self-care and mental health share a symbiotic relationship, as the practices and behaviors associated with self-care can have a significant impact on one's mental health. By prioritizing self-care, individuals can establish a solid foundation for mental health, equipping themselves with the tools and resources necessary to more effectively navigate life's challenges.

Stress Management: Stress management is one of the most important aspects of the connection between self-care and mental health. Stress is an unavoidable aspect of life, but if not properly managed, it can have devastating effects on mental health. Self-care practices, such as exercise, relaxation techniques, and time management, can assist individuals in managing stress, thereby mitigating its detrimental effects on mental health.

Building Resilience: Self-care also contributes to the development of resilience, which is the capacity to adapt to and recover from adversity. By engaging in self-care practices on a regular basis, individuals can develop a strong sense of self-worth and learn effective coping mechanisms, enabling them to better manage life's challenges and maintain a positive outlook.

Emotional Regulation: Emotional regulation is another essential aspect of mental health, and self-care can assist individuals in developing the skills required to effectively regulate their emotions. Individuals can acquire a deeper understanding of their emotions through self-care practices such as journaling, therapy, and mindfulness exercises, enabling them to respond to emotional stimuli in a healthier manner.

Preventing Burnout: Burnout is a condition of mental, emotional, and physical exhaustion caused by persistent tension and overwork. Individuals can prevent exhaustion and maintain a healthy balance between work, personal life, and mental health by prioritizing self-care and establishing boundaries.

Improving Mental Health Outcomes: Regular self-care practices can enhance mental health outcomes by reducing the severity of symptoms associated with anxiety, depression, and other mental health disorders. By taking care of their physical, emotional, and mental requirements, individuals can create a healing and well-being-promoting environment.

Self-care practices play a crucial role in maintaining mental health and preventing the onset of mental health problems. Individuals can enhance their mental health, well-being, and quality of life by making self-care a priority and incorporating it into their daily routines.

Types of Self-Care Practices for Mental Health and Well-Being

To effectively address mental health and well-being, it is necessary to integrate a variety of self-care practices that address various aspects of an individual's existence. The following are examples of self-care practices that are particularly beneficial to mental health and wellbeing:

Physical Self-Care: Physical health and mental health are intrinsically linked, as the mind and body are intricately interconnected. Physical self-care entails taking care of one's body by engaging in regular exercise, consuming a healthy diet, and getting enough sleep. These practices can enhance mood, reduce tension, and enhance mental health in general.

Emotional Self-Care: Emotional self-care focuses on comprehending and effectively managing emotions, which is essential for maintaining mental health. Journaling, engaging in creative outlets such as painting or writing, practicing mindfulness and meditation, or speaking with a trusted friend, family member, or therapist are examples of activities that promote emotional self-care. These practices can facilitate the emotional processing, self-compassion, and emotional resilience of individuals.

Social Self-Care: Because humans are inherently social, social connections are essential for mental health. Social self-care entails fostering and sustaining healthy relationships with friends, family, and the community. This can be accomplished through consistent communication, participation in social activities, and when necessary, seeking support. Strong social connections can foster a sense of belonging and enable individuals to face life's challenges with greater resilience.

Intellectual Self-Care: Stimulating the mind through intellectual pursuits is an additional method for promoting mental health and well-being. Reading books, attending seminars or classes, acquiring new skills, and engaging in thought-provoking conversations are examples of intellectual self-care. These activities can help preserve cognitive function, enhance self-esteem, and foster a feeling of accomplishment.

Spiritual Self-Care: Spiritual Self-Care Spiritual self-care focuses on connecting with a higher power or discovering a sense of purpose in life, which can have a profound effect on mental health. This form of self-care may consist of meditation, prayer, spending time in nature, or engaging in activities that are consistent with one's values and beliefs. Spiritual self-care can provide an individual with a sense of interior serenity, grounding, and connection to something greater than oneself.

Professional Self-Care: Maintaining a positive work-life balance is necessary for mental health and well-being. Professional self-care includes establishing boundaries at work, managing tension, delegating tasks, and, when necessary, seeking assistance from colleagues or supervisors. Individuals can prevent exhaustion and maintain a healthy balance between their personal and professional lives if they prioritize professional self-care.

By incorporating these various forms of self-care into daily routines, individuals can holistically address their mental health and well-being requirements, resulting in a more balanced, satisfying existence.

Tips for Incorporating Self-Care into Daily Life

Self-care can be difficult to incorporate into daily life, particularly when competing priorities and responsibilities exist. Individuals can, however, effectively incorporate self-care practices into their regimens, thereby promoting their mental health and well-being. Here are some suggestions for integrating self-care into everyday life:

Self-Care as a Priority: Recognize the significance of self-care and make it a priority in your existence. Consider self-care activities to be on par with work, family, and other responsibilities. Schedule time specifically for self-care practices, and adhere to the schedule as consistently as feasible.

Establish Self-Care Objectives That Are Attainable: Establish self-care objectives that can be readily incorporated into daily routines. A 10-minute meditation or brief walk, for instance, can be more manageable than an hour-long session. Increase the duration or intensity of self-care activities gradually as they become habitual.

Develop a Personalized Self-Care Plan: Create a personalized self-care plan that includes specific activities and practices tailored to the individual's requirements and preferences. Consider incorporating diverse self-care practices, such as physical, emotional, social, intellectual, spiritual, and professional self-care, in order to create a holistic approach to mental health and well-being.

Establish Boundaries: Establish boundaries to safeguard personal time and energy, thereby enabling regular self-care practices. Communicate with family, friends, and coworkers regarding the significance of self-care and the need to set aside time for personal well-being.

Practice Mindfulness: Implement mindfulness techniques, such as meditation or deep breathing exercises, to aid in stress management and enhance mental health. Mindfulness can be practiced in a variety of contexts and circumstances, making it a flexible self-care technique.

Seek Assistance: Enlist the aid of friends, family, or coworkers to hold you accountable for your self-care objectives. Sharing your self-care journey with others can encourage and motivate you to maintain your commitment to your health.

Be Flexible and Adaptable: Being flexible and adaptable is essential when integrating self-care practices into daily routines, as life is unpredictable. If a specific activity or plan fails, be willing to attempt new strategies or modify your objectives to better fit your needs and circumstances.

Celebrate Progress: Acknowledge and celebrate your progress in the incorporation of self-care into your daily existence. Recognizing accomplishments, regardless of size, can increase motivation and emphasize the significance of self-care.

Individuals can effectively promote mental health and overall well-being by incorporating self-care into their daily lives, resulting to a more balanced, fulfilling existence.

Summary & Conclusion

It is impossible to exaggerate the importance of self-care for mental health and well-being. By nurturing a deeper comprehension of self-care and its connection to mental health, individuals can build a solid foundation for a balanced, fulfilling existence. Through various self-care practices that tend to physical, emotional, social, intellectual, and spiritual requirements, individuals can holistically address their well-being and develop the resiliency necessary to navigate life's obstacles.

Self-care may initially be difficult to incorporate into daily routines, but with dedication, commitment, and a personalized approach, it can become an integral part of one's life. Individuals can effectively prioritize their mental health and well-being by setting realistic objectives, developing a self-care plan, establishing boundaries, and seeking support.

Self-care is an essential aspect of maintaining and enhancing mental health. It enables people to take charge of their wellbeing and cultivate a positive outlook. By embracing and incorporating self-care into daily life, individuals can not only improve their own well-being but also positively impact their relationships, careers, and communities. Self-care is an investment in a happier, healthier, and more satisfying existence.

Chapter 8:
Different self-care practices and how to incorporate them into your daily routine

Introduction:
Self-Care in Modern Life

In today's fast-paced, always-connected world, tension and exhaustion have become more common. Work, relationships, and societal expectations can leave us feeling exhausted and overburdened. It is more crucial than ever to prioritize self-care in order to preserve our physical and mental health.

Self-care comprises a vast array of activities that foster personal development, relaxation, and restoration. It is a proactive approach that focuses on the mind, body, and spirit to ensure our health, contentment, and longevity. By devoting time and effort to self-care, we are better equipped to face the challenges of life and develop resilience.

This chapter will provide a comprehensive overview of various self-care practices and practical advice for incorporating them into your daily life. By grasping the significance of self-care and incorporating it into your life, you can improve your mental and physical health, strengthen your relationships, and cultivate a greater sense of self-awareness and self-compassion.

As we venture deeper into the various facets of self-care, we will examine physical self-care practices, such as exercise, nutrition, and sleep, which are essential for maintaining the optimal functioning of our bodies. In addition, we will discuss mental self-care practices, such as managing tension, cultivating emotional awareness, and establishing strong social connections to promote psychological health. Finally, we will investigate spiritual self-care practices that emphasize mindfulness, meditation, connecting with nature, and cultivating gratitude in order to nourish our souls and nurture a sense of purpose and meaning in life.

Self-care is a journey that requires dedication and perseverance, but the rewards are well worth the effort. You can enhance your quality of life and become the finest version of yourself by implementing these practices.

Physical Self-Care: Building a Strong Foundation for Overall Well-being

Self-care entails taking care of one's body to ensure optimal functioning, prevent disease, and promote longevity. By prioritizing physical self-care, we can increase our vitality, enhance our demeanor, and improve our overall health. This section will delve into three essential elements of physical self-care: exercise, nutrition, and sleep, investigating their significance and providing suggestions for incorporating them into your daily life.

Fueling the Body and Mind with Exercise

Regular Exercise is Essential for Overall Health

Reduces the risk of chronic diseases (such as cardiovascular disease, diabetes, and obesity).
Improves mood and alleviates depression and anxiety symptoms
Enhances energy levels and cognitive performance

Types of Exercises:

- Aerobic, strength training, and flexibility exercises
- Aerobic exercises (e.g., sprinting, swimming, and dancing) promote cardiovascular health. cardiovascular health improvement
- Resistance training (such as weightlifting and resistance bands) strengthens muscle and bone
- Flexibility exercises (yoga, stretching, etc.) equilibrium and injury prevention
- Recommendations: thirty minutes, five days per week

The American Heart Association recommends at least 150 minutes of aerobic exercise per week at a moderate intensity or 75 minutes of vigorous exercise.
Include resistance training at least twice per week

Tips:

- Find activities you appreciate, establish attainable objectives, and use technology to monitor your progress.
- Choose activities that align with your passions to ensure long-term adherence.
- Break your objectives down into smaller, more attainable milestones to maintain your motivation.
- Utilize fitness applications and wearable technology to track your progress and hold yourself accountable.

Nutrition: Nourishment of the Body Internally
Importance of a Nutritious Diet

- o Provides nutrients essential for optimal body function
- o Supports immune function and aids in disease prevention
- o Encourages optimal weight management and increases vitality
- o Fruits, vegetables, entire cereals, and lean proteins are examples of nutrient-dense foods.
- o Prioritize a range of vitamin and mineral-rich, colorful fruits and vegetables.
- o Whole grains (such as brown rice, quinoa, and whole wheat bread) provide sustained energy and fiber.
- o Select lean proteins (such as chicken, fish, legumes, and seeds) for muscle growth and repair.

Recommendations: dining mindfully, planning meals, and remaining hydrated
Practice mindful dining by savoring each mouthful and paying attention to your body's signals of appetite.
Plan ahead to ensure a balanced diet and avoid harmful options.
Consume at least 8 containers (64 ounces) of water per day to maintain appropriate hydration.

Tips: Cooking at home, reducing processed foods, and dining mindfully are suggestions.
Prepare dishes at home so that you can monitor the ingredients and portion sizes.
Reduce your consumption of processed foods high in added sugars, unhealthy lipids, and sodium.
Avoid restrictive regimens and practice moderation to foster a healthy relationship with food.

Restoring the Body and Mind through Sleep
Importance of sleep for physical and mental health Supports immune function, cognitive performance, and emotional regulation Aids in the healing and repair of cells and tissues Contributes to the mending and regulation of emotions
Reduces the risk of chronic health problems (such as cardiovascular disease, obesity, and diabetes).

Sleep Hygiene:

- o Establishing a bedtime routine and creating a sleep-friendly environment comprise good sleep hygiene.
- o A nighttime ritual signals to the body that it is time to settle down and prepare for sleep.
- o Create an environment conducive to sleep by eliminating distractions, maintaining a comfortable temperature, and investing in high-quality linens.
- o Recommendations: 7-9 hours per night

Mental Self-Care: Nurturing the Mind for Emotional Resilience and Psychological Well-being

Self-care for the mind focuses on behaviors that promote emotional and psychological health. By caring for our mental health, we can increase our resilience, strengthen our relationships, and improve our overall quality of life. In this section, we will examine three crucial components of mental self-care: stress management, emotional awareness, and social connections. We will discuss their significance and offer suggestions for incorporating them into daily life.

Stress Management: Regaining Balance and Control

- Importance of stress management for holistic health
- Chronic stress is detrimental to physical health, increasing the risk of cardiovascular disease, obesity, and other chronic conditions.
- High levels of tension can impair cognitive performance, decision-making, and memory.
- Stress can contribute to mental health issues such as anxiety and depression if it persists for an extended period of time.
- Techniques: meditative practices of profound breathing and progressive muscle relaxation
- Meditation and mindful walking are examples of mindfulness practices that cultivate present-moment awareness and reduce tension.
- Deep breathing exercises, such as diaphragmatic and 4-7-8 breathing, activate the relaxation response in the body.
- Progressive muscle relaxation involves contracting and relaxing various muscle groups to reduce tension and promote relaxation.

Recommendations: Routinely Engage in Stress-Relieving Activities

- Utilize stress management techniques on a daily basis, even when you do not feel overburdened, in order to develop resiliency.
- Experiment with various techniques to determine what meets your specific requirements best.

Tips:

- Identifying stressors, establishing limits, and seeking assistance
- Recognize the stressors in your life and devise strategies to eliminate or reduce them.
- Set limits for your work, relationships, and personal responsibilities to avoid overextending yourself.
- Reach out for support and guidance to friends, family, or mental health professionals when necessary.

Emotional Intelligence:

- Understanding and Communicating Your Emotions
- Understanding and expressing emotions are crucial
- Emotional intelligence promotes healthy communication and enhances relationships.
- Identifying and addressing emotions can prevent emotional suppression, which can result in mental health problems.
- Emotional awareness fosters personal development and self-awareness.

Journaling, Self-reflection, and Therapy are Techniques.

- Journaling can aid in emotional processing, pattern recognition, and gaining insight into your emotional landscape.
- Meditation or silent time can deepen emotional awareness and self-understanding.
- A mental health professional can provide a secure environment for exploring emotions and developing coping mechanisms.

Recommendation: Daily Practice of Emotional Awareness

Make time daily to assess your emotions, determine their origins, and address them in a healthy manner.

Be receptive to experiencing both positive and negative emotions as part of a healthy emotional existence.

Tips:

- Embracing vulnerability, self-compassion, and, if necessary, seeking professional assistance
- Permit yourself to be vulnerable by expressing your emotions with dependable family and acquaintances.
- Self-compassion is demonstrated by recognizing and embracing your emotions without judgment or criticism.
- Seek the assistance of a therapist or counselor if you have difficulty managing your emotions on your own.

Social Connections: Cultivating Meaningful Relationships for Mental Health

- Importance of maintaining healthy relationships for mental health
- Strong social connections provide emotional support, increase contentment, and diminish feelings of isolation.
- Socially connected individuals have reduced depression and anxiety rates.
- Relationships with significance contribute to a sense of belonging and purpose.

- o Recommendations: maintaining existing relationships and establishing new ones
- o Communicate frequently with loved ones to maintain and strengthen ties.
- o Make an attempt to create new

Spiritual Self-Care: Nurturing the Soul and Fostering a Sense of Purpose

Spiritual self-care emphasizes practices that foster inner serenity, personal growth, and a deeper connection to oneself, others, and the world. By cultivating our spiritual health, we can instill in our lives a sense of purpose, meaning, and fulfillment. In this section, we will examine three essential components of spiritual self-care: mindfulness and meditation, connecting with nature, and gratitude and reflection. We will discuss their significance and offer suggestions for incorporating them into daily life.

Meditation and Mindfulness: Cultivating Presence and Inner Peace

Importance of Mindfulness for Psychological Health

- o Practicing mindfulness increases self-awareness, affective regulation, and tension reduction.
- o Regular mindfulness practice can enhance cognitive function, concentration, and judgment.
- o Mindfulness promotes a higher sense of tranquility and well-being.
- o Techniques: mindfulness, loving-kindness, and body scan meditation
- o Mindfulness meditation cultivates present-moment awareness by focusing on the respiration, bodily sensations, or thoughts.
- o Meditation on loving-kindness promotes the growth of compassion and empathy for oneself and others.
- o Body scan meditation involves focusing on various areas of the body in order to promote relaxation and body awareness.

Recommendations:

- o Daily practice and locating a calm area
- o Engage in mindfulness practices on a consistent basis to reap the full benefits and establish a routine.
- o Find a place where you can practice in peace and without interruptions.

Tips:

- o Guided meditation apps and practicing patience
- o Especially if you are new to meditation, use guided meditation applications or online resources for support.

- Be patient with yourself as you cultivate your meditation practice, recognizing that it is a skill that requires time and effort to develop.

Connecting with Nature: Recognizing the Restorative Potential of the Natural World

Nature's Significance for Spiritual Well-Being

- It has been demonstrated that spending time in nature reduces tension, improves temperament, and increases sentiments of well-being.
- Connecting with nature can instill astonishment, amazement, and an appreciation for the majesty and interconnectedness of life.
- Nature can facilitate self-reflection, personal development, and spiritual inquiry.
- Recommendations: spending time outdoors, engaging in outdoor activities
- Attempt to spend time in nature every day, even if it's just a brief stroll in a nearby park.
- Engage in outdoor pursuits such as hiking, cycling, and bird-watching to strengthen your connection to nature.

Tips:
- Walking, gardening, and visiting parks and natural areas
- Include nature excursions in your daily regimen to experience the rejuvenating effects of nature.
- Engage in horticulture or plant care to connect with nature and experience the fulfillment of nurturing life.
- Visit local parks, nature reserves, or natural landmarks to immerse yourself in diverse natural environments and broaden your understanding of the world around you.

Gratitude and Reflection: Cultivating a Grateful Attitude

Importance of Thankfulness for Health

- There is a correlation between gratitude and increased contentment, life satisfaction, and well-being.
- Gratitude can change our perspective from ruminating on negative experiences to appreciating the positive aspects of life.
- Practicing gratitude can strengthen relationships and cultivate a stronger sense of interdependence.

Techniques:

- Gratitude journal, daily reflection

- ○ Maintain a daily gratitude journal to chronicle the things for which you are thankful, thereby reinforcing an attitude of gratitude.
- ○ Set aside time each day for contemplation and gratitude, focusing on the positive aspects of your existence.

Recommendations:

- ○ Integrate daily gratitude practices
- ○ Establish a daily gratitude practice, such as writing in a journal of gratitude or reflecting on positive experiences before bed.
- ○ Share your appreciation with others, acknowledging their actions or presence in your life.

Tips for Enhancing Gratitude:

- ○ Focusing on modest moments and practicing mindfulness
- ○ Appreciate the significance of minor moments of happiness, beauty, and connection in your daily existence.
- ○ Deepening your awareness of positive experiences through mindfulness can help you cultivate a greater sense of gratitude.

Integrating spiritual self-care practices into your daily routine can have a significant impact on your overall health. By engaging in mindfulness and meditation, connecting with nature, and cultivating an attitude of gratitude and reflection, you can nourish your soul, cultivate a sense of purpose and meaning, and experience a greater sense of life satisfaction. Embrace these practices with an open heart and a commitment to personal development, and you will observe your spiritual wellbeing flourish.

Summary & Conclusion: Embracing Self-Care as a Pathway

This chapter has covered a variety of self-care practices that incorporate the physical, mental, and spiritual aspects of health. You can create a more balanced, fulfilling, and meaningful existence by prioritizing and incorporating these practices into your daily routine. Self-care is an essential component of maintaining overall health and well-being in a demanding and ever-changing world.

Prioritize physical self-care by engaging in regular exercise, consuming a well-balanced diet, and obtaining sufficient rest. Enhance your mental health by managing stress, cultivating emotional awareness, and cultivating social relationships. Encourage spiritual well-being through mindfulness and meditation, interacting with nature, practicing gratitude and reflection, and connecting with one's inner self.

Remember, as you embark on your self-care journey, that change requires patience and perseverance. Be patient with yourself and adapt your practices to your specific requirements and preferences. Recognize your progress and the commitment you are making to put your well-being first.

Self-care is ultimately a continuous process of self-discovery, development, and transformation. You can improve your overall health, strengthen your relationships, and cultivate a greater sense of self-awareness and self-compassion by devoting time and effort to caring for your mind, body, and spirit. Embrace self-care as a means to wholeness and well-being, and evolve into your finest self.

Chapter 9:
Maintaining Physical and Emotional Wellness as Part of Self-Care for Mental Health

Introduction: Physical & Emotional Wellness

In today's fast-paced society, mental health has become an essential component of overall health. In addition to psychological factors, a holistic approach to mental health also considers physical and emotional dimensions. Self-care, which entails engaging in activities and practices that promote personal health and pleasure, is an essential component of mental health maintenance. Individuals can develop resilience, reduce tension, and improve their quality of life by cultivating their physical and emotional health. In addition, practicing self-care can lead to a greater comprehension of one's requirements, desires, and limitations, resulting in a more balanced and satisfying existence.

This chapter seeks to provide a comprehensive comprehension of the significance of physical and emotional wellness for mental health self-care. It will explore the relationships between physical health, emotional well-being, and mental health, illustrating the interdependence of these aspects of wellness. This chapter will also present practical strategies for incorporating physical and emotional self-care practices into daily life, with the aim of arming readers with the tools they need to enhance their mental health and well-being as a whole. In conclusion, guidance will be provided on attaining a balance between physical, emotional, and mental health requirements, with an emphasis on the significance of self-awareness, flexibility, and consistency in self-care practices.

By understanding and embracing the vital role of physical and emotional wellness in mental health, individuals can make more informed self-care decisions and develop a deeper appreciation for the interconnected nature of wellness.

The Importance of Physical Wellness in Self-Care for Mental Health

Physical wellbeing is essential for self-care and mental health. A healthy body is more resistant to stress and better equipped to deal with life's obstacles. This section will examine the relationship between physical and mental health, highlighting the bidirectional nature of the relationship and highlighting the impact of exercise, nutrition, and sleep on mental health.

The Relationship Between Physical and Mental Health

Bi-Directional Relationship: Physical and mental health are interdependent, with each influencing the other in a circular fashion. Poor physical health can contribute to mental health issues such as depression and anxiety, whereas mental health issues can exacerbate physical maladies and diminish overall health. By fostering physical health, individuals can establish a solid foundation for mental well-being and enhance their capacity to face the challenges of life.

Exercise and Mental Health: Regular physical activity is associated with numerous benefits for mental health, including improved mood, reduced tension, and enhanced cognitive function. Physical activity stimulates the release of endorphins, which are natural mood enhancers, and promotes neuroplasticity, which enhances brain health and resilience. By incorporating exercise into their routines of self-care, individuals can improve their physical and mental health.

Diet and Mental Health: What we eat has a direct effect on our mental health. A diet abundant in essential nutrients, such as vitamins, minerals, and healthful lipids, promotes optimal cognitive function and emotional health. A diet deficient in essential nutrients, on the other hand, can contribute to mood imbalances, cognitive difficulties, and an increased risk of mental health problems. Individuals can improve their mental health and overall wellness by making informed nutritional decisions.

Physical Wellness Strategies

Regular Exercise: Developing a consistent exercise routine is essential for obtaining the mental health benefits of physical activity. A well-rounded fitness program can integrate a variety of exercises, including aerobic, strength training, flexibility, and balance exercises. The frequency, duration, and intensity of recommendations can be tailored to individual requirements and preferences. Setting realistic objectives, finding pleasant activities, and enlisting social support are methods for remaining motivated and overcoming barriers to exercise.

Healthy Nutrition: A balanced diet is a vital component of both physical and mental health. Consuming a variety of nutrient-dense foods, such as fruits, vegetables, whole cereals, lean proteins, and healthy fats, while limiting intake of processed foods, added carbohydrates, and harmful fats, is fundamental to a healthy diet. Certain nutrients, such as omega-3 fatty acids and B vitamins, are essential for mental health and mood regulation. In order to make healthier food choices, it is recommended to plan meals in advance, purchase with a schedule, and learn to read nutrition labels.

Sleep Hygiene: Appropriate sleep hygiene is essential for both physical and mental health. The establishment and maintenance of optimal sleep patterns can enhance temperament, cognitive function, and overall health. Creating a consistent sleep schedule, establishing a soothing bedtime routine, and optimizing the sleep environment are strategies for promoting good sleep hygiene. Conditions such as insomnia and sleep apnea can contribute to mood imbalances, cognitive difficulties, and an increased risk of developing mental health issues. Consultation with a healthcare professional is advised for those with persistent sleep issues.

Individuals can establish a solid foundation for mental health and overall well-being by incorporating these physical wellness practices into their self-care regimens.

The Importance of Emotional Wellness in Self-Care for Mental Health

Emotional health is an essential component of self-care and mental health. The ability to effectively manage and express emotions, deal with stress, and maintain healthy relationships has a significant impact on mental health. This section will examine the relationship between emotional wellness and mental health, with a concentration on the function of emotional regulation, the effects of stress, and the significance of social connections.

The Relationship Between Emotional and Mental Health

Mental Health and Emotional Regulation: Emotional regulation is the capacity to recognize, comprehend, and manage one's emotions in a healthy and adaptive manner. Effective emotional regulation is essential for mental health because it fosters resilience and enables individuals to manage with adversity. Inversely, difficulties in emotional regulation can increase a person's susceptibility to mental health problems like anxiety, depression, and mood disorders.

Stress and Emotional Health: Stress is an unavoidable aspect of life, and the manner in which individuals manage stress can have a significant impact on their emotional health. Chronic tension can have a negative effect on mental health, leading to anxiety, irritability, and melancholy. Developing effective stress management strategies and engaging in self-care activities can assist individuals in lowering their tension levels and preserving their emotional health.

Social Connections and Emotional Health: Humans are social creatures, and robust, supportive relationships are necessary for emotional health. Positive social relationships can provide a buffer against stress and a sense of belonging and purpose. In contrast, social isolation and dysfunctional relationships can exacerbate emotional distress and increase the risk of mental health problems.

Psychological Health Strategies

Mindfulness and Meditation: Mindfulness, the practice of maintaining a nonjudgmental awareness of the present moment, can be a useful tool for promoting emotional health. Meditation and other mindfulness practices can help people cultivate self-awareness, manage tension, and develop healthier emotional responses. Tips for incorporating mindfulness and meditation into daily life include setting aside daily dedicated time, beginning with brief sessions, and experimenting with various meditation techniques to find the best fit.

Stress Management: Identification and management of stressors are essential for maintaining emotional health. Techniques for reducing tension include deep breathing, progressive muscle relaxation, visualization, and hobbies or leisure activities. Individuals who develop a personalized stress management plan can navigate stressful situations more effectively and maintain emotional equilibrium.

Social Connections: Establishing and maintaining solid social networks is essential for psychological health. Strategies for improving communication and interpersonal skills may include active listening practice, expressing empathy, and developing assertiveness. Developing healthy boundaries and managing conflict requires setting clear expectations, respecting the boundaries of others, and seeking compromise or resolution in difficult circumstances.

By focusing on emotional wellness and incorporating these strategies into their self-care routines, individuals can foster resilience, reduce tension, and promote mental health and well-being overall.

Achieving Balance Between Physical and Emotional Wellness for Optimal Mental Health

The promotion of optimal mental health requires striking a balance between physical and emotional wellness. While each component of wellness is vital in and of itself, genuine well-being is attained when all elements are harmoniously integrated. This section will discuss techniques for establishing a self-care routine that addresses both physical and emotional requirements, as well as techniques for monitoring and modifying self-care practices to maintain balance.

Integrating Physical and Emotional Practices of Self-Care

Developing a Self-Care Regimen: Creating a self-care regimen that addresses both physical and emotional requirements is the first step in attaining balance. This may include allocating time for regular exercise, organizing healthy meals, practicing mindfulness, engaging in stress-relieving activities, and cultivating social connections.

Individuals can create a more comprehensive approach to mental health by integrating a variety of self-care practices to address multiple facets of well-being.

Maintaining Consistency and Motivation: For long-term benefits, it is essential to adhere to a self-care routine. Setting realistic objectives, prioritizing self-care activities, and establishing a regular schedule can foster consistency. Individuals can maintain motivation by recalling the reasons for their self-care practices, celebrating their progress, and enlisting the support of friends and family.

Flexibility and Adaptability in Self-Care Practices: Life is full of changes, and self-care routines may need to be modified to accommodate these shifts. Individuals can modify their self-care practices to better meet their current requirements when they embrace flexibility and adaptability, promoting a more sustainable approach to mental health and well-being.

Adjusting and Monitoring Self-Care Practices

Self-Awareness and Self-Reflection: Developing self-awareness is essential for sustaining a balance between physical and emotional health. By routinely ruminating on their self-care practices, individuals are able to identify areas for improvement and make the necessary modifications. This may involve evaluating the efficacy of various self-care activities, identifying indicators of imbalance, or identifying areas where additional support is required.

Identifying Signs of Imbalance: Signs of imbalance between physical and emotional health include persistent fatigue, mood fluctuations, concentration difficulties, and changes in appetite or sleep patterns. By monitoring these indicators, individuals can proactively resolve imbalances and preserve their mental health.

Adjusting Self-Care Practices: When imbalances are identified, it is necessary to adjust self-care practices accordingly. This may involve increasing or decreasing the frequency of certain activities, investigating new self-care techniques, or seeking professional assistance to address particular concerns. Individuals can create a more personalized and effective approach to mental health and well-being by remaining receptive to change and adaptation.

Obtaining a balance between physical and emotional health is essential for promoting optimal mental health, to conclude. Individuals can cultivate resilience and improve their overall well-being by incorporating a variety of self-care practices, maintaining consistency and motivation, and monitoring and modifying their routines. Self-awareness, adaptability, and a dedication to ongoing self-care practices are essential to achieving this equilibrium.

Summary & Conclusion: The Importance of Sleep

Ultimately, nurturing physical and emotional wellness is essential for promoting mental health and overall well-being. Individuals can develop resiliency, reduce stress, and improve their quality of life by grasping the intricate connections between these facets of health and by engaging in a comprehensive self-care regimen. This holistic approach to mental health recognizes that genuine well-being is attained when all components are harmoniously integrated.

Developing and maintaining a self-care routine that addresses both the physical and psychological aspects of health requires self-awareness, motivation, and flexibility. By routinely ruminating on their self-care practices, individuals can identify areas for improvement, make necessary adjustments, and develop a more individualized mental health strategy. In addition, seeking support from friends, family members, or professionals can provide additional guidance and encouragement, reinforcing the significance of social connections to emotional health.

Ultimately, the commitment to ongoing self-care practices is the key to attaining a harmonious equilibrium between physical, emotional, and mental health. As individuals prioritize their well-being and devote time and effort to cultivating their minds and bodies, they can enjoy a balanced and satisfying existence. It is essential to remember that self-care is an ongoing process, and that a commitment to physical and emotional wellness will sustain mental health and overall well-being over time.

Chapter 10:
The Importance of Sleep for Mental Health

Introduction:
Why is Sleep so Important?

Sleep is an essential component of our existence, playing a vital role in maintaining our physical and mental health. It is a necessary restorative process that enables the body and mind to recover, regenerate, and prepare for daily challenges. In recent years, a growing body of evidence has highlighted the intricate relationship between sleep and mental health, highlighting the significance of understanding this relationship for overall health.

Mental health incorporates our emotional, psychological, and social well-being, influencing our thoughts, feelings, and actions. It also influences how we deal with tension, interact with others, and make decisions. Sleep is just as essential for our mental health as it is for our physical health. Lack of sleep, poor sleep quality, and sleep disorders can have significant effects on our temperament, cognition, and overall mental state.

This chapter examines the significance of sleep for mental health by discussing the role of sleep in maintaining mental health, examining the various stages of sleep and their functions, examining the effects of sleep deprivation on mental health, and examining the relationship between sleep disorders and mental health problems. In addition, we provide evidence-based strategies for enhancing sleep quality in order to improve mental health. Individuals can significantly contribute to their mental health and well-being by grasping the significance of sleep and adopting effective strategies for maintaining good sleep hygiene.

The Role of Sleep in Maintaining Mental Health

Sleep influences numerous aspects of our emotional, cognitive, and psychological well-being, and plays a multifaceted role in maintaining mental health. This section will examine the important functions of sleep in maintaining mental health, such as emotional regulation, memory consolidation and learning, stress reduction, and neuroplasticity.

Emotional Management
Sleep is essential for emotional regulation because it enables the brain to consolidate and process the emotional experiences of the day. During sleep, specifically REM sleep,

the brain reorganizes and integrates emotional information, allowing us to more effectively process and regulate our emotions. The amygdala, which is responsible for processing emotions, especially negative ones, becomes less reactive during sleep, resulting in a more balanced emotional state and a lower risk of developing mood disorders such as depression and anxiety. In addition, REM sleep has been demonstrated to assist in erasing fear-based memories, thereby reducing anxiety and post-traumatic stress disorder (PTSD) symptoms.

Memory Enhancement and Learning

Memory consolidation and learning require rest. During profound sleep, specifically NREM sleep, the brain consolidates new information and strengthens neural connections, allowing individuals to better retain and recall memories. This procedure is particularly essential for the consolidation of procedural and declarative memory. A decent night's sleep has been associated with enhanced cognitive function, problem-solving, and creativity. In addition, research has demonstrated that sleep can improve perception and facilitate more effective problem-solving.

Stress Management

The production of stress hormones, such as cortisol, is regulated by sleep. A sufficient amount of sleep can reduce cortisol levels and facilitate a more balanced stress response. This, in turn, can reduce anxiety and enhance mental health overall. In addition, it has been discovered that sleep regulates the production of other hormones and neurotransmitters, such as serotonin, dopamine, and adrenaline, which play an important role in mood regulation, motivation, and the body's stress response.

Neuroplasticity

Neuroplasticity, the brain's capacity to establish and reorganize synaptic connections in response to learning and experience, is a crucial aspect of mental health maintenance. It has been demonstrated that sleep promotes the growth of new neurons and strengthens existing neural connections, thereby enhancing neuroplasticity. This procedure is crucial for learning, memory consolidation, and emotional regulation. By fostering neuroplasticity, sleep contributes to our capacity to adapt, learn, and develop emotionally and cognitively, thereby promoting mental health.

Sleep's influence on emotional regulation, memory consolidation and learning, stress reduction, and neuroplasticity are essential for maintaining mental health. Obtaining sufficient and high-quality sleep is essential for promoting optimal mental health and well-being.

The Stages of Sleep and Their Functions

Sleep is a multi-staged physiological process with distinct characteristics and functions for each stage. To comprehend the significance of sleep, one must comprehend these stages and their functions in maintaining mental health. Non-Rapid Eye Movement (NREM) sleep and Rapid Eye Movement (REM) sleep are the two fundamental categories of sleep. Each stage has distinct functions and plays an indispensable role in promoting mental health.

NREM (non-rapid eye movement) Sleep

NREM sleep comprises between 75% and 80% of the total sleep cycle and is characterized by weaker brain waves and decreased muscle activity. It is further divided into N1, N2, and N3 stages. Each of these phases serves a distinct purpose:

N1 Sleep: This is the lowest stage of slumber and marks the transition from wakefulness to sleep. During this stage, the brain generates brain waves with a low amplitude and varied frequency, the heart rate and respiration calm down, and muscle tension begins to decrease. Although N1 sleep does not contribute substantially to memory consolidation or learning, it is a crucial transitional stage to the deeper stages of sleep.

N2 Sleep: The presence of sleep spindles (bursts of rapid brain activity) and K-complexes (large, sluggish brain waves) distinguishes N2 sleep. This stage is characterized by decreased muscle activity, heart rate, and body temperature compared to N1. N2 sleep contributes to memory consolidation, specifically for motor skills and procedural memories.

N3 Sleep: N3 is the deepest stage of NREM sleep, also known as slow-wave sleep or delta sleep. The brain produces sluggish, high-amplitude delta waves during this stage. N3 sleep is essential for memory consolidation, especially declarative memories, and has restorative functions such as tissue restoration, growth hormone release, and immune system support. This stage is also essential for preserving cognitive function and promoting mental health in general.

Rapid Eye Movement (REM) Sleep

20-25% of the sleep cycle is REM sleep, which is characterized by rapid eye movement, vivid hallucinations, and increased cerebral activity. During this stage, the brain produces brain waves with varied frequencies, akin to those observed during wakefulness. Significantly decreased muscle tone results in transient paralysis that prevents individuals from pursuing their aspirations. REM sleep is essential for several functions related to mental health:

Emotional Regulation: REM sleep is essential for processing and integrating emotional experiences, allowing individuals to more effectively modulate their emotions. This stage of sleep has been associated with decreased activity in the amygdala, which processes negative emotions, and increased activity in the prefrontal cortex, which is responsible for higher-order cognitive functions and emotional regulation.

Memory Consolidation and Learning: REM sleep contributes to the consolidation of procedural and declarative memories, thereby enhancing learning and problem-solving skills. It is also associated with increased creativity and insight, allowing individuals to come up with novel solutions to difficult problems.

Neuroplasticity: As with NREM sleep, REM sleep promotes neuroplasticity by fostering the formation and consolidation of new neural connections. This is an essential process for learning, memory consolidation, and emotional regulation.

In conclusion, the different stages of sleep, such as NREM and REM sleep, play crucial roles in maintaining mental health. Each stage contributes to essential functions such as emotional control, memory consolidation, learning, and neuroplasticity. Understanding these stages and their functions in mental health highlights the significance of adequate and high-quality sleep for overall health.

Consequences of Sleep Deprivation on Mental Health

Whether acute or chronic, sleep deprivation can have significant effects on mental health. Sleep deprivation impacts mood, cognitive function, and the ability to manage with stress, resulting in both short-term and long-term mental health problems. This section will examine the effects of sleep deprivation on mental health, with a particular concentration on mood disorders, cognitive impairment, and an increased risk of psychiatric disorders.

Mood Disorders
Depression and anxiety can develop as a result of chronic sleep deprivation. Insufficient sleep can disrupt the production and balance of neurotransmitters responsible for modulating mood, such as serotonin and dopamine. Consistently sleeping less than six hours per night is associated with an increased risk of developing depression and anxiety, according to studies. In addition, sleep disturbances are common symptoms of existing mood disorders, creating a pernicious cycle in which poor sleep exacerbates mental health problems and mental health problems further disrupt sleep.

Cognitive Impairment
Sleep deprivation can result in cognitive impairments such as difficulty concentrating, memory issues, and diminished problem-solving skills. Lack of sleep impairs the brain's capacity to consolidate memories, process information, and adapt to novel situations. Even one night of insufficient sleep can impair cognitive function and

decision-making, according to research. Chronic sleep loss can contribute to a decline in cognitive performance and an increased risk of neurodegenerative diseases, such as Alzheimer's.

Enhanced Probability of Psychiatric Disorders

There is a link between sleep deprivation and an increased risk of developing psychiatric disorders such as bipolar disorder, schizophrenia, and PTSD. Sleep disturbances can exacerbate the symptoms of these conditions and contribute to their development. Those with bipolar disorder, for instance, frequently experience sleep disturbances during both manic and depressive episodes, with reduced sleep serving as a common catalyst for mania. Similarly, sleep disturbances are a defining characteristic of PTSD, as traumatic experiences can result in nightmares and heightened arousal during sleep.

Ineffective Emotional Control and Social Functioning

Sleep deprivation can impair emotional regulation, resulting in increased emotional reactivity, irritability, and stress management difficulties. This can strain interpersonal relationships and impact social functioning negatively. Sleep-deprived individuals are more likely to misinterpret social signals and exhibit impaired empathy, further contributing to social difficulties and isolation, according to research.

Reduced Stress Resilience

Adequate sleep is necessary for developing stress resistance and fostering healthy coping mechanisms. Sleep deprivation can impair the body's ability to regulate stress hormones, such as cortisol, resulting in increased stress responses and a diminished capacity to face daily challenges. This can contribute to the development of stress-related mental health problems, including anxiety disorders and exhaustion, over time.

In conclusion, sleep deprivation can have devastating effects on mental health, contributing to mood disorders, cognitive impairments, an increased risk of psychiatric disorders, impaired emotional regulation, and diminished stress resilience. Getting enough sleep and addressing sleep disturbances are essential for sustaining optimal mental health and well-being overall.

Relationship Between Sleep Disorders and Mental Health Issues

Complex and bidirectional, the relationship between sleep disorders and mental health issues is multifaceted. Sleep disorders can contribute to the development or worsening of mental health problems, and mental health problems can also cause or exacerbate sleep disorders. This section will investigate the association between common sleep disorders, such as insomnia, sleep apnea, and restless legs syndrome, and mental health concerns.

Insomnia

Insomnia, which is characterized by difficulty falling asleep, remaining unconscious, or enduring non-restorative sleep, is significantly linked to mental health problems. According to studies, insomniacs have an increased risk of developing melancholy, anxiety, and other psychological disorders. Insomnia is also a prevalent symptom of preexisting mental health problems, creating a vicious cycle in which poor sleep contributes to mental health issues and mental health issues exacerbate insomnia. Effective insomnia treatment with cognitive-behavioral therapy for insomnia (CBT-I) or medication can substantially enhance mental health outcomes.

Sleep Apnea

Sleep apnea, a disorder characterized by repetitive breathing pauses during sleep, has been linked to a variety of mental health problems. The most prevalent form of sleep apnea, obstructive sleep apnea (OSA), has been linked to an increased risk of depression, anxiety, and cognitive impairment. Frequent sleep interruptions caused by sleep apnea can result in chronic sleep deprivation, aggravating mental health problems. The use of continuous positive airway pressure (CPAP) devices or other interventions to treat sleep apnea can enhance sleep quality and mental health.

Restless Legs Syndrome

Restless legs syndrome (RLS) is a neurological disorder characterized by an involuntary impulse to move the legs, which is frequently accompanied by unpleasant sensations. RLS frequently disrupts sleep, resulting in sleep deprivation and its attendant mental health effects. The prevalence of depression and anxiety is greater among RLS patients compared to the general population, according to research. The treatment of RLS with medication or changes in lifestyle can alleviate symptoms, enhance sleep quality, and improve mental health.

Circadian Rhythm Disorders

In disorders of the circadian rhythm, such as delayed sleep-wake phase disorder, advanced sleep-wake phase disorder, and irregular sleep-wake rhythm disorder, the timing of sleep and arousal is disrupted. These conditions can result in protracted sleep deprivation and misalignment between the body's internal rhythm and the external environment, thereby contributing to mood disorders, anxiety, and cognitive impairments. In order to realign the body's internal clock and enhance mental health, light therapy, melatonin supplementation, and chronotherapy are frequently used to treat circadian rhythm disorders.

In conclusion, the connection between sleep disorders and mental health problems is intricate and intertwined. Sleep disorders, such as insomnia, sleep apnea, restless legs syndrome, and circadian rhythm disorders, can contribute to the development or worsening of mental health problems, while mental health problems can also cause or exacerbate sleep disorders. Understanding and addressing the interaction between sleep disorders and mental health is essential for promoting optimal mental health and well-being overall.

Strategies for Improving Sleep Quality

Improving the quality of sleep is essential for enhancing mental health and well-being. Incorporating strategies supported by scientific evidence and maintaining good sleep hygiene can significantly improve sleep quality and aid in the prevention of sleep disorders. This section will outline effective strategies for enhancing sleep quality, such as establishing a consistent sleep schedule, creating a sleep-friendly environment, implementing healthy sleep practices, and seeking professional assistance as necessary.

Establish a Regular Sleep Routine

Regarding slumber, consistency is essential. Establishing a regular sleep schedule by going to bed and rising up at the same time every day, even on the weekends, helps regulate the body's internal rhythm and improves sleep quality. This is the recommended quantity of sleep for most adults: 7-9 hours per night.

Develop a Sleep-Friendly Setting

Creating a slumber environment that is comfortable and conducive is essential for promoting restorative sleep. Make sure the chamber is calm, dark, and chilly, as these are conducive to sleep. Consider utilizing blackout curtains, earplugs, and white noise devices to reduce disturbances. Invest in a supportive mattress and cushions that provide comfort and support.

Adopt Sound Sleep Practices

Adopting healthy sleep practices can enhance the quality of sleep and prevent sleep disorders. Some essential practices to adopt include:

- Limiting exposure to displays and blue light prior to nighttime, as they can inhibit the production of melatonin, the hormone that induces sleep.
- Participating in relaxation techniques, such as deep breathing, meditation, or progressive muscle relaxation, in order to help soothe the mind and prepare the body for slumber.
- Avoiding stimulants, such as caffeine and nicotine, in the hours before bed, as they can disrupt sleep.
- Consuming alcohol in moderation, as it can impair sleep quality and exacerbate sleep disorders.
- Regularly exercising, but avoiding intense exercises close to nighttime, as they can heighten alertness and make it difficult to fall asleep.

Develop a Bedtime Routine

Developing a pre-sleep routine can alert the body that it is time to relax and prepare for sleep. Engage in body and mind-relaxing activities, such as reading, having a warm bath, and performing mild stretches. As they can interfere with sleep, avoid engaging in stimulating or distressing activities before nighttime.

Seek Professional Assistance When Necessary

If sleep problems persist despite implementing these techniques, or if a sleep disorder is suspected, it is essential to consult a healthcare professional or sleep specialist. They can assist in identifying the root cause of sleep problems and recommend appropriate treatment options, such as cognitive-behavioral therapy for insomnia (CBT-I), medication, and lifestyle changes.

Improving sleep quality is crucial for promoting improved mental health and well-being overall. Establishing a consistent sleep schedule, creating a sleep-friendly environment, adopting healthy sleep practices, establishing a pre-sleep routine, and seeking professional assistance when necessary are strategies for improving sleep quality. Individuals can substantially improve their sleep quality and contribute to their mental health and well-being by implementing these strategies.

Summary & Conclusion

Sleep's significance for mental health cannot be emphasized. Sleep facilitates emotional regulation, memory consolidation, learning, and neuroplasticity, all of which are essential for maintaining mental health. Various stages of sleep, including NREM and REM sleep, contribute to these vital functions, highlighting the importance of adequate and high-quality sleep for overall health.

Sleep deprivation and sleep disorders can have severe effects on mental health, resulting in mood disorders, cognitive impairments, an increased risk of psychiatric disorders, impaired emotional regulation, and diminished stress resilience. Understanding and addressing the connection between sleep disorders and mental health issues is crucial for promoting optimal mental health and well-being.

By implementing effective strategies for enhancing sleep quality, such as establishing a consistent sleep schedule, creating a sleep-friendly environment, adopting healthy sleep habits, and establishing a pre-sleep routine, individuals can significantly improve their sleep quality and contribute to their mental health and well-being.

The significance of sleep for mental health cannot be denied. Obtaining sufficient and high-quality sleep is not only essential for maintaining mental health, but also a pillar of overall wellbeing. Individuals can support their mental health and lead healthier; more fulfilling lives by recognizing the importance of sleep and implementing evidence-based strategies to enhance sleep quality.

Chapter 11:
The Role of Nutrition in Mental Health

Introduction:
Nutrition in Mental Health

Expanding Perspectives on the Significance of Nutrition to Mental Health In recent years, researchers, healthcare professionals, and the general public have paid increasing attention to the role of nutrition in mental health. The importance of a balanced diet in maintaining both physical and mental health is now widely acknowledged. Proper nutrition has been shown to aid in the prevention of mental health disorders, alleviate their symptoms, and enhance overall quality of life. Moreover, as our understanding of the complex relationship between the brain and the intestine, also known as the gut-brain axis, continues to expand, the role of nutrition in mental health becomes more evident.

Purpose and Scope of the Chapter: An Exhaustive Analysis This chapter's objective is to provide a thorough examination of the role of nutrition in mental health. This chapter intends to serve as a valuable resource for readers interested in comprehending the complex relationships between diet and mental health, drawing on current scientific research and expert recommendations.

The chapter's scope includes the following essential areas:

- An analysis of the biochemical and physiological mechanisms linking nutrition to brain function and mental health.
- Identification of essential nutrients for optimal mental health and a comprehensive analysis of their specific functions in promoting mental health.
- An examination of diverse dietary patterns and their effects on mental health, including a discussion of food variety and quality.
- An analysis of the relationship between nutritional deficiencies and mental health disorders, as well as a discussion of the potential benefits of nutritional supplementation as a complementary therapy.
- Recommendations for enhancing mental health through nutrition, including dietary guidelines, suggestions, and strategies for overcoming obstacles to adopting a mentally healthy diet.
- A consideration of current knowledge deficits and prospective research opportunities in the field of nutrition and mental health.

By providing a well-organized, evidence-based account of the role of nutrition in mental health, this chapter hopes to empower readers to make informed dietary decisions and support their mental health through informed nutritional practices.

The Connection between Nutrition and Mental Health: A Multifaceted Relationship

The Building Blocks of Mental Health: Biochemistry of Nutrients and Their Effect on Brain Function The biochemistry of nutrients and their influence on brain function is a fascinating and intricate field of study. Nutrients serve as the building elements for numerous brain processes, influencing its structure, function, and health as a whole. Here, we explore some of the most important mechanisms by which nutrients affect brain function:

Synthesis and Function of Neurotransmitters: Neurotransmitters are chemical molecules that allow brain cells to communicate. Amino acids, vitamins, and minerals play crucial roles in neurotransmitter synthesis, metabolism, and regulation. Tryptophan, for instance, is a precursor to serotonin, a neurotransmitter involved in mood regulation, while tyrosine is a precursor to dopamine, a neurotransmitter involved in motivation and reward.

Neuronal Structure and Maintenance: Fatty acids, such as omega-3s, contribute to the structural integrity of neuronal membranes, which is vital for appropriate signal transmission and brain function as a whole. In addition, certain nutrients, such as choline, play a role in the synthesis of phospholipids, which constitute a substantial portion of neuronal membranes.

Neuroprotection and Repair: Antioxidants, such as vitamins C and E, and various phytonutrients found in fruits and vegetables, aid in protecting the brain from oxidative stress, which can result in cellular damage and impaired cognitive function. In addition, nutrients such as zinc, magnesium, and B vitamins play crucial roles in DNA repair and cellular health maintenance.

Brain Energy Metabolism: The brain is an energy-intensive organ that requires a constant supply of glucose and other nutrients in order to function optimally. B vitamins such as thiamine, riboflavin, and niacin are essential for energy metabolism in the brain, while minerals such as magnesium and manganese are required for numerous enzymatic processes involved in the production of energy.

The Function of Neurotransmitters and Hormones in Mental Health: Chemical Brain Messengers Neurotransmitters and hormones play crucial roles in mental health by modulating mood, cognition, and other essential aspects of brain function.

Following are a few examples of the crucial functions neurotransmitters and hormones play in mental health:

Mood Regulation: Neurotransmitters including serotonin, dopamine, and norepinephrine are involved in mood and emotion regulation. These neurotransmitters can contribute to mental health disorders such as depression and anxiety when they are out of equilibrium. Intake of nutrients, particularly amino acids and B vitamins, can influence the production and function of these neurotransmitters in a direct or indirect manner.

Stress Response: In response to physical or emotional tension, the hormone cortisol, also known as the "stress hormone," is produced. Chronic stress and elevated cortisol levels can contribute to a variety of mental health problems, including anxiety and depression. Vitamin C and omega-3 fatty acids are able to modulate cortisol levels and promote a healthful stress response.

Cognitive Function and Memory: Neurotransmitters such as acetylcholine and glutamate are indispensable for cognitive function, learning, and memory. Choline, a precursor to acetylcholine, and antioxidants, which protect against oxidative stress, are indispensable for optimal cognitive function.

Sleep and Circadian Rhythms: Sleep and circadian rhythms are regulated by the hormone melatonin, which is produced by the pineal gland. Tryptophan, magnesium, and vitamin B6 all play a role in the synthesis and regulation of melatonin, which can impact mental health via sleep quality and circadian rhythm regulation.

In conclusion, the relationship between nutrition and mental health is multifaceted and profoundly anchored in the brain's biochemistry. All of these processes, including neurotransmitter synthesis, neuronal structure maintenance, neuroprotection, and energy metabolism, are essential for optimal brain function and mental health. Dietary intake regulates the balance and function of neurotransmitters and hormones, which are essential for mood regulation, stress response, cognitive function, and sleep. By comprehending the intricate relationship between nutrition and mental health, individuals can make dietary decisions that support their mental health and overall brain health.

Key Nutrients for Optimal Mental Health: Essential Components for a Healthy Mind

Essential Nutrients for Mental Health: Vitamins, Minerals, and Fatty Acids A range of essential nutrients, including vitamins, minerals, and fatty acids, play significant roles in supporting mental health. Some of the key nutrients that have been found to be particularly important for optimal brain function and mental well-being include:

Omega-3 Fatty Acids: These essential fatty acids, particularly EPA (eicosapentaenoic acid) and DHA (docosahexaenoic acid), are critical for brain health. They are involved in maintaining the structural integrity of neuronal membranes, modulating inflammation, and supporting neurotransmitter function. Omega-3 fatty acids are primarily found in fatty fish, such as salmon, mackerel, and sardines, as well as in plant sources like flaxseeds, chia seeds, and walnuts.

B Vitamins: B vitamins, including B6, B9 (folate), and B12, are essential for the production and metabolism of neurotransmitters and the regulation of homocysteine levels, which have been linked to an increased risk of depression and cognitive decline. Rich sources of B vitamins include whole grains, lean meats, eggs, dairy products, leafy green vegetables, and fortified cereals.

Vitamin D: Often referred to as the "sunshine vitamin," vitamin D plays a crucial role in maintaining mental health by regulating neurotransmitters like serotonin and dopamine. Low levels of vitamin D have been associated with an increased risk of depression and other mental health disorders. The primary source of vitamin D is sunlight exposure, but it can also be obtained from fatty fish, fortified dairy products, and supplements.

Magnesium: This essential mineral is involved in over 300 biochemical processes in the body, including those related to brain function and mental health. Magnesium plays a critical role in neurotransmitter synthesis, nerve function, and stress response regulation. Magnesium-rich foods include whole grains, nuts, seeds, leafy green vegetables, and legumes.

Zinc: Zinc is essential for brain development, neurotransmitter function, and the regulation of the stress response. Low levels of zinc have been linked to depression, anxiety, and cognitive impairment. Rich sources of zinc include oysters, red meat, poultry, beans, nuts, and whole grains.

The Importance of Each Nutrient in Supporting Mental Health
Each of the key nutrients mentioned above plays a unique and indispensable role in supporting mental health:

Omega-3 Fatty Acids: They help reduce inflammation, support neuronal membrane structure, and modulate neurotransmitter function, thus promoting overall brain health and reducing the risk of mental health disorders like depression and anxiety.

B Vitamins: They are critical for the synthesis and metabolism of neurotransmitters, which directly influence mood regulation, cognitive function, and stress response. Adequate intake of B vitamins can help prevent mental health issues related to neurotransmitter imbalances.

Vitamin D: It regulates neurotransmitters like serotonin and dopamine, which are crucial for mood stability and overall mental well-being. Maintaining optimal vitamin D levels can help reduce the risk of depression and other mood disorders.

Magnesium: It supports neurotransmitter synthesis, nerve function, and stress response regulation, which are all essential components of mental health. Adequate magnesium intake can help improve mood, reduce anxiety, and promote overall cognitive function.

Zinc: It contributes to brain development, neurotransmitter function, and stress response regulation, which are all critical for mental health. Ensuring optimal zinc levels can help prevent mental health issues like depression, anxiety, and cognitive impairment.

By incorporating a diverse range of nutrient-dense foods into their diets, individuals can support optimal mental health.

Dietary Patterns and Mental Health: The Impact of Food Choices on Emotional Well-Being

The Impact of Various Diets on Mental Health: Diets of the Mediterranean, Ketogenic, and Plant Origin Various dietary patterns have been investigated for their potential effects on mental health, with some exhibiting more optimistic results than others. Here, we discuss the relationship between three prevalent diets and mental health:

Mediterranean Diet: Dietary characteristics of the Mediterranean diet include a high intake of vegetables, fruits, whole grains, legumes, nuts, fish, and olive oil, moderate consumption of dairy products, poultry, and red wine, and a low intake of red meat and processed foods. This diet has been associated with improved mental health, including a lower risk of depression, anxiety, and cognitive decline, likely due to its high content of anti-inflammatory and antioxidant nutrients, omega-3 fatty acids, and other essential nutrients.

Ketogenic Diet: The ketogenic diet is a high-fat, low-carbohydrate eating plan that has acquired popularity due to its potential weight loss and cognitive benefits. While some studies have demonstrated improvements in mood and cognitive function in individuals following a ketogenic diet, additional research is required to ascertain its long-term effects on mental health. A well-formulated ketogenic diet should include a diversity of nutrient-dense foods, including verdant greens, non-starchy vegetables, nuts, seeds, and healthful lipids, to ensure adequate nutrient intake for optimal brain health.

Plant-Based Diet: A plant-based diet emphasizes the consumption of foods derived from plants, such as fruits, vegetables, whole cereals, legumes, nuts, and seeds, while limiting or eschewing animal products. Diets founded on plants have been linked to enhanced mental health, including a decreased risk of depression and anxiety. The mental health benefits of a plant-based diet are likely due to its high antioxidant, fiber, and other essential nutrient content, as well as its potential anti-inflammatory effects. Vitamin B12, iron, and omega-3 fatty acids are typically found in animal products; therefore, individuals following a plant-based diet must ensure they consume adequate amounts of these nutrients.

The Importance of Food Variety and Quality for Mental Health Promotion
Diverse and high-quality foods are crucial for promoting mental health through nutrition. Consuming a wide variety of nutrient-dense foods ensures that individuals receive all the vitamins, minerals, and other essential nutrients required for optimal cognitive function and mental health. In addition, a focus on food quality, such as selecting whole, minimally processed foods over highly processed and nutrient-poor alternatives, can have a substantial effect on mental health.

Highly processed foods, which are frequently high in added carbohydrates, unhealthy fats, and artificial additives, have been linked to increased inflammation and oxidative stress, both of which are detrimental to brain function and mental health. In contrast, whole foods, such as fruits, vegetables, whole cereals, lean proteins, and healthy lipids, contain an abundance of nutrients that promote cognitive health and mental well-being.

In conclusion, adopting a balanced and diverse dietary pattern that emphasizes whole, nutrient-dense foods, such as the Mediterranean or plant-based diet, can significantly enhance mental health outcomes. By focusing on food variety and quality, individuals can ensure that their minds receive the essential nutrients for optimal mental health.

Nutritional Deficiencies and Mental Health Disorders: Uncovering the Links

The Relationship between Nutritional Deficiencies and Specific Mental Health Disorders
Deficiencies in nutrition can have a significant impact on mental health, with certain deficiencies associated to specific mental disorders. Among the most significant

associations between nutritional deficiencies and mental health disorders are the following:

Depression: Omega-3 fatty acids, B vitamins (especially B6, B9, and B12), vitamin D, and magnesium deficiencies have been linked to an increased risk of depression. These nutrients play important roles in the synthesis and function of neurotransmitters, as well as in the regulation of inflammation and oxidative stress, which can contribute to the development of depression.

Anxiety: Magnesium, zinc, and the B vitamins are nutrient deficiencies associated with anxiety. These nutrients are essential for the regulation of neurotransmitter function, nerve function, and the stress response, all of which are vital components of anxiety management.

Attention Deficit Hyperactivity Disorder (ADHD): Deficiencies in omega-3 fatty acids, zinc, iron, magnesium, and B vitamins have been linked to ADHD. These nutrients are essential for neurotransmitter synthesis, brain development, cognitive function regulation, and attention regulation.
Cognitive decline and dementia have been linked to deficiencies in nutrients such as omega-3 fatty acids, B vitamins, vitamin D, and antioxidants. These nutrients play crucial roles in maintaining brain structure, preventing oxidative stress, and supporting cognitive function.

Potential Benefits of Nutritional Supplements in the Treatment of Mental Health Disorders

In addressing nutrient deficiencies and promoting mental health, nutritional supplementation may be beneficial. It is essential to note, however, that supplements should be used as a supplement to a healthy diet and not as a replacement for a balanced, nutrient-dense diet. Among the potential benefits of nutritional supplements in the treatment of mental disorders are:

Depression: Supplementation with omega-3 fatty acids, specifically EPA, has shown promise in mitigating the symptoms of depression in some individuals. In addition, supplementation with B vitamins, particularly folate, has been shown to alleviate depressive symptoms, particularly when used in conjunction with conventional antidepressant therapy.

Anxiety: Magnesium supplementation has been demonstrated to alleviate anxiety symptoms in individuals with deficient magnesium levels. Those with deficiencies in zinc and B vitamins may also benefit from zinc and B vitamin supplements.

ADHD: Some studies have suggested that supplementation with omega-3 fatty acids may alleviate ADHD symptoms in children, particularly those with low omega-3 levels. Individuals with ADHD who are deficient in nutrients such as zinc, iron, and magnesium may also benefit from supplementation with these nutrients.

Cognitive Decline and Dementia: Although additional research is necessary, some evidence suggests that supplementation with omega-3 fatty acids, B vitamins, and antioxidants may help delay cognitive decline and reduce the risk of dementia in individuals at risk.

Before beginning any supplementation regimen, it is essential to consult a healthcare professional, as individual needs and circumstances vary. In general, addressing nutritional deficiencies through dietary enhancements and, when necessary, targeted supplementation can be an effective strategy for promoting mental health and wellbeing.

Practical Recommendations for Improving Mental Health through Nutrition

Guidelines and Tips for a Mentally Healthy Diet

Consider the following dietary guidelines and recommendations to enhance mental health through nutrition:

Emphasize Whole Foods: Focus on the consumption of nutrient-dense, whole foods, including fruits, vegetables, whole cereals, lean proteins, and healthful lipids. These foods contain essential nutrients that promote optimal brain health and function.

Include a Variety of Foods: To obtain all the necessary vitamins, minerals, and other essential nutrients, include a variety of foods in your diet. Include a variety of colorful fruits and vegetables, whole cereals, lean protein sources, and healthy lipids in your diet.

Consume Omega-3 Rich Foods: Include fatty fish (salmon, mackerel, sardines), flaxseeds, chia seeds, and walnuts in your diet as sources of omega-3 fatty acids. Omega-3 fatty acids promote cognitive health, reduce inflammation, and enhance mood.

Prioritize B Vitamins: Include foods such as whole grains, lean proteins, eggs, dairy products, verdant green vegetables, and fortified cereals in your diet to consume adequate quantities of B vitamins.
Optimize vitamin D levels: Ensure adequate vitamin D intake through exposure to sunlight, consumption of vitamin D-rich foods such as fatty salmon and fortified dairy products, or, if necessary, supplementation.

Minimize Processed Foods and Added Sugars: Minimize your consumption of highly processed foods, which can be high in added sugars, harmful lipids, and artificial additives; these can contribute to inflammation, oxidative stress, and poor mental health.

Stay Hydrated: Consume sufficient water throughout the day to maintain appropriate hydration, as dehydration can impair cognitive function and mood. Pay attention to your appetite and satiety signals, and consume leisurely in order to savor your food and foster a healthful relationship with food.

Identifying and Addressing Potential Obstacles and Barriers to Adopting a Mentally Healthy Diet
It is essential to recognize that adopting a diet that promotes mental health can be difficult due to factors such as time constraints, financial constraints, and social influences. Here are some recommendations for overcoming these obstacles:

Plan Your Meals and Snacks: Planning your meals and refreshments in advance can help you save time and consume a nutrient-dense diet. Consider cooking in bulk and freezing dishes to save time on hectic days.

Shop Wisely: Look for sales and discounts on nutritious foods, and when possible, contemplate purchasing in volume. Choose preserved or tinned fruits and vegetables if fresh produce is prohibitively expensive or unavailable.

Make Straightforward Swaps: Replace processed foods and munchies with whole-grain crackers, fresh produce, and almonds.

Seek Social Support: Share your objectives with family and friends, and consider joining a community group or online forum dedicated to healthful nutrition and mental health.

Consult a Specialist: Consider consulting a registered dietitian or nutritionist if you find it difficult to adopt a diet that promotes mental health or if you require personalized advice.

Individuals can better their mental health through nutrition and support their overall well-being by adhering to these recommendations and addressing potential obstacles.

Future Research and Conclusions: Advancing Our Understanding of Nutrition and Mental Health

Discuss Current Gaps in Knowledge and Areas for Future Research

Despite the fact that research has substantially advanced our comprehension of the connection between nutrition and mental health, there are still knowledge gaps that require further investigation. These are some areas for future research:

Personalized Nutrition: Investigating the role of individual genetic, metabolic, and environmental factors in determining the optimal diet for mental health, given that nutritional requirements and responses may vary from person to person.

Long-Term Effects of Particular Diets: Examining the long-term effects of different dietary patterns, such as ketogenic or plant-based diets, on mental health outcomes in diverse populations.

Action mechanisms include: Clarifying the underlying biological mechanisms by which particular nutrients or dietary patterns affect mental health, such as the role of intestinal microbiota, inflammation, and oxidative stress.

Nutritional Supplementation: Conducting well-designed, randomized, controlled trials to evaluate the efficacy and safety of different nutritional supplements in the prevention and treatment of mental health disorders.

Access to Nutritious Food: Investigating the impact of food accessibility, affordability, and cultural factors on mental health, as well as investigating interventions to enhance access to nutritious foods in underserved communities.

Highlight the Importance of Nutrition to Mental Health and Summarize the Key Points

In conclusion, nutrition plays an essential role in mental health, with specific nutrients and dietary patterns having substantial effects on emotional health. A diet rich in whole foods and essential nutrients that is well-balanced and diverse can support brain function and overall mental health.

Important Aspects of This Chapter Include:

- The relationship between nutrition and mental health stems from the biochemistry of nutrients and their influence on brain function, neurotransmitters, and hormones.
- Vitamins, minerals, and fatty acids, among other essential nutrients, play crucial roles in maintaining mental health.
- Several dietary patterns, including the Mediterranean and plant-based diets, have been linked to better mental health outcomes.
- Nutritional deficiencies may play a role in the development of mental health disorders, and targeted supplementation may be useful in addressing these deficiencies.
- Adopting a diet that promotes mental health involves emphasizing whole foods, ingesting a diversity of nutrient-dense foods, and addressing potential obstacles and challenges.

Ultimately, prioritizing nutrition and adopting a healthy diet can have a significant positive effect on mental health and wellbeing. As research in this field continues to advance, a more comprehensive understanding of the intricate relationship between nutrition and mental health will emerge, guiding the development of targeted interventions and individualized dietary recommendations for enhanced mental health outcomes.

Chapter 12:
The Benefits of Exercise for Mental Health

Introduction:
Exercise in Mental Health

In recent years, there has been a growing interest in the complex relationship between physical activity and mental health, as mounting evidence supports the role of exercise in maintaining and enhancing mental health. As the prevalence of mental health disorders continues to rise worldwide, researchers and health professionals have made it a top priority to identify accessible and effective methods for promoting mental health. With its numerous physical and mental benefits, exercise has emerged as a potent tool in this pursuit.

In this chapter, we will examine the various facets of physical activity and how they contribute to improved mental health. The physiological mechanisms underlying the mood-enhancing effects of exercise, such as the release of endorphins and enhanced sleep quality, will be discussed. In addition, we will investigate the effect of exercise on specific mental health disorders, such as depression and anxiety, and the cognitive advantages of physical activity, such as improved memory, learning, concentration, and focus.

The purpose of this chapter is to provide a firm comprehension of the crucial role exercise plays in promoting mental health through a comprehensive review of research and examples. In addition, we will provide advice and recommendations to help readers integrate physical activity into their daily lives and experience the transformative impact of exercise on their mental health. Individuals can take a proactive approach to enhancing their overall quality of life by comprehending the benefits of exercise for mental health and adopting an active lifestyle.

The Physiological Effects of Exercise on Mental Health

The physiological effects of exercise on mental health are multidimensional and intricate, involving multiple interconnected mechanisms. These effects not only enhance our emotional health, but they also prevent us from developing mental health conditions. In this section, we will examine the physiological mechanisms that contribute to the mental health benefits of exercise.

Endorphins and Other Neurotransmitters: Their Function

Endorphins, also known as "feel-good" compounds, are naturally occurring neurotransmitters produced by the brain that mitigate pain and enhance mood. Endorphins and other essential neurotransmitters such as serotonin, dopamine, and norepinephrine are released as a result of physical activity. These chemicals play an important role in modulating mood, motivation, and pleasure and reward sensations.

The increase in neurotransmitter levels after exercise has been linked to a decrease in tension, anxiety, and depression, as well as an increase in well-being and contentment. This mood-enhancing effect is commonly referred to as the "runner's high," but it can occur after any form of physical activity.

Superior Sleep Quality

Sleep is necessary for optimal mental health because it allows the brain to rest, rejuvenate, and consolidate memories. Inadequate sleep quality or duration has been linked to an increased risk of developing mood disorders, anxiety, and cognitive impairments.

By stimulating the production of melatonin, the hormone responsible for modulating sleep, exercise can help regulate the body's sleep-wake cycle, also known as the circadian rhythm. Regular physical activity has been shown to increase the amount of profound, restorative sleep, which is essential for maintaining appropriate cognitive function, emotional regulation, and mental health as a whole.

Reduction of Stress and Resilience

Physical activity has a significant influence on the body's stress response, mitigating the detrimental impacts of stress on mental health. Physical activity increases the synthesis of brain-derived neurotrophic factor (BDNF), an essential protein for optimal brain function that promotes the development and survival of neurons. It has been demonstrated that BDNF contributes to the brain's resistance to stress, thereby preventing the development of stress-related mental health disorders.

In addition, exercise helps reduce levels of cortisol, the primary stress hormone in the body, which can have detrimental effects on mental health if elevated for an extended period of time. By reducing cortisol levels and promoting the release of neurotransmitters that enhance mood, exercise can effectively counteract the negative effects of stress on mental health.

Effects that Inhibit Inflammation

Chronic inflammation has been linked to the onset of a variety of mental health conditions, including depression and anxiety. Exercising promotes the release of anti-inflammatory cytokines and decreases the production of pro-inflammatory cytokines, which have been shown to have anti-inflammatory effects on the body. This decrease in inflammation protects the brain from harm and promotes optimal cognitive and emotional functioning, thereby contributing to an overall improvement in mental health.

In conclusion, the physiological effects of exercise on mental health are diverse and interconnected, involving the release of mood-enhancing neurotransmitters, improvements in sleep quality, reductions in stress, and anti-inflammatory effects. These mechanisms function synergistically to promote mental health and prevent the onset of mental health disorders.

Exercise and Mental Health Disorders

The relationship between physical activity and mental health disorders is a developing field of study, with numerous studies highlighting the beneficial effects of exercise on a variety of conditions. This section will discuss how physical activity can help prevent or ameliorate symptoms of mental health disorders such as melancholy, anxiety, and post-traumatic stress disorder (PTSD).

Depression and Exercise

Depression is a prevalent and incapacitating mental disorder characterized by persistent feelings of sorrow, hopelessness, and a lack of interest or enjoyment in activities. Exercise has been demonstrated to be an effective treatment for mild to moderate depression, with some studies suggesting that it may be as effective as antidepressant medication or psychotherapy for certain individuals.

Several factors, including the release of mood-enhancing neurotransmitters, increased production of BDNF, and reduced inflammation, contribute to the antidepressant effects of exercise. These physiological changes promote neuroplasticity and enhance overall brain function, leading to mood and emotional well-being enhancements.

In addition to its function as a stand-alone treatment, exercise can also be used in conjunction with other interventions, such as medication and therapy, to enhance their efficacy and improve overall treatment outcomes.

Workout and Anxiety

Anxiety disorders are characterized by excessive concern, fear, or agitation, and they can have a significant impact on a person's daily existence. Physical activity has been found to be effective for reducing anxiety symptoms and increasing overall mental health. Regular physical activity aids in relieving tension, promoting relaxation, and fostering a sense of accomplishment and mastery, all of which can help combat feelings of anxiety and dread.

Aerobic exercise, such as running, swimming, or cycling, has been shown to be particularly effective for reducing anxiety symptoms, according to research. Exercise is believed to have anxiolytic effects due to the release of endorphins and other neurotransmitters, in addition to the stress-buffering effects of increased BDNF production and decreased cortisol levels.

Physical Activity and Post-Traumatic Stress Disorder (PTSD)

Post-traumatic stress disorder is a mental health condition that can develop after exposure to a traumatic event. It is characterized by intrusive memories, flashbacks, and elevated levels of stress and anxiety. While more research is necessary to completely comprehend the relationship between exercise and PTSD, preliminary studies indicate that physical activity may help reduce symptoms and enhance the mental health of those with the disorder.

Exercise may ameliorate PTSD symptoms by promoting the release of mood-enhancing neurotransmitters, lowering cortisol levels, and increasing the production of BDNF, which can enhance emotional regulation and stress resistance. In addition, physical activity can enhance the quality of sleep, which is frequently disturbed in PTSD patients and can exacerbate symptoms.

Exercise as part of a comprehensive PTSD treatment strategy, alongside cognitive-behavioral therapy (CBT) and exposure therapy, may enhance treatment outcomes and promote long-term recovery.

In conclusion, exercise can play a significant role in the prevention and treatment of numerous mental health disorders, such as depression, anxiety, and PTSD. Individuals can enhance their mental health and well-being by engaging in regular physical activity.

Cognitive Benefits of Exercise

The cognitive benefits of exercise extend beyond its effect on mental health disorders, as research indicates that regular physical activity improves multiple aspects of cognitive function in individuals. In this section, we will discuss the cognitive benefits of exercise, such as improved memory, learning, concentration, and focus, as well as its potential preventive effects against age-related cognitive decline and neurodegenerative diseases.

Enhanced Learning and Memory

It has been demonstrated that exercise promotes the development of new brain cells, particularly in the hippocampus, which is responsible for learning and memory. This process, known as neurogenesis, can result in enhanced memory and cognitive function, both of which are essential for maintaining mental health.

Physical activity also increases the production of BDNF and other growth factors that promote the survival, development, and plasticity of neurons, thereby contributing further to enhanced learning and memory. In addition, it has been demonstrated that exercise improves the efficacy of brain networks involved in memory processing, resulting in enhanced consolidation and retrieval of memories.

Improved Concentration and Focus

Attention and concentration, which are crucial cognitive abilities for routine functioning and academic performance, can be significantly affected by physical activity. Physical activity has been shown to enhance focus and concentration by increasing oxygen and nutrient delivery to the brain, thereby increasing blood flow to the brain.

In addition, exercise can improve the function of brain regions associated with attention and executive control, resulting in enhanced cognitive flexibility and the ability to filter out distractions. As well as the general population, individuals with attention deficit disorders may benefit from these advantages.

Protection Against Cognitive Decline with Age

Regular exercise has been associated with a reduced risk of age-related cognitive decline and neurodegenerative diseases, such as Alzheimer's and Parkinson's. Enhancing neuroplasticity, decreasing inflammation, and promoting the development of new neurons and synapses, exercise promotes brain health and cognitive reserve.

Physical activity can also aid in maintaining the integrity of the blood-brain barrier, which plays a crucial role in shielding the brain from hazardous substances and preserving brain health overall. These protective effects of exercise may help elderly individuals delay the onset of cognitive decline and maintain cognitive function.

Cognitive Wellness and Neuroplasticity

Neuroplasticity is the capacity of the brain to reorganize and change in response to new experiences, learning, and challenges. Exercising increases the production of BDNF, other growth factors, and neurotransmitters, which support the growth, survival, and adaptation of neurons.

This enhanced neuroplasticity enables the brain to deal with stress and other challenges more effectively and promotes optimal cognitive function throughout the lifespan. By regularly engaging in physical activity, individuals can employ the power of exercise to improve brain health and promote cognitive resilience.

The cognitive benefits of exercise include enhancements in memory, learning, focus, and concentration, as well as prevention against age-related cognitive decline. Individuals can support optimal brain function and maintain good mental health throughout their lifetimes by incorporating physical activity into their daily routines.

Practical Tips and Recommendations for Incorporating Exercise

Incorporating physical activity into one's daily routine can have a substantial impact on mental health and well-being. However, beginning and maintaining an exercise routine can be difficult for many people. This section will provide suggestions for incorporating exercise into your daily routine in a way that makes it pleasurable and sustainable.

Find Interests You Enjoy

Participating in physical activities that you genuinely appreciate is one of the most crucial aspects of maintaining a regular exercise routine. When you anticipate your exercises, you are more likely to adhere to them over the long term. Experiment with various tension-relieving activities, such as swimming, running, dancing, and yoga, to determine which ones offer you the most pleasure and stress relief.

Establish Realistic Objectives

Setting fitness objectives that are attainable and realistic can increase motivation and help you maintain consistency in your exercise routine. Start with modest, manageable objectives, such as walking 30 minutes per day or attending a group fitness class once per week, and progressively increase the intensity and duration of your workouts as you advance. Ensure that you celebrate your accomplishments along the way, as this will increase your motivation and dedication.

Schedule Your Exercises

The key to obtaining the mental health benefits of exercise is consistency. To ensure that physical activity becomes an integral part of your daily routine, schedule your workouts as you would any other essential appointment or commitment. By setting aside specific time for exercise, you prioritize your mental health and increase the likelihood that you will adhere to your exercise regimen.

Establish a Support System

Having a support system can help you remain accountable and motivated throughout your fitness journey. Consider recruiting a workout partner, enrolling in a group fitness class, or joining a local sports league in order to remain on track. Sharing your exercise objectives and progress with peers, family, or online communities can also be motivating.

Consider Your Body
It is essential to pay attention to your body and modify your workout accordingly. While it is crucial to challenge yourself, overtraining and disregarding discomfort can result in injuries and setbacks. Include leisure days and recovery activities, such as stretching, foam rolling, and moderate yoga, to promote the restoration of your body and prevent overtraining.

Combine Mental and Physical Exercises
The mental health benefits of exercise are enhanced when combined with mental exercises. Activities like yoga, tai chi, and mindfulness-based exercises, which combine physical movement with mental concentration and relaxation techniques, can help to reduce tension, enhance concentration, and promote overall well-being.

Include Physical Activity in Your Daily Routine
Find methods to implement movement into your daily routine, in addition to scheduled exercises. Take the stairs instead of the elevator, go for a walk during your lunch break, or host a dance party in the living room with your family. These short bouts of activity can contribute to enhanced mental health over time.

In conclusion, incorporating physical activity into your daily routine can have a significant impact on your mental health and well-being. By adhering to these suggestions and guidelines, you can develop a pleasurable and sustainable exercise regimen that promotes optimal mental health and improves your quality of life.

Summary & Conclusion

The indisputable link between physical activity and mental health highlights the significance of incorporating physical activity into our daily lives. Regular exercise has numerous benefits, including the release of mood-enhancing neurotransmitters, improved sleep quality, stress reduction, enhanced cognitive function, and a reduced risk of mental health disorders.

Individuals can make informed decisions and adopt an active lifestyle that promotes their mental health if they have a thorough comprehension of the various aspects of exercise and their effects on mental health. Individuals can seamlessly incorporate exercise into their daily routine, making it a sustainable and enjoyable habit, by adhering to practical tips and recommendations such as finding pleasurable activities, setting realistic goals, and building a support system.

Exercise not only benefits our mental health but also promotes our overall well-being, allowing us to live healthier, happier, and more fulfilling lives. As we continue to prioritize mental health in our society, it is imperative that we recognize the power of exercise as a crucial instrument in our pursuit of optimal mental health and well-being.

Chapter 13:
The Impact of Stress on Self-Care and How to Manage it

Introduction:
Stress Management in Self-Care

Our personal and professional lives, relationships, and daily activities are permeated by stress. People are frequently confronted with multiple demands and responsibilities in today's fast-paced society, which can contribute to elevated stress levels. If not properly managed, this tension can have far-reaching effects on one's mental health and well-being. Understanding the relationship between tension and self-care is therefore of the utmost importance.

Self-care refers to the conscious actions and behaviors that individuals engage in to maintain and improve their physical, emotional, and mental health. It plays an important role in promoting mental health, nurturing resiliency, and enhancing overall life satisfaction. Despite its pervasive influence on one's capacity to engage in self-care practices, however, the impact of stress on self-care is frequently disregarded.

In this chapter, we will delve deeper into the relationship between stress and self-care, examining how stress affects mental health and how it can interfere with self-care routines. We will also discuss the significance of stress management as a vital component of self-care, as well as the prevalent stressors that can have an impact on one's self-care practices. The presentation of practical stress management techniques and their benefits for self-care and mental health will provide readers with actionable strategies for managing tension and enhancing their wellbeing. Finally, we will investigate real-world examples and case studies illustrating the positive influence of effective stress management on self-care and mental health.

This chapter seeks to provide readers with a comprehensive comprehension of the significance of stress management in promoting mental health and well-being by examining the complex relationship between stress and self-care. This information will enable readers to recognize the impact of stress on their own self-care practices and provide them with the tools and strategies necessary to effectively address and manage   stress.

The Relationship Between Stress and Self-Care

Stress and self-care have a complex and multifaceted relationship. Stress can influence self-care practices in a variety of ways, frequently compromising an individual's ability to maintain a healthy life balance. In contrast, self-care activities can assist individuals in managing tension and mitigating its negative impacts on mental health. In this section, we will examine the various facets of the relationship between stress and self-care, including the ways in which stress can impede self-care practices and the role self-care plays in stress management.

The Effect of Stress on Self-Care

Stress can be a significant barrier to self-care, making it more difficult for people to engage in activities that promote their health. Among the ways in which tension can impede self-care are:

Reduced Motivation: High levels of stress can result in feelings of overabundance, exhaustion, and even helplessness, which can reduce an individual's motivation to engage in self-care activities.

Limited Time and Vitality: When mental and emotional resources are depleted by stress, it can be difficult for a person to prioritize self-care.

Negative Coping Strategies: In response to stress, individuals may adopt detrimental coping strategies, such as obesity, substance abuse, or excessive screen time, which can further compromise self-care and well-being.

Self-Care as an Antidote to Stress: Self-care practices can be a potent buffer against the negative effects of stress, despite the obstacles that stress can pose to self-care. Self-care activities can aid in stress management by:

Building Resilience: Regular self-care practices can promote mental and emotional resilience, making it simpler for individuals to deal with stressors and maintain a sense of equilibrium in their lives.

Enhancing Well-Being: Self-care activities, such as exercise, relaxation, and socialization, can enhance well-being by boosting mood, reducing anxiety, and improving overall mental health, which can make it simpler to manage stress.

Providing a Sense of Control: Self-care activities can provide individuals with a sense of control over their own well-being, which can be especially beneficial when confronted with external stressors that may be beyond their control.

Relationship Between Stress and Self-Care
Each factor influences the other in a two-way relationship between tension and self-care. Chronic stress can impede self-care practices, whereas insufficient self-care can exacerbate stress, producing a negative feedback cycle. In contrast, effective self-care can mitigate the negative effects of stress on mental health and overall health. As a result, individuals who wish to maintain a healthy balance in their lives and enhance their ability to manage with stress must comprehend the interdependence between stress and self-care.

In conclusion, the relationship between stress and self-care is dynamic and multifaceted, with each factor affecting the other. Individuals seeking to maintain mental health and well-being must be aware of the ways in which stress can impede self-care and the role self-care plays in providing a buffer against stress. By addressing stress and prioritizing self-care, individuals can break the cycle of stress undermining their well-being and develop greater resilience to life's challenges.

The Effects of Stress on Mental Health

Stress can have a significant impact on a person's mental health, influencing their emotions, cognitive functioning, and well-being as a whole. While stress is a normal aspect of life and can even be beneficial in certain situations, chronic or excessive stress can cause or exacerbate a variety of mental health issues. In this section, we will examine the various ways in which stress can impact mental health, emphasizing the significance of stress management for maintaining mental health.

Psychological Effects of Stress
Emotional consequences are one of the most noticeable effects of stress on mental health. Chronic tension can result in a variety of emotional disorders, such as:

Anxiety: Persistent tension can induce anxiety, dread, and apprehension, making it challenging for individuals to unwind or feel at ease.

Depression: Long-term tension can contribute to feelings of melancholy, hopelessness, and loss of interest in previously enjoyable activities.

Irritability: Stress can increase a person's propensity for frustration, wrath, and impatience, which can strain relationships and impair social functioning.

Psychological Effects of Stress

In addition to its emotional effects, stress can impair cognitive performance. Among the cognitive repercussions of stress are the following:

Impaired Memory: High levels of stress can impair the consolidation, retrieval, and utilization of memories, making it difficult to remember information or acquire new skills.

Reduced Attention and Focus: Stress can make it difficult for individuals to concentrate on tasks, resulting in decreased productivity and an increased likelihood of making mistakes.

Impaired Decision-Making: Stress can impair discernment, leading to rash or impetuous decisions that may not be in a person's best interests.

Stress and Psychological Disorders

Chronic stress can contribute to the onset or deterioration of mental health disorders such as anxiety disorders, melancholy, and post-traumatic stress disorder (PTSD). Long-term exposure to stress can alter the structure and function of the brain, making individuals more susceptible to mental health problems. Moreover, tension can exacerbate the symptoms of mental health disorders, making them more difficult to manage and treat.

Stress' Importance in Burnout

Burnout is a condition of emotional, mental, and physical exhaustion induced by protracted and excessive stress, which is commonly encountered in high-pressure work environments. Burnout can have detrimental effects on mental health, causing cynicism, detachment, and a diminished sense of accomplishment. Additionally, it can contribute to the development of anxiety, depression, and other mental health problems.

In conclusion, stress can have extensive effects on mental health, influencing emotions, cognitive functioning, and overall wellbeing. Chronic stress can contribute to the onset or exacerbation of mental health disorders and increase the likelihood of exhaustion. Therefore, stress management is essential for maintaining psychological health and preventing the negative effects of stress on mental health.

The Importance of Managing Stress in Maintaining Self-Care

Stress management is essential for maintaining self-care and promoting mental health as a whole. It can be difficult for individuals to engage in self-care activities and maintain a healthy balance in their lives when tension levels are high. In this section, we will discuss the significance of stress management in maintaining self-care, emphasizing the benefits of stress management and its role in breaking the cycle of tension eroding well-being.

Breaking the Stress and Self-Care Cycle
As previously discussed, there is a bidirectional relationship between stress and self-care, with stress functioning as a barrier to self-care and insufficient self-care exacerbating stress. Effective stress management is essential for breaking this cycle and preventing stress's negative effects on mental health and well-being. Individuals can reduce the impact of stress on their self-care practices and develop healthier coping mechanisms by learning to recognize and address stressors.

Fostering Resilience
Resilience, which is the capacity to adapt and recuperate from adversity, requires that stress be effectively managed. Individuals who are resilient are better able to manage with stressors, maintain a sense of balance in their lives, and enjoy better mental health outcomes. By prioritizing stress management and self-care, individuals can increase their resilience and improve their ability to navigate life's challenges.

Promoting Psychological
Effective stress management is essential for promoting mental health and preventing the onset or deterioration of mental health disorders. By addressing stress and engaging in self-care practices, individuals can reduce the risk of anxiety, depression, and other mental health issues by mitigating the emotional and cognitive impacts of stress.

Enhancing Overall Well-Being
It is essential to manage tension in order to improve comprehensive well-being, which includes physical, emotional, and mental health. When stress is effectively managed, individuals can experience an improvement in mood, a boost in vitality, and a greater sense of life satisfaction. In turn, this can make it simpler for people to engage in self-care activities and maintain a healthy life balance.

Beneficial Individuals
Effective stress management equips individuals with the tools and strategies necessary to deal with stressors and take charge of their health. When people feel

equipped to manage stress, they are more likely to prioritize self-care and make decisions that promote their mental health and well-being as a whole.

In conclusion, stress management is of uttermost significance for self-care and mental health promotion. Effective stress management plays an essential role in supporting a healthy and balanced lifestyle by breaking the cycle of stress undermining self-care, cultivating resilience, promoting mental health, enhancing overall well-being, and empowering individuals. Individuals can improve their self-care practices and, ultimately, their mental health and well-being by prioritizing stress management.

Common Stressors and Their Impact on Self-Care Practices

There are numerous stressors that individuals may encounter in their daily lives, each of which has the potential to interfere with self-care practices and negatively affect mental health. By comprehending the effects of prevalent stressors on self-care, individuals can be better prepared to recognize and resolve these stressors, thereby minimizing their impact on well-being. This section will examine prevalent stressors and their potential impact on self-care practices.

Job-Related Tension
Work-related stress is a widespread problem caused by factors such as heavy responsibilities, short deadlines, job insecurity, and interpersonal conflicts. This form of stress can have a substantial impact on self-care practices by devouring time and energy, causing fatigue, and diminishing motivation to engage in self-care activities.

Financial Stress
Concerns about income, debt, or financial security can be a significant source of anxiety and concern for a large number of individuals. This tension can have a negative impact on self-care practices by diverting attention and resources away from self-care activities, causing feelings of helplessness, and contributing to undesirable coping mechanisms, such as obesity or substance misuse.

Relationship Stress
Relationship stress, such as conflicts with family members, intimate partners, or acquaintances, can have a negative impact on self-care practices. Emotional exhaustion, decreased motivation to engage in self-care activities, and increased reliance on detrimental coping mechanisms, such as isolation or emotional food, can result from relationship stress.

Health-Related Anxiety
Health-related stress, which can be caused by personal health issues or concerns about the health of loved ones, can also have an effect on self-care behaviors. This form of stress can result in feelings of being overburdened, a preoccupation with

health concerns, and a disregard for self-care activities that promote mental and physical health.

Time Management Stress

The difficulty of juggling multiple responsibilities, such as work, family, and personal interests, can result in time management anxiety. This form of tension can make it challenging for people to prioritize self-care, as they may lack the time or stamina to engage in self-care activities.

Understanding the impact of these common stressors on self-care practices is crucial for those who wish to maintain a healthy balance in their lives and enhance their ability to manage with stress. By recognizing these stressors and their effects on self-care, individuals can take proactive measures to resolve them, reduce their impact, and prioritize self-care as a means of bolstering their mental health and well-being.

Practical Stress Management Techniques and Their Benefits for Self-Care and Mental Health

To mitigate the effects of stress on self-care and mental health, it is necessary to develop effective stress management techniques. By incorporating these techniques into their daily lives, individuals can better manage tension, improve their self-care routines, and enhance their overall health. In this section, we will examine the benefits of practical stress management techniques for self-care and mental health.

Observance and Meditation

Mindfulness and meditation practices cultivate present-moment awareness and a nonjudgmental attitude toward one's thoughts and emotions. By promoting relaxation, enhancing emotional regulation, and enhancing self-awareness, these techniques can help individuals manage tension.

Self-Care and Mental Health Benefits:
- o Decreased anxiety and depression
- o Improved emotional well-being
- o Increased stress tolerance

Exercise

Regular physical activity has been shown to reduce stress hormones, enhance mood, and increase energy levels, making it an effective stress management technique.

Self-Care and Mental Health Benefits:
- o Decreased anxiety and depression
- o Improved sleep quality
- o Improved well-being overall

Management of Time and Priorities
Developing time management and prioritization skills can help individuals manage stress by enabling them to allocate their time and resources more effectively to activities that promote their well-being.

Benefits for Self-Care and Mental Health:
- o Decreased feelings of overwhelm and exhaustion
- o Improved capacity to engage in self-care activities
- o Enhanced sense of control and accomplishment

Social Support
Maintaining strong social connections and seeking support from friends, family, or support groups can aid in stress management and provide a sense of belonging and mutual comprehension.

Self-Care and Mental Health Benefits:
- o Decreased feelings of isolation and loneliness
- o Improved capacity to manage stress
- o Increased well-being overall

Relaxation Techniques
Relaxation techniques, such as deep breathing exercises, progressive muscle relaxation, and guided imagery, can aid in the management of stress by promoting a sense of calm and reducing physiological stress responses.

Self-Care and Mental Health Benefits:
- o Decreased anxiety and tension
- o Improved sleep quality
- o Enhanced stress tolerance

Limiting Behavior
Setting healthy boundaries involves establishing limits on one's time, energy, and emotional investment in various facets of life, including work, relationships, and social obligations. This can aid in stress management by ensuring that individuals have sufficient time and resources for self-care activities.

Benefits for Self-Care and Mental Health:
- o Decreased feelings of overwhelm and exhaustion
- o Improved capacity to engage in self-care activities
- o Enhancement of overall well-being

Individuals can better manage stress, improve their self-care practices, and support their mental health and well-being by incorporating these stress management techniques into their daily activities. These techniques can help to reduce the impact of stress on self-care and promote a healthier, more balanced lifestyle if they are practiced regularly.

Real-Life Examples and Case Studies

Examining real-world examples and case studies can assist in demonstrating the effect of effective stress management on self-care and mental health. These examples can provide valuable insight into how individuals have effectively implemented stress management techniques to enhance their self-care and mental health.

Mindfulness in the Workplace: A Case Study

Due to strict deadlines, lengthy hours, and problematic relationships with colleagues, Julia, a marketing manager, was experiencing high levels of work-related stress. She chose to integrate mindfulness meditation into her daily regimen, devoting ten to fifteen minutes each morning to the practice. Julia observed improved emotional regulation, increased concentration, and a greater sense of calm at work as a result. Julia was able to create a healthier work-life balance and engage in self-care activities such as exercise and spending time with loved ones by managing her tension through mindfulness, thereby enhancing her mental health.

Exercise and Social Support for Managing Stress: A Case Study

John, a single parent with two children, struggled to balance work and family responsibilities. His inability to manage his stress led to feelings of exhaustion and estrangement from his children. John joined a local running club in an effort to reduce his tension and enhance his self-care. The combination of regular exercise and social support from fellow runners assisted John in lowering his stress levels, improving his mood, and fortifying his relationships with his children. John was able to establish a healthier, more balanced lifestyle by prioritizing stress management through physical activity and social support.

Setting Boundaries for Improved Mental Health: A Case Study

Due to her demanding scholastic timetable and numerous extracurricular activities, Sophia, a college student, was experiencing high levels of anxiety. She frequently neglected self-care, resulting in a decline in mental health. Sophia decided to establish limits on her time and energy by selecting activities that aligned with her priorities and learning to say "no" to other commitments. Consequently, she was able to reduce her stress levels, make time for self-care activities such as regular sleep and relaxation, and ultimately enhance her mental health.

Stress Management and Therapy for Anxiety Relief: A Case Study

Michael, a young professional, struggled with chronic anxiety that negatively impacted his relationships and daily life. A therapist provided him with a variety of stress management techniques, including deep breathing exercises, progressive muscle relaxation, and cognitive restructuring, after he sought professional assistance.

Michael was able to better manage his anxiety, engage in self-care activities such as spending time with friends and pursuing interests, and improve his overall mental health by routinely exercising these techniques.

These real-world examples and case studies illustrate the profound effect that effective stress management has on self-care and mental health. Individuals can improve their self-care practices, support their mental health, and enhance their overall quality of life by employing effective stress management techniques.

Summary & Conclusion

It is difficult to exaggerate the impact of stress on self-care and mental health. Individuals must recognize the intricate relationship between stress and self-care, as well as the mental health impacts of stress. By comprehending the significance of stress management in maintaining self-care, individuals can begin to address the common stressors that affect their self-care practices and wellbeing as a whole.

Techniques for stress management, such as mindfulness and meditation, exercise, time management and prioritization, social support, relaxation techniques, and establishing boundaries, can provide substantial benefits for self-care and mental health. These techniques enable individuals to take charge of their health and develop resilience, thereby enhancing their capacity to face life's challenges.

This chapter's real-world examples and case studies further illustrate the profound impact that effective stress management can have on self-care and mental health. Individuals can create healthier, more balanced lifestyles that benefit their mental health and well-being as a whole by incorporating stress management techniques into their daily routines.

Self-care and mental health are promoted significantly by stress management. Individuals can improve their self-care practices and, consequently, their mental health and quality of life by grasping the relationship between stress and self-care, addressing prevalent stressors, and incorporating practical stress management techniques.

Section III. Mindfulness and Meditation

Chapter 14:
Definition of Mindfulness and How it Relates to Mental Health

Introduction:
What is Mindfulness?

In today's fast-paced world, mental health issues such as tension, anxiety, and depression have become increasingly prevalent, affecting the lives of innumerable individuals. As a result, there is a growing interest in discovering effective methods to promote mental health and resilience. The practice of mindfulness is one such approach that has garnered significant attention in recent years. Mindfulness, which is rooted in ancient traditions but supported by modern science, provides a potent and accessible method for enhancing mental health and well-being.

This chapter will explore mindfulness and its relationship to mental health in depth. Beginning with a distinct definition of mindfulness, we will examine its underlying principles and theories as they relate to mental health. We will discuss the numerous mental health benefits of mindfulness, including tension reduction, anxiety management, and relief from depressive symptoms. We will offer guidance on how to incorporate mindfulness practices into daily life by emphasizing the significance of mindfulness in maintaining mental health.

In addition to examining the role of mindfulness in therapeutic approaches such as Mindfulness-Based Stress Reduction (MBSR), Mindfulness-Based Cognitive Therapy (MBCT), and Acceptance and Commitment Therapy (ACT), we will provide an overview of different mindfulness techniques that can be used to improve mental health. To further illustrate the transformative power of mindfulness, we will provide real-world examples and case studies illustrating the positive effects of effective mindfulness management on mental health.

This chapter seeks to equip readers with the knowledge and practical tools necessary to improve their mental health by incorporating mindfulness practices into their daily lives through a well-structured and evidence-based examination of mindfulness and mental health.

Defining Mindfulness and its Relationship with Mental Health
What is Mindfulness?

Mindfulness is a mental state attained through the deliberate practice of focusing one's attention on the present moment while noticing and accepting one's thoughts, emotions, and bodily sensations without judgment or emotional reaction. It is a skill that can be developed through a variety of techniques, such as meditation, yoga, deep breathing, or simply being fully present and involved in daily activities. Mindfulness encourages individuals to cultivate a greater awareness of their inner and outer experiences, fostering a healthier connection with oneself and the world.

Relationship between Mindfulness and Psychological Health
The relationship between mindfulness and mental health is supported by a number of fundamental principles and theories:

Cognitive and Emotional Regulation: Mindfulness encourages individuals to observe their thoughts and emotions without becoming immersed in them or acting impulsively. This nonjudgmental awareness facilitates the development of improved cognitive and emotional regulation skills, resulting in a greater capacity to manage tension and negative emotions.

Non-Attachment: Non-attachment, or letting go of the need to control every aspect of our existence, is a fundamental tenet of mindfulness. By practicing non-attachment, individuals can learn to embrace the impermanence of thoughts, emotions, and experiences, nurturing a more adaptable and flexible outlook in response to life's challenges.

Self-Compassion: Mindfulness encourages an attitude of kindness and compassion toward oneself. Individuals can develop a healthier relationship with themselves by cultivating self-compassion, which in turn contributes to enhanced mental health and well-being.

Neuroplasticity: According to research, regular mindfulness practice can result in structural and functional brain changes. These alterations are associated with enhanced cognitive functioning, affective regulation, and stress resilience, which all contribute to improved mental health.

Individuals can develop a healthier relationship with themselves and the world around them by embracing the principles of mindfulness and cultivating a nonjudgmental awareness of their thoughts, emotions, and experiences. This increased self-awareness enables the identification and management of negative thought patterns, emotions, and behaviors, ultimately nurturing a greater sense of mental health and resilience.

The Effects on Mindfulness on Mental Health
A expanding corpus of research supports the myriad mental health benefits of mindfulness. Key areas where mindfulness has been demonstrated to have a significant impact include:

Stress Reduction: One of the most extensively researched benefits of mindfulness is its capacity to reduce tension. Individuals can develop adaptive responses to stressful circumstances by cultivating a nonreactive, nonjudgmental awareness of stressors. This ability to manage stress more effectively can result in lower levels of cortisol, the primary stress hormone in the body, and a reduction in stress-related symptoms such as irritability, sleep disturbances, and physical distress.

Anxiety Management: Mindfulness-based interventions have been shown to reduce anxiety symptoms because they encourage individuals to observe their apprehensive thoughts and emotions without judgment or resistance. This increased self-awareness enables individuals to recognize and interrupt habitual patterns of apprehensive thinking, as well as to develop healthier coping strategies.

Depression Alleviation: Mindfulness-based therapies, such as Mindfulness-Based Cognitive Therapy (MBCT), can reduce symptoms of depression and prevent relapse in individuals with a history of recurrent depression, according to research. Mindfulness can contribute to more effective management of depressive symptoms by cultivating a greater awareness of negative thought patterns and encouraging self-compassion.

Improved Emotional Regulation: By encouraging individuals to observe their emotions without becoming overwhelmed or reacting impulsively, mindfulness practices can improve emotional regulation. This heightened emotional awareness can result in a greater capacity to manage difficult emotions and nurture a more balanced emotional state.

Enhanced Well-Being: Mindfulness practice has been associated with increased psychological well-being, as it fosters greater self-awareness, self-compassion, and emotional regulation. Additionally, mindfulness can contribute to enhanced relationships, enhanced resilience, and a greater sense of life satisfaction.

Cognitive Functioning: Research has shown that mindfulness can contribute to improvements in cognitive functioning, including enhanced attention, working memory, and problem-solving skills. These cognitive benefits can contribute to improved mental health by encouraging adaptive thought patterns and decreasing the likelihood of becoming overburdened by life's challenges.

By cultivating and incorporating mindfulness into daily life, individuals can experience numerous positive effects on their mental health, including stress reduction, anxiety management, depression relief, improved emotional regulation, enhanced well-being, and improved cognitive functioning. These advantages demonstrate the transformative potential of mindfulness practices for promoting mental health and resiliency.

The Importance of Mindfulness in Maintaining Health

Integrating mindfulness practices into everyday life is essential for preserving mental health and nurturing a greater sense of well-being. By cultivating mindfulness, individuals can experience a variety of long-lasting benefits to their mental health, such as:

Regular mindfulness practice can assist individuals in developing a heightened awareness of their thoughts, emotions, and behaviors. This increased self-awareness enables them to identify and manage negative patterns, nurturing a healthier mindset and enhanced mental health.

Cultivation of self-compassion and self-acceptance: Mindfulness practice fosters a compassionate and kind attitude toward oneself. Individuals can establish a healthier relationship with themselves by cultivating self-compassion and self-acceptance, leading to a greater sense of mental health and overall life satisfaction.

Mindfulness can improve emotional regulation by teaching individuals to observe their emotions without becoming overwhelmed or reacting impulsively. It can also improve resilience by teaching individuals to observe their emotions without becoming overwhelmed or reacting impulsively. This increased emotional awareness fosters a more balanced emotional state by enhancing the ability to manage difficult emotions. In addition, mindfulness can boost resilience by fostering adaptive thought patterns and assisting individuals in bouncing back from adversity more effectively.

Regular mindfulness practice can play a crucial role in preventing the onset of mental health disorders as well as managing existing conditions. Mindfulness-based interventions, for instance, have been demonstrated to be effective in reducing anxiety, depression, and stress symptoms, as well as preventing relapse in individuals with a history of recurrent depression.

By fostering self-awareness, self-compassion, emotional regulation, and resiliency, incorporating mindfulness into daily life can contribute to a greater sense of overall well-being. In turn, these factors can result in improved relationships, greater life satisfaction, and an enhanced quality of life.

To maintain mental health and reap the full benefits of mindfulness, it is necessary to routinely practice the skill and incorporate it into various aspects of daily life. This can be accomplished through formal practices like meditation, yoga, or deep breathing exercises, as well as informal practices like being fully present and engaged in everyday activities like eating, strolling, or simply listening to others. By cultivating mindfulness consistently, individuals can experience long-lasting benefits to their mental health and well-being.

Mindfulness in Therapy and Techniques for Improving Mental Health

Mindfulness has been incorporated into numerous therapeutic approaches over the years, demonstrating its efficacy in promoting mental health. Among the prominent mindfulness-based therapies and techniques devised to improve mental health are the following:

Mindfulness-Based Stress Reduction (MBSR): MBSR is a structured 8-week program devised by Jon Kabat-Zinn that incorporates mindfulness meditation, yoga, and group discussions to educate people how to effectively manage stress. MBSR has been shown to enhance mental health, reduce tension, and alleviate anxiety and depression symptoms.

Mindfulness-Based Cognitive Therapy (MBCT) is a group-based 8-week program that integrates cognitive-behavioral therapy with mindfulness practices. It was designed to assist individuals with a history of recurrent depression prevent relapse, but has also proven effective in treating anxiety and other mental health conditions.

Acceptance and Commitment Therapy (ACT): ACT is a form of cognitive-behavioral therapy that incorporates mindfulness techniques to assist individuals in developing psychological flexibility, decreasing experiential avoidance, and cultivating a more adaptive response to negative thoughts and emotions.

Dialectical Behavior Therapy (DBT) is a comprehensive treatment approach devised by Marsha Linehan, initially for individuals with borderline personality disorder but subsequently expanded to treat a variety of mental health disorders. Mindfulness skills are one of the fundamental components of DBT, along with emotion regulation, distress tolerance, and interpersonal effectiveness.

In addition to these therapeutic approaches, several mindfulness techniques can be independently employed to enhance mental health:

Mindful Breathing: Focusing on the respiration is a simple yet effective method for cultivating mindfulness. Focusing on the sensation of the in-and-out breath can help ground the mind in the present moment and promote a sense of calm and tranquility.

Body Scan Meditation: This mindfulness practice entails systematically drawing attention to various regions of the body, from the cranium to the toes. Individuals can develop a greater sense of body awareness and release physical tension by observing sensations such as tension and relaxation.

Mindful Eating: Mindful dining entails focusing on the experience of eating, relishing each mouthful, and being aware of hunger and satiety signals. This practice can aid in fostering a healthier relationship with food and preventing emotional consumption.

Meditation on Loving-Kindness (Metta) involves cultivating sentiments of affection and compassion toward oneself and others. By reiterating phrases such as "May I be happy, may I be healthy, and may I be safe," people can increase their self-compassion and emotional well-being.

Mindful Walking: Attention is paid to the physical sensations of walking, such as the sense of the feet contacting the ground or the movement of the thighs, during mindful walking. This practice can be implemented into daily life by engaging in brief meditative walks or by bringing awareness to the act of walking during routine activities.

Individuals can experience significant improvements in their mental health and well-being by incorporating mindfulness into therapeutic approaches and practicing various mindfulness techniques.

Real-Life Examples and Case Studies

Numerous case studies and real-world examples demonstrate the transformative power of mindfulness in promoting mental health and well-being. These accounts provide a view into the lives of individuals whose mental health has significantly improved as a result of incorporating mindfulness practices into their daily lives.

Overcoming Stress and Burnout: A high-level executive working in a highly demanding and competitive environment was suffering from chronic stress and exhaustion. By participating in a Mindfulness-Based Stress Reduction (MBSR) program, the executive learned to more effectively manage stress by incorporating mindfulness practices such as meditation and mindful breathing into daily life. As a consequence, they experienced a significant decrease in tension levels, better sleep, and an improvement in their overall well-being.

Managing Anxiety: A college student with generalized anxiety disorder discovered respite from anxiety by practicing mindfulness meditation. By devoting time each day to focusing on their respiration and observing their thoughts without judgment, the student was able to develop healthier anxiety-management coping strategies. They reported a significant decrease in anxiety symptoms and an increase in mental well-being over time.

Coping with Depression: middle-aged man with a history of recurrent depression sought out mindfulness-based cognitive therapy (MBCT) in order to manage his depressive symptoms. The man learned to recognize and embrace his negative thoughts and emotions without judgment through the 8-week MBCT program, enabling him to develop healthier coping strategies. As a consequence, his mental health improved significantly and he was better equipped to prevent future depressive episodes.

Enhancing Emotional Regulation: A young woman who struggled with emotional regulation and frequent mood fluctuations began practicing mindfulness techniques, such as body scan meditation and loving-kindness meditation, to improve her emotional regulation. She gained a greater awareness of her emotions and a greater capacity to manage them without becoming overwrought as time passed. As a result, she experienced more stable emotions and a greater sense of mental health.

Improving Relationships: couple with communication issues and frequent conflicts decided to enroll in a mindfulness-based couples therapy program in order to improve their relationship. By exercising nonjudgmental awareness of their own emotions and those of their companion, the couple was able to improve their communication skills and strengthen their relationship.

These real-world examples and case studies illustrate the transformative power of mindfulness practices by promoting mental health and resiliency. Individuals can experience significant improvements in their mental health and overall quality of life by incorporating mindfulness into daily life and therapeutic approaches.

Summary & Conclusion

Mindfulness is a potent instrument that can have a profound effect on mental health and well-being overall. Individuals can develop a greater sense of self-awareness, self-compassion, and emotional regulation through the practice of focusing their attention on the present moment and embracing thoughts, emotions, and somatic sensations without judgment. Mindfulness' numerous benefits, which include stress reduction, anxiety management, depression relief, and enhanced cognitive functioning, demonstrate its significance in maintaining mental health and fostering resilience.

Mindfulness has been effectively incorporated into a variety of therapeutic approaches, including MBSR, MBCT, ACT, and DBT, demonstrating its efficacy in improving mental health outcomes. In addition, a variety of mindfulness practices, including mindful breathing, body scan meditation, mindful dining, loving-kindness meditation, and mindful walking, can be incorporated into daily life to promote mental health.

Case studies and real-world examples further illustrate the transformative potential of mindfulness practices for enhancing mental health and quality of life as a whole. By consistently cultivating mindfulness and integrating it into various aspects of daily life, individuals can experience long-lasting benefits to their mental health and realize the full potential of this potent practice.

Chapter 15: Benefits of Mindfulness and Meditation

Introduction: Deeper Dive into the Benefits

The Transformative Power of Mindfulness and Meditation

It is not uncommon in today's fast-paced world to feel exhausted by the constant flow of information, deadlines, and personal responsibilities. Mindfulness and meditation have emerged as potent instruments for cultivating mental clarity, emotional equilibrium, and a sense of inner calm amidst the turmoil. These practices, which are rooted in ancient wisdom, have acquired widespread popularity in recent years due to the growing body of scientific evidence supporting their numerous benefits for mental health, physical health, emotional well-being, and productivity.

Mindfulness, the practice of devoting nonjudgmental and compassionate attention to the present moment, can be cultivated through various forms of meditation or incorporated into daily activities. Meditation, on the other hand, involves concentrating the mind on a particular object, thought, or activity in order to attain a state of mental clarity and emotional calmness. There are numerous meditation techniques, but they all have the same objective: to cultivate self-awareness and inner peace.

This chapter will examine the transformative power of mindfulness and meditation, as well as their numerous benefits and scientific efficacy. We will also provide examples of individuals whose lives have undergone profoundly positive changes as a result of these practices. Finally, we will provide practical advice and direction on how to incorporate mindfulness and meditation into your daily life, enabling you to tap into their potential for personal development, enhanced well-being, and overall life satisfaction.

Mental Health Benefits
Stress Reduction
Stress reduction is one of the most widely acknowledged mental health benefits of mindfulness and meditation. Chronic stress can negatively impact both mental and physical health, contributing to anxiety, depression, cardiovascular disease, and a compromised immune system. Mindfulness and meditation help regulate cortisol, the primary stress hormone in the body, and activate the parasympathetic nervous system, which is responsible for the relaxation response. This process enables individuals to better control their tension levels, resulting in enhanced mental health and well-being.

Managing Anxiety and Depression

Mindfulness and meditation have been discovered to be effective methods for coping with anxiety and depression. These practices teach individuals to become more conscious of their thoughts and emotions, enabling them to identify negative thought patterns and prevent rumination. In turn, this increased awareness promotes self-compassion and healthier coping strategies, thereby alleviating anxiety and depression symptoms.

A study published in JAMA Internal Medicine found that mindfulness meditation helped individuals with generalized anxiety disorder reduce their anxiety and depression symptoms. In addition, mindfulness-based cognitive therapy (MBCT) has been shown to be effective in preventing depression relapse in recurrently depressed individuals.

Enhanced Cognitive Performance

Regular meditation practice has been associated with enhanced cognitive function, such as enhanced concentration, memory, and problem-solving skills. These advantages are attributable to changes in brain structure and function brought about by meditation.

A Harvard Medical School study, for instance, found that regular meditation practice increased gray matter density in the hippocampus, a region of the brain associated with memory and learning, and the prefrontal cortex, which plays a crucial role in attention and emotional regulation. Meditation has also been shown to increase the thickness of the corpus callosum, the structure that connects the two hemispheres of the brain, resulting in improved communication between brain regions and enhanced cognitive performance.

Mental Toughness and Emotional Intelligence

By fostering self-awareness and emotional regulation, mindfulness and meditation can also enhance resilience and emotional intelligence. Individuals can gain a greater understanding of their emotional impulses and responses by learning to observe and embrace their thoughts and emotions without judgment. This understanding enables the development of healthier coping mechanisms, resulting in increased resilience in the face of adversity.

Mindfulness and meditation practices also improve emotional intelligence, which is the capacity to recognize, comprehend, and manage one's own emotions as well as those of others. Developing emotional intelligence can result in enhanced interpersonal relationships, communication, empathy, and compassion.

Mindfulness and meditation have numerous mental health benefits, including stress reduction, improved anxiety and depression management, enhanced cognitive function, and increased resilience and emotional intelligence. Those who routinely engage in these practices can enhance their quality of life and well-being as a result of these advantages.

Physical Health Benefits

Not only do mindfulness and meditation have profound effects on mental health, but they also provide numerous benefits for physical health. Contributing to overall health and well-being, these practices can boost immune function, reduce blood pressure, and improve sleep quality.

Enhanced Immune Performance

Mindfulness and meditation practices positively affect the immune system, according to research. It has been discovered that these practices increase the production of antibodies, which are proteins that help the body recognize and neutralize hazardous substances, and activate natural killer cells, which play an essential role in the body's defense against viruses and cancer cells. This results in a stronger defense against diseases and infections, thereby promoting physical health overall.

A study published in the journal Psychosomatic Medicine found that participants in an eight-week mindfulness-based stress reduction (MBSR) program had a greater immune response than a control group. After receiving a flu vaccine, the participants had higher levels of antibodies, suggesting that mindfulness practices can enhance the immune system's capacity to combat infections.

Reduce Blood Stress

Mindfulness and meditation practices have been discovered to aid in lowering blood pressure by promoting relaxation and decreasing the production of stress hormones. Hypertension is a major risk factor for cardiovascular diseases such as heart attack and stroke. Mindfulness and meditation can contribute to improved cardiovascular health by lowering blood pressure.

A meta-analysis of multiple studies published in the Journal of Hypertension revealed that those who practiced meditation, particularly transcendental meditation, experienced significant reductions in blood pressure. Meditation could be a valuable addition to conventional hypertension treatments, according to the review.

Better Sleep

A sufficient amount of sleep is necessary for maintaining physical health because it permits the body to repair and regenerate cells, consolidate memories, and regulate hormones. Mindfulness and meditation can enhance the quality of sleep by helping individuals unwind, calm their minds, and fall slumber more quickly. This can result in a more pleasant night's sleep and increased daytime vitality.

A study conducted by researchers at the University of California, Los Angeles found that participants who practiced mindfulness meditation slept significantly better than a control group that received education on sleep hygiene. Insomnia, depression, and fatigue were also reduced in the group that meditated.

Reduced Persistent Pain

Chronic pain can have a significant impact on an individual's quality of life, and mindfulness and meditation practices have been shown to reduce pain intensity and improve pain management. By cultivating nonjudgmental awareness of pain sensations and establishing healthier responses to pain, chronic pain conditions can be alleviated.

According to a study published in the Journal of Pain, individuals with chronic low back pain who participated in an eight-week MBSR program encountered significant reductions in pain intensity and improvements in physical functioning when compared to a control group. The fact that the MBSR group used less pain medication suggests that mindfulness practices can be an effective complement to conventional pain management techniques.

In conclusion, mindfulness and meditation offer a variety of physical health benefits, including enhanced immune function, reduced blood pressure, enhanced sleep, and decreased chronic pain. By incorporating these practices into their daily routines, individuals can improve their well-being and live a healthier, more fulfilling existence.

Emotional Well-Being Benefits

Mindfulness and meditation also have profound effects on emotional health, resulting in improved emotional regulation, increased contentment and life satisfaction, and enhanced interpersonal relationships. These advantages can contribute to an existence that is more balanced and fulfilling.

Enhanced Emotional Management

One of the primary advantages of mindfulness and meditation is their capacity to assist individuals in better regulating their emotions. By fostering self-awareness and self-compassion, these practices allow people to observe and embrace their emotions without judgment or resistance. This nonjudgmental awareness promotes healthier coping mechanisms and facilitates an emotionally balanced state.

According to a study published in Frontiers in Human Neuroscience, individuals who participated in a mindfulness-based intervention exhibited increased activation in brain regions associated with emotional regulation, suggesting that mindfulness training can lead to enhanced emotional control and stability.

Happiness and Life Satisfaction Rise

By cultivating a nonjudgmental awareness of the present moment, mindfulness and meditation practices can also contribute to increased contentment and life satisfaction. This consciousness fosters gratitude, contentment, and an appreciation for life's basic pleasures. In addition, mindfulness and meditation can aid in the development of a more optimistic outlook by reducing negative thought patterns and fostering self-compassion.

Over the course of several weeks, individuals who practiced loving-kindness meditation experienced significant increases in positive emotions such as happiness, affection, and gratitude, according to a study conducted at the University of North Carolina. This rise in positive emotions was also associated with enhancements in personal resources, such as increased mindfulness, social support, and a sense of life's purpose, which contributed to greater life satisfaction.

Better Relationships
By fostering empathy, compassion, and effective communication, mindfulness and meditation practices can have a positive effect on interpersonal relationships. These practices can help individuals become more attuned to their own and others' emotions, resulting in deeper connections and stronger relationships.

A study published in the Journal of Marital and Family Therapy, for instance, discovered that couples who participated in a mindfulness-based relationship enhancement program experienced significant improvements in relationship satisfaction, closeness, and acceptance. In addition, the couples reported decreased levels of tension and anxiety, which can further contribute to healthier relationships.

In addition, mindfulness and meditation can help individuals develop better conflict resolution skills by promoting emotional regulation and enhancing the capacity to respond thoughtfully and empathetically to difficult situations. This can result in more harmonious personal and professional relationships.

Mindfulness and meditation have significant and far-reaching benefits for emotional health, including improved emotional regulation, increased pleasure and life satisfaction, and enhanced relationships. By engaging in these practices, individuals can cultivate greater emotional balance and well-being, resulting in a life that is more fulfilling and harmonious.

Productivity Benefits
Mindfulness and meditation can also have a positive effect on productivity by increasing concentration, fostering creativity, and promoting time management. These benefits can result in increased productivity and achievement in both personal and professional endeavors.

Improved Concentration and Focus
By training the mind to maintain awareness on a particular object, thought, or activity, mindfulness and meditation are known to enhance focus and attention. This enhanced concentration can be applied to various facets of life, resulting in increased productivity and the capacity to complete tasks more efficiently.

A study published in the journal Psychological Science discovered that participants who underwent a brief mindfulness training were better able to sustain their attention on a difficult task than the control group. Mind-wandering, a prevalent obstacle to productivity, was also reduced in the mindfulness group.

Improved Creativity

Mindfulness and meditation can also encourage individuals to be more present, receptive to new ideas and perspectives, and open to new perspectives. By reducing the influence of self-critical thoughts and quieting the mind, these practices can create a mental space conducive to creative problem-solving and innovative thought.

A study published in the journal Mindfulness found that participants who engaged in open-monitoring meditation, a practice involving the nonjudgmental observation of one's thoughts and emotions, experienced greater divergent thinking and generated more creative ideas than a control group.

Successful Time Management

Mindfulness and meditation practices can improve time management skills by fostering increased self-awareness and the ability to effectively prioritize tasks. These practices can assist individuals in identifying and overcoming procrastination, distractions, and other impediments to productivity. In addition, mindfulness can improve decision-making abilities, allowing for a more effective allocation of time and resources.

A study published in the journal Frontiers in Psychology found that mindfulness training is associated with enhanced time management skills and decreased procrastination among college students. The study found that mindfulness practice helped students cultivate greater self-compassion and self-regulation, which contributed to their increased productivity.

Reduced Fatigue

Mindfulness and meditation practices can help prevent burnout, a protracted state of physical and emotional exhaustion that is frequently the result of prolonged stress and excessive work burden. By promoting stress reduction, emotional regulation, and self-care, these practices can assist individuals in maintaining a healthy work-life balance, resulting in increased productivity and job satisfaction.

According to a study published in the Journal of Occupational Health Psychology, nurses who participated in an eight-week MBSR program experienced significant reductions in burnout symptoms such as emotional exhaustion and depersonalization. The study also found that the nurses' well-being and job satisfaction improved.

In conclusion, mindfulness and meditation have substantial productivity benefits, including enhanced focus and attention, enhanced creativity, effective time management, and reduced fatigue. Individuals can realize their complete potential, attain greater success, and experience a more fulfilling and balanced existence by incorporating these practices into their daily routines.

Real-life Examples and Scientific Studies

Mindfulness and meditation have a transformative effect, as evidenced by a growing corpus of scientific evidence and numerous real-world examples. The section that follows will emphasize some illuminating anecdotes and critical studies that demonstrate the potential of these practices to improve lives.

Real-life Examples

Through his program, Jon Kabat-Zinn, the creator of mindfulness-based stress reduction (MBSR), has helped thousands of people manage with stress, anxiety, and chronic pain. Numerous healthcare professionals have been inspired by Kabat-Zinn's work to incorporate mindfulness practices into their treatment strategies, leading to widespread adoption and recognition of the benefits of mindfulness and meditation.

Andy Puddicombe, a former Buddhist priest and co-founder of the widely used meditation application Headspace, has made mindfulness and meditation accessible to millions of individuals. Through his app and guided meditation sessions, Puddicombe has assisted people of all walks of life in reducing tension, enhancing mental health, and enhancing their overall wellbeing.

Dan Harris, a correspondent for ABC News, suffered a panic attack on live television, prompting him to investigate mindfulness and meditation. He discovered that these practices substantially improved his mental health and well-being, which inspired him to write the best-selling book "10% Happier" and establish a popular podcast with the goal of making meditation more accessible and enticing to a wider audience.

Scientific Research

MRI scans revealed that participants who completed an eight-week MBSR program experienced an increase in gray matter density in brain regions associated with learning, memory, affective regulation, and self-awareness, according to a groundbreaking study conducted by Harvard Medical School researchers. This study provided compelling evidence that mindfulness and meditation can lead to structural changes in the brain, which may have long-term positive effects on mental health and well-being.

A study published in the journal JAMA Internal Medicine found that mindfulness meditation helped individuals with generalized anxiety disorder reduce their anxiety and depression symptoms. This study provides evidence that mindfulness and meditation can be effective strategies for managing mental health issues, even in clinical populations.

A meta-analysis of 47 trials involving over 3,500 participants, published in JAMA Internal Medicine, found that mindfulness meditation programs had moderate evidence of reducing anxiety, melancholy, and pain, and low evidence of reducing stress and enhancing mental health-related quality of life. These findings provide additional evidence of the prospective health benefits of mindfulness and meditation for a wide range of individuals and health conditions.

This section provides convincing evidence of the transformative power of mindfulness and meditation through the use of real-world examples and scientific research. As more people turn to mindfulness and meditation to improve their mental health, physical health, emotional well-being, and productivity, it is evident that these practices have the potential to have a substantial impact on the lives of individuals and on society as a whole.

Practical Tips for Incorporating Mindfulness and Meditation into Your Daily Routine

Including mindfulness and meditation in your daily routine need not be difficult or time-consuming. By adhering to these guidelines, you can incorporate these practices into your daily life and begin reaping their numerous benefits.

Start Small

As you become more acclimated with the practice, progressively increase the duration of your daily meditation sessions from 5 to 10 minutes. Consistency is more essential than the duration of your sessions, so strive for daily practice, even if it's only a few minutes.

Create a Specialized Area

Create a peaceful and comfortable space for meditation at home. This area should be devoid of distractions and provides a tranquil environment. A designated space for meditation can help you establish a routine and convey to your mind that it's time to concentrate and unwind.

Develop a Routine

Setting periods for mindfulness and meditation practice can make incorporating them into your daily routine more manageable. Numerous individuals find it beneficial to meditate first thing in the morning or before night. Experiment with various times to determine what works best for you, and strive for consistency.

Utilize Meditation-Guided Apps or Audio

Guided meditation apps and audio recordings can be an invaluable resource for beginners. These resources provide step-by-step instructions and can assist you in establishing a firm foundation for your practice. Headspace, Calm, and Insight Timer are three well-known meditation applications.

Employ Mindful Breathing

Breathing mindfully is a basic yet effective technique that can be practiced anywhere and at any time. Focus your attention on your breath, observing the sensations of inhaling and exhaling without judging or attempting to control your respiration. This practice can assist you in cultivating mindfulness and refocusing your attention on the present.

Be Compassionate and Patient with Yourself

Developing a regular mindfulness and meditation practice requires time, and you may face obstacles along the way. Remember to be patient and kind with yourself as you continue to learn and develop. Realize that it is normal for your mind to wander during meditation and that the objective is not to eliminate thoughts, but rather to become aware of them and tenderly return your focus to the present.

Participate in Mindful Activity

In addition to formal meditation practice, you can integrate mindfulness into daily activities such as dining, commuting, and performing housework. By paying attention to the sensations, sounds, and scents around you during these activities, you can cultivate greater present-moment awareness and appreciation.

Attend Classes on Group Meditation or Mindfulness

Attending group meditation sessions or classes on mindfulness can provide support, direction, and motivation to help you maintain your practice. As you progress on your mindfulness voyage, connecting with like-minded individuals can also provide motivation and inspiration.

By following these practical guidelines, you can incorporate mindfulness and meditation into your daily routine and begin to reap the numerous mental health, physical health, emotional well-being, and productivity benefits they offer. Remember that consistency is essential, and that with time and effort, you will likely observe positive changes in your life.

Summary & Conclusion

Mindfulness and meditation have the potential to substantially enhance mental health, physical health, emotional well-being, and productivity, among other benefits. By engaging in these practices, individuals can achieve greater self-awareness, enhanced emotional regulation, reduced tension and anxiety, enhanced focus and attention, and an enhanced sense of well-being.

Numerous real-world examples and scientific studies demonstrate the transformative potential of mindfulness and meditation. Individuals from all aspects of life can begin to experience the transformative potential of these practices if they are made accessible and alluring.

Including mindfulness and meditation in your daily routine need not be difficult or time-consuming. With suggestions and resources such as guided meditation apps and mindfulness classes, anyone can begin to adopt and integrate these practices into their daily lives.

In conclusion, mindfulness and meditation are effective ways to improve mental health, physical health, emotional well-being, and productivity. By committing to a consistent practice, individuals can cultivate greater self-awareness, resiliency, and balance in their lives, resulting in a more satisfying and harmonious existence. Embrace the power of mindfulness and meditation to live a healthier, happier, and more successful existence.

Chapter 16:
Simple Mindfulness and Meditation Techniques for Beginners

Introduction:
Techniques for Beginners

In today's fast-paced society, tension, anxiety, and exhaustion are all too prevalent. As a consequence, people are looking for ways to alleviate the stresses of modern life and improve their health. Mindfulness and meditation have emerged as effective means of addressing these challenges, providing numerous benefits for mental and physical health, emotional well-being, and productivity. There is a plethora of information and techniques available to those who wish to embark on a mindfulness and meditation journey, given their growing popularity. However, this can make it difficult for novices to know where to begin.

This chapter attempts to provide a thorough, yet approachable, introduction to mindfulness and meditation for beginners. This chapter provides a clear and concise comprehension of the fundamental principles and techniques by analyzing the fundamentals of these practices. In addition, it explores the numerous benefits of mindfulness and meditation, supported by scientific research and real-world examples, to provide a firm foundation for the positive effects these practices can have on an individual's life.

In addition, this chapter offers suggestions and advice for those who wish to incorporate mindfulness and meditation into their daily lives. By providing readers with straightforward and effective techniques, this book will pave the way for enhanced mental health and well-being.

By the conclusion of this chapter, readers will have a comprehensive comprehension of mindfulness and meditation, their benefits, and how to incorporate them into their daily lives. This journey can result in significant positive changes that promote a healthier, more balanced, and more satisfying existence.

Understanding Mindfulness and Meditation
Definition of Mindfulness
Mindfulness is the practice of cultivating present-moment awareness while recognizing and accepting one's thoughts, emotions, and bodily sensations without judgment. Mindfulness, which has its roots in Buddhist philosophy, has become a

widely recognized, secular practice in Western psychology and mental health. By cultivating mindfulness, people can obtain a greater sense of control over their thoughts and emotions, thereby improving their wellbeing.

Origins of Mindfulness
- Historical roots in Buddhist teachings and practices
- The role of mindfulness in the Noble Eightfold Path
- The introduction of mindfulness to Western psychology by Jon Kabat-Zinn

Meditation Definition
Meditation is a compilation of techniques designed to cultivate mental clarity, concentration, and emotional balance. While the origins of meditation lie in various spiritual traditions, secular forms have acquired widespread popularity due to their demonstrated positive effects on mental health and well-being. There are numerous varieties of meditation, such as concentration, mindfulness, and loving-kindness meditation, each with its own approach and benefits.

Origins of Meditation
- Ancient practices in Hinduism, Buddhism, and other spiritual traditions
- The emergence of secular meditation in modern Western culture

The Relationship Between Mindfulness and Meditation
While mindfulness and meditation are related concepts, they are not interchangeable. Mindfulness is a mental state of being present and aware, while meditation is a practice that helps cultivate this state. Mindfulness meditation, a specific form of meditation, is the practice of developing mindfulness by focusing on the breath, bodily sensations, or thoughts and feelings as they arise. It is important to understand the distinction and relationship between these terms to gain a comprehensive understanding of their individual and combined benefits.

Numerous Varieties of Meditation Techniques

- **Mindfulness Meditation:** observing thoughts, feelings, and sensations as they arise without judgment
- **Concentration Meditation:** focusing on a single point, such as the breath, a mantra, or a visual object
- **Loving-Kindness Meditation (Metta):** cultivating emotions of self- and other-directed affection, compassion, and benevolence.
- **Body Scan Meditation** consists of meticulously examining the body in order to develop awareness of physical sensations and promote relaxation.
- **Guided Meditation:** following a pre-recorded script or a teacher who offers guidance throughout the meditation session.

This section provides a firm foundation for comprehending the techniques and practices associated with these terms by investigating the fundamental concepts of mindfulness and meditation. This comprehension is essential for successfully incorporating mindfulness and meditation into one's life and obtaining their numerous benefits.

Benefits for Mental Health
Mindfulness and meditation practices provide numerous mental health benefits, including reduced anxiety and depression, improved emotional regulation, and enhanced cognitive function. The positive effects of mindfulness and meditation on mental health are supported by scientific research and real-world examples.

Reduced Anxiety and Mood Disorders
Mindfulness-based interventions, such as mindfulness-based stress reduction (MBSR) and mindfulness-based cognitive therapy (MBCT), have been demonstrated to effectively reduce anxiety and depressive symptoms. These practices help individuals develop a nonjudgmental awareness of their thoughts and emotions, enabling them to disengage from negative thought patterns and manage their mental health more effectively.

Research on MBSR and MBCT
- **MBSR:** This eight-week program developed by Jon Kabat-Zinn has been shown to reduce tension, anxiety, and depression in a variety of populations, including those with chronic pain and medical conditions.
- **MBCT:** This program was developed by Zindel Segal, Mark Williams, and John Teasdale. Research has demonstrated its efficacy in reducing depression relapse rates among recurrently depressed individuals.

Mindfulness Exercise Examples for the Management of Anxiety and Depression
- **Concentrated Breathing:** Focusing on the breath can help to ground the mind in the present and alleviate feelings of anxiety and depression.
- **Body Scan** involves meticulously monitoring the body to develop awareness of physical sensations, which promotes relaxation and reduces anxiety.
- **Thought Labeling:** Individuals can disengage from negative thought patterns associated with anxiety and depression by observing and labeling their thoughts as they occur, without judgment.

Enhanced Emotional Control
Mindfulness and meditation can improve emotional regulation by increasing self-awareness and the capacity to effectively regulate emotions. By cultivating a nonjudgmental awareness of thoughts and emotions, individuals can better identify their emotional triggers and respond more adaptively to difficult circumstances.

The Function of Mindfulness in Emotional Control
- Mindfulness promotes self-awareness, enabling individuals to better recognize and manage their emotions.
- Individuals can cultivate greater emotional stability and resiliency by witnessing their emotions without judgment.

Examples of Emotional Intelligence-Developing Meditation Exercises
Meditation on loving-kindness (Metta) involves cultivating sentiments of love, compassion, and benevolence toward oneself and others, thereby nurturing emotional health and empathy.
Focusing on the breath or other somatic sensations can help individuals develop a greater awareness of their emotional states, thereby enhancing their ability to regulate emotions through mindfulness meditation.

By comprehending the mental health benefits of mindfulness and meditation, individuals can make educated decisions about incorporating these practices into their daily lives. Developing a consistent practice can lead to substantial improvements in mental health, nurturing resilience and emotional stability in the face of life's challenges.

Benefits for Physical Health

Not only do mindfulness and meditation practices enhance mental health, but they also have a substantial effect on physical health. According to research, these practices can aid in lowering blood pressure, enhancing cardiac health, boosting immune function, and reducing chronic pain, among other advantages.

Reduced Blood Pressure and Improved Cardiovascular Health

Multiple studies have demonstrated that meditation, particularly transcendental meditation, can reduce blood pressure and enhance cardiac health. Meditation induces a relaxation response, which reduces stress hormones, slows the pulse rate, and increases blood flow.

Research on Transcendental Meditation and Cardiovascular Health

- According to a review of studies published in the journal Hypertension of the American Heart Association, transcendental meditation led to significant reductions in blood pressure.
- According to a study published in the journal Circulation, those who practice transcendental meditation have a 48% lower incidence of heart attack and stroke than those who receive conventional treatment.

Relationship Between Stress Reduction and Cardiovascular Health

- Chronic stress has been linked to increased cardiovascular disease risk factors, such as hypertension and inflammation.
- Mindfulness and meditation practices can aid in stress reduction and relaxation, resulting in enhanced cardiovascular health.

Enhanced Immune Performance

Research has established a link between mindfulness practices and enhanced immune response. These practices aid in reducing tension and promoting relaxation, thereby enhancing the immune system's capacity to function optimally.

Mindfulness and Immune System Response Research

- According to a study published in Psychosomatic Medicine, those who participated in an eight-week mindfulness-based stress reduction (MBSR) program exhibited greater immune system activity than those who did not.
- Another study published in the journal Brain, Behavior, and Immunity found that mindfulness meditation increased antibody production in response to a flu vaccine, indicating improved immune function.

The Importance of Relaxation and Stress Reduction for Total Health

- Chronic stress can impair the immune system, increasing susceptibility to illness and infection.

- Mindfulness and meditation practices can support overall health and well-being, including enhanced immune function, by reducing tension and promoting relaxation.

By investigating the physical health benefits of mindfulness and meditation, individuals can gain a deeper understanding of the relationship between mental and physical health. Incorporating these practices into daily life can result in enhanced health outcomes and a heightened sense of equilibrium and vitality.

Benefits for Emotional Well-being

Mindfulness and meditation practices can have a profound effect on emotional health, nurturing increased self-compassion, empathy, stress reduction, and resilience. Individuals can significantly enhance their emotional health and quality of life by cultivating a nonjudgmental awareness of their thoughts, emotions, and physical sensations.

Enhanced Levels of Self-Compassion and Empathy

Self-compassion and empathy are indispensable for emotional health. Mindfulness and meditation practices, especially loving-kindness meditation, can aid in the development of these characteristics by nurturing a compassionate and nonjudgmental attitude toward oneself and others.

The Role of Loving-Kindness Meditation in Cultivating Empathy

- Loving-kindness meditation, or Metta, entails generating sentiments of love, compassion, and benevolence towards oneself, loved ones, acquaintances, strangers, and even adversaries.
- According to scientific research, practicing loving-kindness meditation can increase positive emotions, decrease negative emotions, and increase empathy and compassion.

Self-compassion Exercise Examples to Promote Emotional Health

- **Self-Compassion Break:** During times of tension or emotional pain, individuals can halt, acknowledge their suffering, and offer themselves kind words or actions.
- **Gratitude Journaling:** Recording daily moments of gratitude can assist in diverting attention away from negative emotions and fostering a greater sense of well-being and self-compassion.

Stress Reduction and Enhanced Resilience

Mindfulness and meditation practices can help individuals reduce tension and develop greater resistance to adversity. By cultivating present-moment awareness and acceptance without judgment, individuals can better manage tension and respond more adaptively to challenging situations.

Mindfulness and Meditation's Influence on Stress Reduction
- o Numerous studies have shown that mindfulness-based interventions, such as mindfulness-based stress reduction (MBSR), are effective at reducing tension and enhancing psychological well-being.
- o Mindfulness and meditation practices help individuals develop greater awareness of their thoughts and emotions, enabling them to disengage from detrimental thought patterns and manage tension more effectively.

Techniques for Building Resilience During Difficult Times
- o **Mindful Breathing:** Taking a few moments to concentrate on the breath can help to ground the mind in the present, thereby reducing tension and promoting relaxation.
- o **RAIN** stands for Recognize, Allow, Investigate, and Non-identification. It is an approach founded on mindfulness that assists individuals in navigating difficult emotions and building resilience.

By investigating the benefits of mindfulness and meditation for emotional well-being, individuals can receive a deeper understanding of the potential for personal development and transformation that these practices offer. Integrating mindfulness and meditation into daily life can promote emotional health and resiliency, resulting in a greater sense of equilibrium, self-compassion, and overall contentment.

Benefits for Productivity
Mindfulness and meditation practices can also have a substantial impact on productivity by enhancing concentration, fostering creativity, and promoting time management. By cultivating present-moment awareness and mental clarity, individuals can increase their personal and professional efficiency and effectiveness.

Improved Concentration and Focus
By instructing the mind to remain in the present moment, mindfulness and meditation can help individuals develop greater concentration and focus. This can increase productivity by reducing distractions and allowing individuals to focus on their tasks more effectively.

The Role of Mindfulness in Improving Concentration
- o Mindfulness is the practice of devoting nonjudgmental attention to the present moment, which can help individuals develop greater mental clarity and concentration.
- o According to scientific research, regular mindfulness meditation can enhance attention, concentration, and cognitive flexibility.

Examples of Methods to Enhance Concentration and Focus
- o **Mindful Breathing:** Concentrating on the breath for a few minutes can help ground the mind in the present and enhance concentration.
- o **Concentration Meditation:** This practice entails concentrating on a single point, such as the breath, a mantra, or a visual object, in order to train the mind to maintain focused attention.

Improved Creativity
Mindfulness and meditation can also cultivate creativity by fostering mental flexibility, openness, and divergent thought. By cultivating a nonjudgmental awareness of thoughts and emotions, individuals can more effectively access their innate creativity.

How Mindfulness Influences Creativity
- According to research, mindfulness practices can enhance divergent thinking, which is the process of generating multiple ideas and solutions for a given problem.
- By cultivating a nonjudgmental awareness of thoughts and emotions, mindfulness can assist individuals in overcoming mental barriers and more effectively tapping into their creative potential.

Examples of Methods to Foster Creativity
- **Mindful Walking:** Taking a mindful walk in nature or a new setting can stimulate creative thought by fostering an open mind and present-moment awareness.
- **Open-Monitoring Meditation:** This practice entails observing thoughts, emotions, and sensations as they arise without judgment, which can assist individuals in gaining access to their creative insights and ideas.

Successful Time Management
By fostering mental clarity and concentration, mindfulness and meditation can also improve time management skills. Mindfulness practitioners are better able to prioritize tasks, maintain focus on their objectives, and avoid procrastination.

The Importance of Mindfulness in Time Administration
- Mindfulness can assist individuals in becoming more conscious of how they utilize their time and in making more deliberate decisions regarding their priorities.
- By reducing tension and fostering mental clarity, mindfulness can help individuals work more efficiently and effectively, resulting in enhanced time management.

Techniques to Improve Time Management Examples
- **Mindful Goal-Setting:** Taking the time to set clear, realistic goals and evaluate progress on a regular basis can help individuals prioritize tasks and better manage their time.
- **Mindful Breaks:** Including brief mindfulness breaks throughout the day can aid in maintaining concentration, reducing tension, and enhancing overall productivity.

Individuals can acquire a greater appreciation for the potential of mindfulness and meditation to improve their personal and professional lives by grasping the productivity benefits of these practices. Incorporating mindfulness and meditation into daily life can result in enhanced concentration, creativity, and time management, nurturing greater success and satisfaction in all areas of life.

Incorporating Mindfulness and Meditation into Daily Life

Beginners may find incorporating mindfulness and meditation into daily life intimidating, but with a few simple techniques and strategies, these practices can be easily incorporated into routines. Individuals can experience numerous benefits for their mental health, physical health, emotional well-being, and productivity by making mindfulness and meditation a regular practice.

Developing a Consistent Method

To obtain the benefits of mindfulness and meditation, it is crucial to develop a consistent practice. By setting aside time daily, individuals can establish a routine that promotes their health and development.

Guidelines for Establishing a Consistent Routine

- Set aside a specific time each day for mindfulness or meditation, preferably when you will be undisturbed and able to concentrate.
- Begin with brief sessions, such as 5 to 10 minutes per day, and progressively lengthen them as you gain familiarity with the practice.
- Find a peaceful, distraction-free location to practice in.

Integrating Meditation into Everyday Activities

Practicing mindfulness during daily activities such as dining, walking, and commuting involves bringing a focused awareness to the present moment.

Examples of Mindfulness-Based Actions

- **Mindful Eating:** Focus on the flavor, texture, and aroma of your food as you savor each morsel and consume leisurely.
- **Mindful Walking:** While walking, pay attention to the sensation of your feet contacting the ground, the movement of your body, and the cadence of your respiration.
- **Mindful Commuting:** Practice focusing on your breath or simply observing your surroundings without judgment during your daily commute.

Choosing the Correct Meditation Method

It is essential to find a meditation technique that resonates with you and correlates with your personal objectives and inclinations, given the variety of techniques available.

Guidelines for Selecting a Meditation Method

- Experiment with various forms of meditation, such as concentration, mindfulness, and loving-kindness, to determine which one feels most natural and advantageous to you.
- When choosing a meditation technique, consider your objectives and personal preferences. For instance, if you wish to cultivate compassion and empathy,

loving-kindness meditation may be a better choice than concentration meditation.

- o Be flexible with your meditation technique as your objectives and preferences change over time.

Seeking Advice and Assistance

Seeking guidance from experienced practitioners, teachers, or supportive communities can aid beginners in establishing and maintaining a consistent mindfulness and meditation practice.

Resources for Advice and Assistance

- o Local meditation centers and community organizations may provide classes, seminars, and group meditation sessions.
- o Online resources, such as guided meditation applications, websites, and lectures, can offer beginners guidance and support.
- o Books, articles, and research on mindfulness and meditation can provide helpful insights and direction for advancing your understanding and practice.

Individuals can enhance their mental health, physical health, emotional well-being, and productivity by incorporating mindfulness and meditation into their everyday lives. Individuals can fully embrace these transformative practices and improve their overall quality of life by establishing a consistent practice, integrating mindfulness into everyday activities, and seeking guidance and support.

Summary & Conclusion

Embracing Mindfulness and Meditation for a Balanced Life

This chapter examined the transformative power of mindfulness and meditation practices for novices, delving into their numerous advantages for mental health, physical health, emotional well-being, and productivity. Individuals can experience significant improvements in their overall well-being and quality of life by incorporating these practices into daily life, according to research.

Key Points:

o Mindfulness and meditation involve cultivating present-moment awareness and accepting thoughts, emotions, and bodily sensations without judgment.
o These practices provide numerous mental health benefits, including reduced anxiety, depression, and tension, as well as enhanced cognitive function and emotional regulation.
o Physical health benefits include, among others, decreased blood pressure, improved cardiac health, and enhanced immune function.
o Emotional health is enhanced by increased self-compassion, empathy, stress reduction, and resilience.
o Productivity benefits include enhanced concentration and creativity, as well as efficient time management.
o Incorporating mindfulness and meditation into daily life requires establishing a consistent practice, incorporating mindfulness into daily activities, selecting the most effective meditation technique, and seeking guidance and support.

Individuals can engage on a voyage of personal development, self-discovery, and metamorphosis by embracing mindfulness and meditation. The journey may commence with basic practices, but the potential for profound transformation is enormous. Individuals can create a balanced, gratifying, and meaningful existence by cultivating a deeper connection with themselves, cultivating compassion for others, and living in the present moment.

Chapter 17:
The Science Behind Mindfulness and Meditation

Introduction:
What Does the Science Say?

In numerous cultures and spiritual traditions, mindfulness and meditation have been practiced for thousands of years. These ancient practices have acquired immense prominence in the Western world in recent years, transcending their traditional origins and making their way into healthcare, education, and the workplace. The growing corpus of scientific research highlighting the numerous benefits of mindfulness and meditation for mental health, emotional well-being, and productivity can be credited with the rising popularity of these practices.

The purpose of this chapter is to provide a comprehensive comprehension of the scientific basis for mindfulness and meditation. By examining the physiological and psychological processes at play during these practices, we will delve into the intricate relationship between the mind and body, as well as how these practices can facilitate positive change. In addition, we will provide evidence-based explanations and real-world examples to demonstrate the efficacy of mindfulness and meditation in enhancing various aspects of an individual's life.

The chapter will be divided into several crucial components, with each section concentrating on a unique benefit of mindfulness and meditation. These sections will discuss the advantages of mental health, physical health, emotional well-being, and productivity. Within each component, we will discuss the scientific studies and theories that support these claims, as well as provide practical advice and suggestions for incorporating mindfulness and meditation into daily life.

The purpose of this article is to provide readers with a thorough comprehension of the science behind mindfulness and meditation so that they can make informed decisions about incorporating these practices into their lives. By presenting a balanced and evidence-based perspective, we aim to empower readers to leverage the transformative potential of mindfulness and meditation and enhance their well-being as a whole.

The Science of Mindfulness and Meditation

What is Mindfulness?

Mindfulness is a state of mind characterized by heightened awareness of the present instant without judgment or distraction. It involves paying attention to one's thoughts, emotions, physiological sensations, and external stimuli while cultivating acceptance and a sense of wonder. Mindfulness encourages individuals to approach their experiences with openness and non-reactivity, enabling them to develop a more profound understanding of themselves and their surroundings.

What Exactly is Meditation?

Meditation is a mental exercise that seeks to enhance concentration, relaxation, and self-awareness. It involves engaging in various practices designed to cultivate particular mental states or qualities, such as concentration, compassion, or insight. Numerous meditation techniques can be categorized broadly into two categories: focused attention and open monitoring. Open monitoring practices encourage a nonjudgmental awareness of all thoughts, emotions, and sensations that arise in the present moment.

Mindfulness and Meditation's Neurological Mechanisms

Researchers have gained insight into the neurological mechanisms underlying mindfulness and meditation as a result of recent developments in neuroscience. Several important brain regions, including the prefrontal cortex, amygdala, and hippocampus, are affected by these behaviors.

- **The Prefrontal Cortex** is involved in executive functioning, including decision-making, self-regulation, and emotional control. It has been discovered that mindfulness and meditation practices increase the thickness and activation of the prefrontal cortex, resulting in enhanced cognitive and emotional regulation.
- **Amygdala:** The amygdala plays a vital role in the processing of emotional information, particularly anxiety and stress-related data. Mindfulness and meditation have been shown to reduce the amygdala's reactivity, resulting in a diminished stress response and enhanced emotional regulation.
- **Hippocampus:** The hippocampus is essential for memory formation and learning. Mindfulness and meditation have been shown to increase the size and connectivity of the hippocampus, resulting in enhanced memory and learning abilities.

In addition, mindfulness and meditation have been associated with neuroplasticity, the brain's capacity to alter and adapt to new experiences. By routinely engaging in these practices, people can strengthen neural pathways associated with attention, emotional regulation, and compassion, resulting in long-lasting improvements in brain function.

Moreover, mindfulness and meditation can affect the release of various neurotransmitters and hormones, including serotonin, dopamine, and cortisol. These chemical mediators play essential roles in mood regulation, reward processing, and stress response, contributing further to the overall mental and physical health benefits of these practices.

Mental Health Benefits

It has been demonstrated that mindfulness and meditation have a profound effect on mental health. Regular practice of these techniques can result in a variety of positive outcomes, including reduced tension and anxiety, enhanced cognitive function, and improved mood. In this section, we will examine the benefits of mindfulness and meditation on mental health in greater depth.

Reducing Anxiety and Stress

The ability to reduce tension and anxiety is one of the most well-established benefits of mindfulness and meditation. These practices encourage individuals to observe their thoughts and emotions without judgment or reactivity, thereby granting them greater control over their internal experiences. As a consequence, they are better able to regulate their stress response and maintain composure in difficult situations.

Mindfulness-based stress reduction (MBSR), a structured program that incorporates mindfulness and meditation techniques, has been shown to reduce anxiety and stress-related symptoms, according to research. Multiple studies have demonstrated that mindfulness-based stress reduction (MBSR) can contribute to significant reductions in stress, anxiety, and negative mood, as well as improvements in overall psychological well-being.

Improving Cognitive Capacity and Concentration

Mindfulness and meditation have also been found to enhance cognitive function, especially in the areas of attention, memory, and executive control. Individuals can increase their concentration and mental clarity by training their minds to remain focused and in the present moment.

Various cognitive domains, including working memory, sustained attention, and cognitive flexibility, can be enhanced through mindfulness and meditation practices, according to scientific research. Problem-solving, decision-making, and information processing may become more efficient as a result of these enhancements.

Against Depression

Mindfulness and meditation can play a significant role in reducing depressive symptoms and preventing relapse in those with a history of depression. By cultivating nonjudgmental awareness and self-compassion, these practices can assist individuals in developing healthier coping strategies and breaking the cycle of depressive negative thought patterns.

Research has demonstrated the effectiveness of mindfulness-based cognitive therapy (MBCT) in treating depression. MBCT integrates mindfulness practices with traditional cognitive therapy techniques. Multiple studies have demonstrated that MBCT can substantially alleviate depressive symptoms and reduce the risk of relapse in people with recurrent depression.

In addition to formal therapy, incorporating mindfulness and meditation into daily life can provide ongoing support for the management of depressive symptoms. By cultivating greater self-awareness, emotional control, and mental resilience, these practices can assist individuals in navigating the challenges of daily life with greater ease and well-being.

Physical Health Benefits

Mindfulness and meditation can have positive effects on physical health in addition to their positive effects on mental health. Among other benefits, these practices can contribute to enhanced cardiovascular health, a stronger immune system, and better sleep quality. In this section, we will examine in greater depth the physical health benefits of mindfulness and meditation.

Bringing down Blood Pressure

Mindfulness and meditation have been shown to improve cardiovascular health, specifically by lowering blood pressure. Hypertension, or high blood pressure, is a significant risk factor for cardiovascular disease, the leading cause of mortality worldwide. By fostering relaxation and reducing tension, these practices can help regulate blood pressure and promote cardiac health overall.

Meditation, specifically transcendental meditation and mindfulness-based interventions, has been shown in multiple studies to reduce blood pressure. These practices have been shown to reduce both systolic and diastolic blood pressure, suggesting that they may be an effective adjunct to standard hypertension treatment.

Improving the Immune System

The immune system plays a vital function in defending the body against disease and infection. Stress has been shown to have a negative influence on immune function, making it imperative to effectively manage stress to maintain optimal health. Mindfulness and meditation can strengthen the immune system by reducing tension and fostering relaxation.

Researchers have discovered a correlation between mindfulness, meditation, and enhanced immune function. Those who practice mindfulness and meditation have higher levels of natural killer cells, an immune cell type responsible for combating infections and cancer cells, according to studies. In addition, it has been discovered that these practices reduce inflammation, a key factor in many chronic diseases.

Enhanced Sleep Quality

Sleep is essential for sustaining overall health and well-being, and sleep disturbances such as insomnia can have detrimental effects on mental and physical health. Mindfulness and meditation have been found to enhance sleep quality by promoting relaxation and reducing tension, two common causes of sleep problems.

Multiple studies have demonstrated the efficacy of mindfulness and meditation practices, such as mindfulness-based stress reduction (MBSR) and mindfulness-based therapy for insomnia (MBTI), for enhancing sleep quality and diminishing insomnia symptoms. By cultivating greater self-awareness and emotional control, individuals can develop healthier sleeping patterns and enjoy deeper, more restorative sleep.

Enhancing Emotional Well-being and Productivity

In addition to their positive effects on mental and physical health, mindfulness and meditation can also enhance emotional well-being and productivity. These practices can aid in the development of emotional intelligence, the improvement of interpersonal relationships, and the enhancement of workplace performance. This section will examine the positive effects of mindfulness and meditation on emotional health and productivity.

Improving Emotional Control and Resilience

Mindfulness and meditation practices can facilitate greater emotional regulation and resiliency in individuals. By cultivating a nonjudgmental awareness of one's thoughts and emotions, a person can learn to respond more effectively to their emotions, rather than being controlled by them. This can result in an increase in emotional intelligence and resilience to stress and adversity.

Mindfulness and meditation can help individuals develop healthier emotional responses and coping strategies, according to research. Studies have shown that these practices can lead to decreased emotional reactivity, enhanced emotional regulation, and increased stress resistance. These benefits can lead to enhanced interpersonal relationships and emotional health as a whole.

Increasing Productivity and Innovation

Meditation and mindfulness can also have positive effects on workplace productivity and creativity. By promoting mental clarity, concentration, and emotional regulation, these practices can assist individuals in becoming more productive and creative at work.

Numerous studies have demonstrated that mindfulness and meditation enhance workplace productivity and creativity. It has been discovered that employees who practice mindfulness and meditation exhibit enhanced concentration, decision-making, and problem-solving skills, resulting in enhanced job performance and satisfaction. Moreover, these practices have been linked to increased creativity and innovative thinking, which are essential for success in today's fast-paced, dynamic workplace.

Individuals can integrate mindfulness and meditation into their daily work routines by engaging in brief mindfulness exercises, such as concentrated breathing or body assessments, throughout the day. Regular mindfulness practice pauses can assist employees in recharging, refocusing, and maintaining a balanced, productive workday.

Practical Tips for Incorporating Mindfulness and Meditation
Establishing a Routine

For the full benefits of mindfulness and meditation to be realized, consistency is essential. Individuals can cultivate a habit that becomes an integral part of their lives by establishing a daily practice routine. Tips for creating a daily practice schedule include setting aside a specific time of day, locating a calm and comfortable space, and progressively increasing the length of practice as one gains comfort with the techniques.

Choosing the Appropriate Method

It is essential for a person to discover a meditation technique that aligns with his or her personal objectives and inclinations, given the abundance of methods available. Others may find open monitoring techniques, such as body surveys, more beneficial than focused attention practices, such as concentrating on the respiration. Individuals can determine the practices that best suit their requirements and lifestyles by experimenting with a variety of methods.

Meditation in Daily Life

In addition to formal meditation practice, people can incorporate mindfulness into daily activities. Simple methods to incorporate mindfulness into daily life include paying attention to the breath while performing routine duties, engaging in mindful dining, and engaging in mindful walking or movement. These "mindful moments" throughout the day can assist individuals in maintaining a consistent level of awareness and presence, resulting in enhanced well-being and quality of life.

Summary & Conclusion

Mindfulness and meditation provide numerous benefits for mental health, physical health, emotional well-being, and productivity. The science behind these practices illuminates their efficacy in reducing tension, anxiety, and depression, as well as augmenting cognitive function, emotional regulation, and resilience. In addition, mindfulness and meditation contribute to enhanced physical health outcomes, such as reduced blood pressure, a strengthened immune system, and improved sleep quality.

Understanding the neurological mechanisms underlying mindfulness and meditation enables individuals to appreciate the mind and body-transforming power of these practices. As they consistently engage in these practices, they can experience enduring improvements in cognitive function and well-being.

To maximize the benefits of mindfulness and meditation, individuals should establish a consistent practice routine, investigate various techniques to determine the most suitable approach, and integrate mindfulness into daily activities. By doing so, they can establish a firm basis for personal development, self-awareness, and improved quality of life.

As mindfulness and meditation continue to acquire recognition in the fields of healthcare, education, and the workplace, their role in promoting overall well-being grows. This chapter seeks to empower readers to incorporate mindfulness and meditation into their lives and experience the transformative effects of these primordial practices by providing evidence-based insights and practical advice. Mindfulness and meditation can become potent instruments for personal development, self-awareness, and enhanced well-being, enabling individuals to live a more balanced, fulfilling, and healthy life through continued dedication and practice.

Chapter 18:
How Mindfulness and Meditation Can Help with Stress and Anxiety

Introduction:
How this helps with Stress & Anxiety

Stress and anxiety have become pervasive in today's fast-paced world, negatively affecting our mental and physical health, relationships, and overall quality of life. As individuals contend with increasingly demanding work schedules, societal expectations, and personal obligations, it is crucial that they discover effective methods to reduce tension and anxiety. The practice of mindfulness and meditation is one of the most promising methods for addressing these mental health issues. These practices, which are rooted in ancient spiritual traditions and supported by contemporary scientific research, are garnering recognition for their transformative potential.

This chapter will provide a comprehensive examination of the mental health, physical health, emotional well-being, and productivity benefits of mindfulness and meditation. We will examine real-world examples, scientific research, and practical suggestions for incorporating these practices into your daily life. This chapter seeks to equip readers with the knowledge and resources necessary to employ the power of mindfulness and meditation to improve their overall well-being and resilience.

First, we will discuss the mental health advantages of mindfulness and meditation, including their effects on tension and anxiety reduction, mood improvement, and attention enhancement. Next, we will discuss the benefits to physical health, such as immune function, pain management, and cardiac health. Then, we will discuss how mindfulness and meditation can promote emotional health, covering such topics as self-compassion, empathy, and resiliency. Finally, we will delve into the connection between mindfulness, meditation, and productivity, discussing their effects on imagination, decision-making, and time management.

By the conclusion of this chapter, readers will have gained a comprehension of the numerous positive effects mindfulness and meditation can have on their lives and will be equipped with the tools and strategies necessary to incorporate these practices into their daily lives.

Alleviating Stress and Anxiety

Mindfulness and meditation are well-known for their stress-relieving properties. Mindfulness-based stress reduction (MBSR), a program devised in the 1970s by Jon Kabat-Zinn, has been investigated extensively for its efficacy in reducing stress and anxiety symptoms. MBSR integrates yoga and body awareness with mindfulness meditation to educate participants to be present and nonjudgmental towards their experiences. Multiple studies have demonstrated that MBSR and other mindfulness-based interventions can substantially reduce tension and anxiety in a variety of populations, including those with chronic illnesses, college students, and working professionals.

Cognitive restructuring is one of the primary mechanisms by which mindfulness and meditation reduce tension and anxiety. Mindfulness teaches individuals to observe their thoughts without judgment, which enables them to recognize and challenge anxiety-related negative thought patterns. Meditation, especially mindfulness meditation, helps modulate the body's stress response system by reducing the production of stress hormones such as cortisol and promoting relaxation by activating the parasympathetic nervous system.

Enhancing Mood and Emotional Control

Mindfulness and meditation have also been demonstrated to enhance emotional regulation and mood. Individuals can develop a healthier relationship with their emotions by cultivating a nonjudgmental awareness of their thoughts and feelings. This enhanced emotional awareness enables them to recognize and manage negative emotions more effectively, resulting in improved temperament and mental health as a whole.

Meditation has been shown to have a direct effect on the amygdala, the emotional processing region of the brain. Regular meditation practice can reduce amygdala activity, leading to improved emotional regulation and reduced emotional reactivity, according to studies. Moreover, certain forms of meditation, such as loving-kindness meditation (LKM) or Metta, specifically target the cultivation of positive emotions such as love, compassion, and empathy, thereby enhancing mood and emotional health.

Increasing Concentration and Focus

Meditation and mindfulness practices can also enhance concentration and focus. During meditation, the act of being present and paying attention to one's thoughts, emotions, and physiological sensations trains the brain to be more focused and attentive in everyday life. According to research, mindfulness meditation can result in increased attentional stability, decreased mind wandering, and enhanced cognitive flexibility.

Numerous studies have also investigated the effect of meditation on attention training, with participants demonstrating improvements in a variety of attention-related tasks after regular meditation practice. Real-world examples of mindfulness-based interventions in schools and workplaces have demonstrated their potential to improve attention, concentration, and cognitive functioning as a whole. Mindfulness in Schools Project (MiSP) and Mindfulness-Based Attention Training (MBAT) have been implemented in educational and professional contexts to promote mindfulness and enhance participants' attention and focus.

The numerous mental health benefits of mindfulness and meditation include tension and anxiety reduction, enhanced attention and focus, and improved mood and emotional regulation. These practices are potent instruments for those wishing to enhance their mental health and well-being as a whole.

Boosting Immune Function

Mindfulness and meditation have been shown to positively impact physical health, particularly immune function, in addition to their positive effects on mental health. Multiple studies have demonstrated that regular meditation practice can enhance immune function by increasing the production of natural killer cells, which aid in protecting the body against infections and diseases. In addition, studies have demonstrated that mindfulness meditation can reduce the production of pro-inflammatory cytokines, which are proteins implicated in the inflammatory process.

Mindfulness and meditation can help individuals maintain overall physical health and potentially reduce the risk of developing a variety of diseases by reducing inflammation and promoting a stronger immune response. Consider setting aside time each day for a brief meditation session or investigating guided meditation applications to support your practice in order to incorporate meditation into a healthy lifestyle.

Eliminating Chronic Pain

Mindfulness and meditation can play an important role in the management of pain, especially for those with chronic pain. Numerous studies have investigated the efficacy of mindfulness-based interventions, such as MBSR, in reducing the intensity of pain and enhancing pain-related outcomes. Consistently, these studies have found that mindfulness practices can contribute to reduced pain intensity, enhanced coping strategies, and an overall improvement in the quality of life for people with chronic pain.

Mindfulness assists with pain management in part by altering the perception of pain. Individuals can learn to observe their pain without judgment or resistance through the practice of mindfulness, which can alter the way they experience pain and potentially lessen its intensity. Consider practicing mindfulness meditation, body assessments, or gentle yoga to cultivate greater awareness and acceptance of pain sensations to incorporate mindfulness into pain management strategies.

Enhancing Heart Health

Mindfulness and meditation have also been demonstrated to improve cardiovascular health by lowering blood pressure, pulse rate, and other cardiovascular risk factors. Multiple studies have shown that regular meditation practice can result in reduced blood pressure and enhanced heart rate variability, both of which are indicators of a healthy cardiovascular system. Meditation has even been recognized by the American Heart Association as a potential adjunct therapy for cardiovascular disease prevention.

However, it is believed that the relaxation response induced by meditation may help to reduce tension and inflammation, both of which are known risk factors for cardiovascular disease. Real-world examples of meditation programs for heart health include the Heartfulness Project, which uses meditation and other holistic practices to promote heart health.

Mindfulness and meditation have extensive physical health benefits, including improved immune function, reduced chronic pain, and improved cardiac health. By incorporating these activities into their daily routines, individuals can take an active role in promoting their overall physical health and lowering their risk of developing a variety of health problems.

Cultivating Self-Compassion and Empathy

By cultivating self-compassion and empathy, mindfulness and meditation practices can contribute significantly to emotional health. Self-compassion is the practice of treating oneself with tenderness, understanding, and acceptance, particularly in times of failure or distress. Individuals can develop greater self-awareness and recognize when they are being excessively critical or severe towards themselves by practicing mindfulness. This awareness makes room for the practice of self-compassion, resulting in increased emotional resilience and well-being overall.

It has been demonstrated that meditation, particularly loving-kindness meditation (LKM) or Metta, increases empathy and emotional intelligence. By emphasizing the cultivation of love, compassion, and benevolence toward oneself and others, LKM enables individuals to cultivate a more profound understanding of the emotions and experiences of others. This increased sensitivity fosters stronger bonds and more fulfilling relationships.

Consider incorporating LKM or other self-compassion-focused meditations into your routine to cultivate self-compassion and empathy through mindfulness. In addition, make it a habit to recognize and challenge self-critical thoughts as they arise, substituting them with gentler and more supportive self-talk.

Improving Relationships

Mindfulness practice can have a profound effect on interpersonal relationships. Mindfulness can help individuals communicate more effectively, manage conflicts, and develop stronger relationships with others by fostering greater self-awareness, emotional regulation, and empathy. Multiple promising studies have investigated the effects of mindfulness-based interventions on couples' communication, relationship satisfaction, and overall relationship quality.

Tips for incorporating mindfulness into everyday interactions include actively listening to others without judgment, pausing before responding to allow for deliberate consideration, and being fully present in conversations. In addition, practicing mindfulness meditation as a couple can be an effective means of strengthening emotional connections and enhancing communication.

Promoting Resilience and Adaptation
Resilience, the capacity to adapt and recover from adversity, is a crucial element of psychological health. Mindfulness and meditation practices can assist individuals in developing greater resilience by enhancing their capacity to manage with stress, regulate emotions, and maintain a balanced perspective during difficult circumstances. Mindfulness practitioners exhibit greater psychological flexibility, which is associated with improved stress management and overall mental health, according to research. Grounding exercises, such as focusing on the breath or physical sensations, to regain balance and composure are among the mindfulness techniques for enhancing resilience in difficult situations. In addition, exercising gratitude, journaling, and other reflective activities can aid in developing a positive outlook and fostering resilience.

In conclusion, emotional health and mindfulness are closely intertwined, with mindfulness practices contributing to the cultivation of self-compassion, empathy, improved relationships, and resilience. By adopting these practices, individuals can achieve greater emotional equilibrium, contentment, and well-being in their lives.

Enhancing Creativity
Mindfulness and meditation can have a profound effect on creativity, which is a crucial aspect of productivity in a variety of personal and professional endeavors. Mindfulness practices facilitate creative thinking and problem-solving by fostering increased self-awareness, emotional regulation, and cognitive flexibility. Divergent thinking is a critical component of creativity that entails the generation of multiple ideas or solutions to a problem. According to research, mindfulness meditation can improve divergent thinking.

Open-monitoring meditation, which promotes the nonjudgmental observation of thoughts, emotions, and sensations and allows for a freer flow of ideas, is one method for incorporating mindfulness into creative activities. In addition, engaging in brief mindfulness exercises or meditations prior to engaging in creative endeavors can help to cleanse the mind and promote a more focused and relaxed state.

Improving Decision-Making

Mindfulness can also enhance decision-making by diminishing cognitive biases and fostering more objective, rational thought. Cognitive fallacies, such as confirmation bias and deferred cost fallacy, can negatively affect decision-making processes by causing individuals to rely on faulty reasoning or make decisions based on emotions rather than rational analysis. By cultivating greater self-awareness and emotional regulation, mindfulness practices can assist individuals in recognizing and overcoming these biases, resulting in improved decision-making.

Studies on meditation and decision-making indicate that regular mindfulness practice can improve decision-making skills by increasing cognitive flexibility and decreasing emotional reactivity. Taking a moment to pause and reflect before making decisions, practicing non-attachment to outcomes, and employing mindful inquiry to investigate assumptions and beliefs that may be influencing decision-making processes are techniques for using mindfulness to make better decisions.

Increasing Efficiency and Time Management

Mindfulness can play an important role in enhancing productivity and time management by fostering task engagement, concentration, and general cognitive functioning. Individuals can become more efficient and effective at completing tasks and managing their time if they develop the ability to be entirely present and attentive. Examples of mindfulness-based interventions in the workplace have demonstrated their potential to enhance employee productivity and time management.

Setting aside regular periods for brief mindfulness exercises or meditation, employing mindful breaks to recharge and refocus throughout the day, and employing mindfulness techniques to manage distractions and maintain focus on tasks at hand are all practical suggestions for incorporating mindfulness into daily routines to increase productivity.

In conclusion, the relationship between mindfulness and productivity is complex, with mindfulness practices enhancing creativity, decision-making, and time management. By incorporating mindfulness and meditation into their daily routines, individuals can increase their productivity and pursue their personal and professional objectives more effectively.

Summary & Conclusion

It is impossible to exaggerate the transformative force of mindfulness and meditation in various aspects of our existence. As discussed in this chapter, these practices offer numerous advantages for mental health, physical health, emotional well-being, and productivity. Mindfulness and meditation can promote improved mental health and well-being by reducing tension and anxiety, enhancing mood, and enhancing concentration. Physically, these practices can enhance immune function, reduce chronic pain, and promote cardiac health, thereby contributing to a healthier, more balanced lifestyle.

On an emotional level, mindfulness and meditation can promote self-compassion, empathy, stronger relationships, and resiliency, resulting in greater satisfaction and contentment. Mindfulness and meditation can substantially increase productivity by enhancing the capacity to think creatively, make better decisions, and manage time more efficiently.

As discussed in this chapter, there are numerous methods to incorporate mindfulness and meditation into daily life, including various meditation techniques, mindfulness exercises, and programs tailored to specific requirements or objectives. By adopting these practices, individuals can take an active role in enhancing their mental, physical, and emotional health, as well as their personal and professional productivity.

In conclusion, mindfulness and meditation are effective methods for cultivating a healthier, more balanced, and more fulfilling existence. By comprehending the numerous benefits of these practices and incorporating them into daily routines, individuals can experience long-lasting positive change, ultimately improving their quality of life.

Chapter 19:
The Impact of Mindfulness and Meditation on Overall Well-Being

Introduction:
How this helps us on Overall Well-being

In today's technology-driven, fast-paced society, tension, anxiety, and exhaustion are increasingly prevalent. Consequently, the quest for effective strategies to improve mental health, physical health, emotional well-being, and productivity has never been more important. Mindfulness and meditation are a promising approach that has garnered significant traction over the past few decades. Modern science has embraced these archaic practices, which have their origins in Eastern metaphysical and spiritual traditions, as potent weapons against the challenges of modern living.

Mindfulness is a mental state characterized by awareness of the present moment, nonjudgment, and acceptance. Mindfulness involves being aware of our thoughts, emotions, and bodily sensations without getting caught up in them or attempting to change them. Meditation, on the other hand, is a set of mental training techniques whose central component is frequently mindfulness. These practices can take a variety of forms, including concentrated attention, open monitoring, and loving-kindness meditation, with each presenting its own benefits and challenges.

Mindfulness and meditation have a substantial impact on well-being and are supported by an increasing corpus of research. It has been demonstrated that these practices enhance mental health by reducing tension, enhancing emotional regulation, and fostering a positive outlook. They can also improve physical health by enhancing immune function, enhancing the quality of sleep, and reducing chronic discomfort. Moreover, mindfulness and meditation promote emotional well-being by cultivating self-awareness, enhancing emotional intelligence, and enhancing interpersonal relationships. Lastly, these practices can increase productivity and performance by enhancing concentration, fostering creativity, and reducing fatigue.

In this chapter, we will examine the science behind mindfulness and meditation, delve into their benefits in terms of mental health, physical health, emotional well-being, and productivity, and provide real-world examples, scientific studies, and practical advice for incorporating these practices into your daily life. By comprehending the extensive effects of mindfulness and meditation, you will be better equipped to take charge of your well-being and lead a more fulfilling existence.

The Science of Mindfulness and Meditation
What is Mindfulness?

- o **Definition and Explanation:** Mindfulness is a mental state characterized by present-moment awareness, non-judgment, and acceptance. It involves deliberately directing our attention to our thoughts, emotions, and bodily sensations without getting caught up in them or trying to change them. This non-reactive observation allows us to better understand ourselves and develop a healthier relationship with our inner experiences.
- o **The History of Mindfulness Practices:** Mindfulness has its roots in ancient Eastern philosophical and spiritual traditions, such as Buddhism, Taoism, and Hinduism. These traditions emphasize the importance of developing awareness, self-knowledge, and mental discipline to alleviate suffering and foster personal growth. In recent decades, mindfulness has been integrated into Western psychology and medicine, giving rise to secular, evidence-based interventions such as Mindfulness-Based Stress Reduction (MBSR) and Mindfulness-Based Cognitive Therapy (MBCT).

What is Meditation?

- **Definition and Explanation:** Mindfulness is a mental state characterized by awareness of the present moment, a lack of judgment, and acceptance. It entails paying attention on purpose to our thoughts, feelings, and bodily sensations without getting caught up in them or attempting to alter them. This nonreactive observation allows us to cultivate a healthier relationship with our inner experiences and a deeper understanding of ourselves.
- **The Historical Development of Mindfulness Practices:** Ancient Eastern philosophical and spiritual traditions, such as Buddhism, Taoism, and Hinduism, are the origins of mindfulness. These traditions emphasize the significance of cultivating awareness, self-awareness, and mental discipline in order to alleviate suffering and promote personal development. Mindfulness has been incorporated into Western psychology and medicine in recent decades, giving rise to secular, evidence-based interventions such as Mindfulness-Based Stress Reduction (MBSR) and Mindfulness-Based Cognitive Therapy (MBCT).

What Exactly is Meditation?

- **Meditation** is a set of mental training techniques designed to promote relaxation, concentration, self-awareness, and personal development. In addition to mindfulness, meditation can involve practices such as visualization, mantra repetition, and body-centered techniques such as yoga and tai chi.
- **Various Forms of Meditation:** There are numerous types of meditation, each with its own objectives and techniques. Typical examples include:
- **Focused Attention Meditation** entails focusing on a single object, such as the breath, a mantra, or a visual image, in order to develop attentional stability and mental clarity.
- **Open Monitoring Meditation** promotes the nonjudgmental observation of the entire field of experience, including thoughts, emotions, and sensations, in order to cultivate awareness and insight.
- **Loving-Kindness Meditation** involves cultivating sentiments of compassion and benevolence toward oneself and others in order to promote empathy, altruism, and emotional health.

The Neuroscience of Meditation and Mindfulness

- **How Mindfulness and Meditation Affect the Brain:** Research indicates that mindfulness and meditation can induce structural and functional changes in the brain, reflecting the brain's remarkable neuroplasticity. The following are key sectors affected by these practices:
- **The Anterior Prefrontal Cortex:** The prefrontal cortex, which is associated with executive functions such as attention, decision-making, and affective

regulation, has been shown to increase in thickness and activity as a result of mindfulness training.
- o **The Amygdala:** This region, which plays a central role in processing emotions and generating stress responses, has been discovered to display decreased activation and volume in experienced meditators.
- o **The Hippocampus**, which is essential for learning and memory, has been shown to increase in gray matter density as a result of mindfulness and meditation training.
- o **The Insula:** The insula, which is involved in interoceptive awareness and empathy, exhibits increased activation during mindfulness and loving-kindness meditation.
- o **The Significance of Neuroplasticity:** Neuroplasticity is the capacity of the brain to reorganize and modify in response to experience. This inherent plasticity enables mindfulness and meditation practices to reshape neural circuits, resulting in long-lasting changes in cognitive function, affective regulation, and well-being. The expanding corpus of research on the neural effects of mindfulness and meditation demonstrates that these practices are not merely relaxation techniques, but rather potent instruments for personal transformation.

Reducing Stress and Anxiety

By cultivating present-moment awareness and nonjudgmental acceptance, mindfulness and meditation interrupt the cycle of rumination and concern, which can exacerbate stress and anxiety. In addition, these practices can promote relaxation by stimulating the parasympathetic nervous system, which opposes the stress response and promotes a state of rest and recuperation.

Research Studies: Multiple studies have demonstrated that mindfulness and meditation are effective in reducing tension and anxiety. For example:

- o **Mindfulness-Based Stress Reduction (MBSR)** entails the following: Jon Kabat-Zinn's eight-week Mindfulness-Based tension Reduction (MBSR) program incorporates mindfulness meditation, mild yoga, and psychoeducation to help participants manage tension, pain, and illness. Numerous studies have demonstrated that MBSR can significantly reduce tension, anxiety, and depressive symptoms.
- o **Transcendental Meditation (TM):** TM is a type of mantra meditation involving the repetition of a specific sound or word to attain a state of relaxed awareness. According to research, TM can effectively reduce anxiety, decrease blood pressure, and enhance mental health in general.

Improving Emotional Control

How Mindfulness and Meditation Improve Emotional Awareness: By promoting nonjudgmental awareness of thoughts and emotions, mindfulness and meditation help individuals develop a more nuanced understanding of their inner experiences. This increased emotional awareness can facilitate the development of more adaptive coping strategies and responses to challenging situations.

Numerous Studies have demonstrated the positive effects of mindfulness and meditation on emotional regulation. For instance:

- **Mindfulness-Based Cognitive Therapy (MBCT):** MBCT is an intervention that integrates mindfulness practices with elements of cognitive-behavioral therapy in order to prevent relapse in individuals with a history of depression. Studies have demonstrated that MBCT can substantially reduce the risk of relapse in individuals with recurrent depression, in part by fostering emotional regulation and decreasing rumination.

Developing a Positive Attitude

How Mindfulness and Meditation Cultivate Gratitude, Optimism, and Self-Compassion Mindfulness and meditation promote a shift in perspective, enabling individuals to recognize and value positive experiences and qualities in themselves and others. These practices can cultivate gratitude, optimism, and self-compassion, resulting in increased happiness and life satisfaction.

Scientific Studies: Numerous studies have emphasized the benefits of mindfulness and meditation for fostering a positive outlook. Examples include:

- Loving-kindness meditation entails cultivating sentiments of tenderness and benevolence toward oneself and others. Research indicates that meditation on loving-kindness can increase positive emotions, empathy, and social connection while decreasing negative emotions and self-critical thoughts.
- Gratitude practices, such as ruminating on things for which one is grateful, have been found to promote well-being, increase positive emotions, and strengthen relationships when incorporated into mindfulness practice.

As we continue to investigate the benefits of mindfulness and meditation, we will delve into their effects on physical health, emotional well-being, and productivity, providing readers with a comprehensive comprehension of the far-reaching influence of these practices on overall well-being.

Benefits for Physical Health
Boosting the Immune System

How Mindfulness and Meditation Support Immune Function: Mindfulness It has been demonstrated that mindfulness and meditation practices positively affect the immune system by reducing tension and promoting relaxation. When stress levels are reduced, the immune system functions more effectively, making the body better able to fight off infections and diseases.

Numerous Research Studies have demonstrated the effect of mindfulness and meditation on immune system function. For example:

- **MBSR and Immune System Biomarkers:** Participants in an 8-week MBSR program experienced an increase in natural killer cells and a reduction in pro-inflammatory cytokines, both of which contribute to a stronger immune response, according to a study.
- **Telomeres** are protective coverings at the extremities of chromosomes that play a crucial role in cellular senescence. According to research, meditation may help maintain telomere length, which may contribute to enhanced immune function and general health.

Enhanced Sleep Quality

How Mindfulness and Meditation Improve Sleep Duration and Quality: By fostering relaxation and reducing tension, mindfulness and meditation contribute to the optimal conditions for a restful night's sleep. These practices can also help address cognitive and emotional factors, such as rumination and anxiety, that contribute to sleep disturbances.

Scientific Studies: Multiple studies have shown that mindfulness and meditation improve sleep quality. Examples include:

- **Mindfulness-Based Insomnia Therapy (MBTI):** This intervention integrates mindfulness practices with behavioral strategies to address both cognitive and physiological causes of insomnia. The MBTI has been shown to effectively enhance sleep quality, decrease sleep latency, and reduce nighttime awakenings.
- **Mindfulness Meditation for Sleep Quality:** A study of elderly adults with sleep disturbances revealed that those who participated in a mindfulness meditation program experienced significant improvements in sleep quality in comparison to a control group that received sleep hygiene education.

Eliminating Chronic Pain

Mindfulness and Meditation can help those with chronic pain develop a more adaptive relationship with their pain by fostering nonjudgmental awareness and acceptance. These practices can also modulate the pain processing pathways in the brain, resulting in reduced pain intensity and enhanced coping.

Research Studies: Numerous studies have demonstrated the benefits of mindfulness and meditation for managing chronic pain. For instance:

- **MBSR for Chronic Pain Conditions:** According to research, individuals with chronic pain conditions, such as fibromyalgia and lower back pain, who participate in MBSR programs can experience significant reductions in pain intensity, improvements in physical functioning, and an increase in quality of life.
- **Mindfulness Meditation for Pain Perception:** According to a study comparing mindfulness meditation to a placebo intervention, participants who practiced mindfulness meditation experienced a significant reduction in pain intensity and unpleasantness, suggesting that mindfulness can modulate pain perception.

Mindfulness and meditation can contribute to improved physical health by promoting a healthier immune system, enhancing sleep quality, and reducing chronic pain, thereby enhancing well-being.

Cultivating Self-Awareness
How Mindfulness and Meditation Foster Self-Awareness:
By promoting the nonjudgmental observation of one's thoughts, emotions, and bodily sensations, mindfulness and meditation practices help individuals gain a more profound understanding of their internal experiences. This enhanced self-awareness can result in increased self-acceptance, personal development, and emotional resilience.

Multiple Research Studies have demonstrated the benefits of mindfulness and meditation for increasing self-awareness. For instance:

- **Mindfulness and Self-Awareness:** According to research, mindfulness practices can enhance self-awareness by strengthening connections between brain regions associated with introspection and self-referential processing, such as the insula and medial prefrontal cortex.
- **Meditation and Emotional Awareness:** According to studies, meditation can improve emotional awareness by increasing activation in brain regions involved in processing emotions and empathy, such as the insula and amygdala.

Improve Emotional Intelligence

How Mindfulness and Meditation Enhance Emotional Intelligence: Emotional intelligence is the capacity to recognize, comprehend, and manage one's own and others' emotions. Meditation and mindfulness practices can enhance emotional intelligence by fostering self-awareness, empathy, and effective emotional regulation.

Scientific Studies: Multiple studies have demonstrated that mindfulness and meditation improve emotional intelligence. For example:

- **Mindfulness Instruction and Emotional Acuity:** Research demonstrates that mindfulness training can enhance emotional intelligence by augmenting an individual's ability to recognize and control their emotions, as well as their capacity for empathy and perspective-taking.
- **Meditation on Loving-Kindness and Empathy:** As stated previously, loving-kindness meditation entails cultivating sentiments of compassion and benevolence toward oneself and others. According to research, this practice can enhance empathy, emotional connection, and prosocial behavior.

Improving Relationships

How Meditation and Mindfulness Improve Interpersonal Relationships: Mindfulness and meditation can improve relationships by enhancing emotional intelligence, empathy, and communication skills. These practices can also aid in the development of healthier attachment styles, the reduction of relationship tension, and the promotion of emotional closeness and fulfillment.

Scientific studies: Numerous studies have demonstrated the interpersonal advantages of mindfulness and meditation. Examples include:

- **Mindful relationships:** According to research, mindful individuals tend to enjoy greater relationship satisfaction, improved communication, and reduced levels of relationship tension.
- **Couples** who meditate together report increased relationship satisfaction, emotional intimacy, and empathy, as well as decreased relationship conflict and tension, according to studies.

Mindfulness and meditation can significantly contribute to emotional well-being by cultivating self-awareness, enhancing emotional intelligence, and fortifying relationships, providing a solid foundation for a more fulfilling and balanced existence.

Productivity and Performance
Improving Focus and Attention

How mindfulness and meditation enhance focus and attention: By training the mind to maintain focus and resist distractions, mindfulness and meditation practices can help individuals develop greater attentional control. Additionally, these practices can enhance cognitive flexibility, allowing individuals to transition between tasks more effectively.

Numerous studies have demonstrated the benefits of mindfulness and meditation for concentration and attention. For example:

- Mindfulness and attentional control: According to research, mindfulness training can improve attentional control by increasing activity in the prefrontal cortex, a brain region associated with executive functions such as attention and decision-making.
- Focused attention meditation and sustained attention: According to studies, practicing focused attention meditation can contribute to improvements in sustained attention, as evidenced by enhanced performance on concentration- and vigilance-demanding tasks.

Fostering Innovation and Problem-Solving
How mindfulness and meditation promote creativity and problem-solving: Mindfulness and meditation can boost creativity by fostering a state of calm alertness, which is conducive to generating novel ideas and forging new connections. These practices can also enhance problem-solving abilities by increasing cognitive flexibility and decreasing cognitive rigidity.

Numerous research studies have demonstrated the effect of mindfulness and meditation on creativity and problem-solving. For instance:

- Open monitoring, meditation, and inspiration: Open monitoring meditation, which entails nonjudgmental observation of the entire field of experience, can increase divergent thinking, which is essential for creative problem-solving, according to research.
- Mindfulness and cognitive flexibility: According to studies, mindfulness practices can improve cognitive flexibility, allowing individuals to adapt to shifting demands and generate multiple solutions to complex problems.

Eliminating Burnout and Improving Resilience
By reducing tension, promoting emotional regulation, and cultivating self-awareness, mindfulness and meditation practices can help individuals manage the demands of work and life more effectively, thereby decreasing the risk of burnout. In addition to

fostering adaptive coping strategies and a growth mindset, these practices can also improve psychological resilience.

Scientific studies: Numerous studies have demonstrated the efficacy of mindfulness and meditation in preventing exhaustion and boosting resilience. For example:

- MBSR and burnout: According to research, participation in MBSR programs can significantly reduce burnout symptoms, such as emotional exhaustion, depersonalization, and diminished personal accomplishment.
- Mindfulness and resilience: According to studies, higher levels of dispositional mindfulness are associated with greater psychological resilience, suggesting that mindfulness practices can help individuals rebound more effectively from adversity.

Mindfulness and meditation can significantly improve productivity and performance, allowing individuals to flourish in their personal and professional lives, by enhancing concentration, fostering creativity, and reducing fatigue.

Establishing a Regular Practice
Choosing the Right Techniques

Assessing Personal Preferences and Goals: To establish a consistent mindfulness and meditation practice, it is essential to select techniques that accord with one's preferences and goals. When selecting practices to integrate into their routine, individuals should consider their level of experience, time constraints, and specific objectives (e.g., tension reduction, enhanced focus, or emotional regulation).

Exploring Various Types of Meditation: There are many different types of meditation, such as focused attention meditation, open monitoring meditation, body scan meditation, and loving-kindness meditation, each with its own approach and benefits. Individuals should investigate various approaches to determine which practices resonate most with them and support their well-being objectives most effectively.

Developing Routine and Consistency

- Establishing a regular meditation practice requires setting aside dedicated practice time, preferably daily at the same time. Developing the discipline and reaping the benefits of mindfulness and meditation requires consistency.
- Beginners should begin with brief meditation sessions (e.g., 5 to 10 minutes) and progressively increase the duration as they become accustomed to the practice. This method can assist individuals in developing a habit without feeling overburdened.

Developing a Conducive Environment

- ○ **Designating a Space for Meditation:** Designating a space for meditation can help individuals establish a consistent practice by providing a distraction-free and supportive environment. This area should be cozy, tranquil, and devoid of superfluous stimuli.
- ○ **Participating in Group Meditation Sessions**, attending seminars or retreats, or seeking guidance from experienced practitioners can provide valuable support and accountability, thereby enhancing motivation and dedication to the practice.

Integrating Meditation into Everyday Activities

- ○ **In Addition to Regular Meditation Sessions**, individuals can cultivate mindfulness throughout their daily lives by bringing present-moment awareness and nonjudgmental acceptance to mundane activities such as eating, walking, and conversing.
- ○ **Implementing Informal Mindfulness Techniques:** Informal mindfulness practices, such as taking brief pauses to concentrate on the breath, performing mini-body surveys, and setting intention reminders, can help strengthen the mindfulness habit and extend its benefits to various aspects of daily life.

Individuals can establish a regular mindfulness and meditation practice that contributes to improved well-being and overall life satisfaction by selecting the appropriate techniques, developing consistency, creating a supportive environment, and integrating mindfulness into daily activities.

Summary & Conclusion

This chapter has examined the profound impact of mindfulness and meditation on overall well-being, focusing on the benefits for mental health, physical health, emotional well-being, and productivity. The evidence-based explanations provided disclose the transformative potential of these practices by demonstrating their far-reaching effects on various aspects of life.

By cultivating mindfulness and meditation, individuals can reduce stress and anxiety, enhance focus and attention, improve emotional regulation, foster self-awareness, strengthen relationships, enhance immune function, and foster creativity and problem-solving skills. These advantages can result in greater life satisfaction and a more balanced, satisfying existence.

To obtain the benefits of mindfulness and meditation, it is necessary to establish a consistent practice that correlates with individual preferences and objectives. Individuals can employ the power of these practices to live a healthier, happier, and more productive life by selecting the appropriate techniques, developing consistency, creating a supportive environment, and integrating mindfulness into daily activities.

In conclusion, mindfulness and meditation provide a transformative path to improved well-being by equipping individuals with the skills to navigate life's challenges with greater comfort, resilience, and self-compassion. By adopting these practices and incorporating them into daily life, readers can embark on a journey of personal development and self-discovery that ultimately results in a more fulfilling and balanced life.

Chapter 20:
Integrating Mindfulness and Meditation into Daily Life

Introduction:
How We Apply to Daily Life

In our modern, fast-paced society, it is simple to feel overburdened by the demands of daily life. Stress, anxiety, and an endless to-do list can result in feelings of exhaustion and dissatisfaction. However, the ancient practices of mindfulness and meditation provide a means of counteracting these negative effects and fostering a greater sense of equilibrium, serenity, and well-being. This chapter examines the many mental, physical, and emotional advantages of incorporating mindfulness and meditation into daily life.

Mindfulness is a mental state attained by concentrating one's attention on the present moment while calmly acknowledging and accepting one's emotions, thoughts, and bodily sensations. Meditation, on the other hand, is a broader practice that incorporates various techniques to promote relaxation, concentration, and awareness, one of which is mindfulness meditation. Individuals can develop the skills necessary to navigate life's challenges with grace, resilience, and equanimity by cultivating mindfulness and meditating.

This chapter will provide an overview of the benefits of mindfulness and meditation, with an emphasis on their effects on mental health, physical health, emotional well-being, and productivity. In addition, it will provide real-world examples, scientific studies, and practical advice to assist readers in incorporating these practices into their daily lives. By incorporating mindfulness and meditation into daily life, readers can experience a transformative transformation in their overall quality of life, becoming better equipped to deal with life's inevitable ups and downs.

Mindfulness-Based Cognitive Therapy (MBCT)
MBCT integrates cognitive-behavioral therapy with mindfulness techniques, focusing on negative thought patterns that contribute to anxiety and depression.
o According to research, MBCT can effectively reduce depressive symptoms and reduce the risk of depressive relapse, even in those with a history of recurrent depression (Kuyken et al., 2015).
o MBCT has also been shown to assist people with generalized anxiety disorder by decreasing concern and rumination (Evans et al., 2008).

Mindfulness-Based Stress Reduction (MBSR)
- o MBSR is an eight-week program that includes mindfulness meditation, body awareness, and gentle yoga to help individuals cope with stress, pain, and illness
- o A meta-analysis of 39 studies revealed that mindfulness-based stress reduction (MBSR) effectively reduced anxiety and depressive symptoms in a variety of populations, including cancer patients, healthcare professionals, and individuals with chronic pain. (Goyal et al., 2014)

Enhanced Cognitive Performance - Increased Concentration and Focus
- o It has been demonstrated that mindfulness meditation improves attention and concentration, as exemplified by enhanced performance on attention-based tasks (Lutz et al., 2009).
- o Long-term meditators had superior attentional performance and more efficient cognitive processing than non-meditators, according to a study (Brefczynski-Lewis et al., 2007).

Superior working memory
- o Working memory is essential for learning, decision-making, and problem-solving; mindfulness meditation has been demonstrated to increase working memory capacity in both adults and adolescents (Quach et al., 2016).
- o According to a study of military personnel, those who participated in an eight-week mindfulness training program exhibited greater working memory capacity and fewer cognitive errors than a control group (Jha et al., 2010).

Reduced Post-Traumatic Stress Disorder (PTSD) Symptoms
- o Mindfulness and meditation have been found to aid PTSD sufferers by reducing symptoms such as intrusive thoughts, emotional detachment, and hyperarousal (Kearney et al., 2013).
- o According to a study of veterans with PTSD, those who participated in a mindfulness-based intervention experienced significant reductions in PTSD symptoms compared to those in the control group (Niles et al., 2018).

Enhanced Stress Resilience
- o Mindfulness and meditation have been shown to help individuals better manage stress by reducing reactivity to stressors and promoting healthier coping strategies (Greeson et al., 2011).
- o A study of college students (Shapiro et al., 2007) found that those who practiced mindfulness meditation had lower stress levels and greater psychological well-being than a control group.

Enhanced Emotional Control and Mental Adaptability
- o Mindfulness meditation has been shown to promote emotional regulation by increasing the capacity to observe and label emotions, thereby diminishing their intensity (Goldin & Gross, 2010).

- o Individuals with social anxiety disorder who participated in an eight-week mindfulness-based intervention exhibited better emotional regulation and fewer anxiety symptoms than those in the control group, according to a study (Goldin et al., 2009).
- o Mindfulness practices can also promote mental flexibility, allowing individuals to better acclimate to altering circumstances and manage stress (Moore & Malinowski, 2009).
- o According to Ortner et al. (2007), older adults who practiced mindfulness meditation demonstrated greater mental flexibility and less negative affect than a control group.

Reduced Reflection and Anxiety

- o Mindfulness and meditation help individuals break free from ruminative and anxious patterns, which can contribute to mental health issues such as depression and anxiety (Hoge et al., 2013).
- o According to a study of individuals with a history of depression, mindfulness-based interventions reduced the frequency and duration of ruminative thoughts, resulting in fewer depressive symptoms.

Enhanced Self-Awareness and Self-Insight

- o Mindfulness and meditation can help individuals develop a greater understanding of their thoughts, emotions, and behaviors, promoting self-awareness and self-insight (Farb et al., 2007)
- o A study on experienced meditators found that they had a greater awareness of their own mental states and were better able to disengage from self-centered thinking compared to non-meditators (Brewer et al., 2011)

Reduced ADHD Symptoms

- o According to Mitchell et al. (2017), mindfulness-based interventions enhance attention, impulsivity, and hyperactivity in both adolescents and adults with ADHD.
- o Adults with ADHD who participated in a mindfulness-based intervention showed significant reductions in inattention, hyperactivity, and impulsivity compared to a control group, according to a study (Schoenberg et al., 2014).

The benefits of mindfulness and meditation for mental health are extensive, ranging from reduced anxiety and depression to improved cognitive functioning and emotional regulation. Individuals can develop the skills necessary to better navigate life's challenges, improve their mental health, and enhance their overall quality of life through consistent practice.

Improved Cardiovascular Health
Reduced Blood Pressure
- Mindfulness meditation has been shown to help lower blood pressure in individuals with hypertension, reducing the risk of cardiovascular diseases (Coulon et al., 2016)
- A meta-analysis of 15 randomized controlled trials found that mindfulness-based interventions led to significant reductions in both systolic and diastolic blood pressure (Park & Finkelstein, 2021)

Enhanced Heart Rate Variability
- Heart rate variability is an indicator of the body's ability to respond to stress; research suggests that mindfulness meditation can improve heart rate variability, promoting cardiovascular health (Mather & Thayer, 2018)
- A study on experienced meditators found that they had higher heart rate variability compared to non-meditators, indicating better stress resilience and adaptability (Lehrer et al., 2018)

Enhanced Immune Function
- Improved immune response
- Research suggests that mindfulness meditation can boost immune function by increasing the production of immune cells and reducing inflammation (Creswell et al., 2016)
- A study on individuals undergoing a mindfulness-based stress reduction program found that they experienced increased immune cell activity compared to a control group (Fang et al., 2010)

Better Sleep - Improved Sleep Quality
- Mindfulness meditation has been shown to improve sleep quality and reduce insomnia symptoms, leading to better overall physical health (Ong et al., 2014)
- A randomized controlled trial found that participants who engaged in a mindfulness-based intervention experienced significant improvements in sleep quality, sleep duration, and reductions in sleep disturbances compared to a control group (Black et al., 2015)

Reduced Chronic Pain - Enhanced Pain Management
- Mindfulness meditation has been found to help individuals better manage chronic pain by promoting nonjudgmental awareness of pain sensations, leading to reductions in pain intensity and distress (Zeidan et al., 2012)
- A meta-analysis of 38 studies found that mindfulness-based interventions were effective in reducing pain, depression, and anxiety in individuals with chronic pain conditions (Hilton et al., 2017)

Healthier Weight Management - Reduced Emotional Eating

- o Mindfulness practices can help individuals develop a healthier relationship with food by promoting mindful eating, reducing emotional eating, and preventing overeating (Katterman et al., 2014)
- o A study on overweight and obese women found that those who participated in a mindfulness-based intervention experienced significant reductions in emotional eating, binge eating, and overall weight loss compared to a control group (Daubenmier et al., 2011)

Improved Gastrointestinal Health - Reduction in Irritable Bowel Syndrome (IBS) Symptoms

- o Mindfulness-based interventions have been shown to alleviate IBS symptoms by reducing stress and promoting relaxation, leading to improved gastrointestinal health (Zernicke et al., 2013)
- o A study on individuals with IBS found that those who participated in an eight-week mindfulness-based intervention experienced significant reductions in IBS symptoms and improved quality of life compared to a control group (Gaylord et al., 2011)

The physical health benefits of mindfulness and meditation are wide-ranging, encompassing improvements in cardiovascular health, immune function, sleep quality, chronic pain management, weight management, and gastrointestinal health. By integrating mindfulness and meditation practices into daily life, individuals can support their overall physical well-being and enjoy a healthier, more vibrant life.

Increased Emotional Intelligence

Enhanced Self-Awareness
- Mindfulness and meditation can help individuals become more attuned to their emotions, leading to greater self-awareness and emotional intelligence (Keng et al., 2011)
- A study on business leaders found that those who engaged in mindfulness meditation experienced increased self-awareness and improved emotional intelligence compared to a control group (Roeser et al., 2013)

Better Understanding of Others' Emotions
- Mindfulness practices can also enhance empathy, enabling individuals to better understand and respond to the emotions of others (Lamothe et al., 2016)
- A study on healthcare professionals found that those who participated in a mindfulness-based intervention experienced increased empathy and compassion towards their patients compared to a control group (Krasner et al., 2009)

Enhanced Self-Compassion - Reduced Self-Criticism
- Mindfulness and meditation can help individuals develop a kinder, more compassionate attitude towards themselves, reducing self-critical thoughts and negative self-talk (Neff & Germer, 2013)
- A study on college students found that those who engaged in mindfulness meditation experienced increased self-compassion and reduced self-criticism compared to a control group (Shapiro et al., 2005)

Improved Emotional Regulation - Greater Emotional Balance
- Mindfulness and meditation can help individuals develop the skills needed to effectively manage their emotions, promoting greater emotional balance and well-being (Hölzel et al., 2011)
- A study on individuals with borderline personality disorder found that those who participated in a mindfulness-based intervention experienced significant improvements in emotional regulation and a reduction in mood-related symptoms compared to a control group (Soler et al., 2012)

Increased Positive Emotions and Life Satisfaction - Boosted Happiness Levels
- Mindfulness and meditation have been shown to increase positive emotions and overall life satisfaction, contributing to greater emotional well-being (Fredrickson et al., 2008)

- A study on working adults found that those who participated in a mindfulness-based intervention experienced increased positive emotions, job satisfaction, and life satisfaction compared to a control group (Hülsheger et al., 2013)

Reduced Loneliness and Improved Social Connections - Enhanced Interpersonal Relationships

- Mindfulness and meditation can help individuals feel more connected to others, reducing feelings of loneliness and enhancing interpersonal relationships (Cacioppo et al., 2013)
- A study on older adults found that those who participated in a mindfulness-based intervention experienced significant reductions in loneliness and increased social engagement compared to a control group (Creswell et al., 2012)

Greater Resilience to Life's Challenges - Improved Coping Strategies
- Mindfulness and meditation can help individuals develop more effective coping strategies for dealing with life's challenges, promoting greater resilience and emotional well-being (Garland et al., 2011)
- A study on cancer patients found that those who engaged in mindfulness meditation experienced increased resilience, better coping strategies, and improved emotional well-being compared to a control group (Carlson et al., 2001)

In summary, the emotional well-being benefits of mindfulness and meditation are numerous and include increased emotional intelligence, enhanced self-compassion, improved emotional regulation, increased positive emotions and life satisfaction, reduced loneliness, and greater resilience to life's challenges. By regularly practicing mindfulness and meditation, individuals can foster greater emotional well-being, leading to more fulfilling and balanced lives.

Productivity Benefits: Enhanced Focus and Concentration
Reduced Mental Distractions
- Mindfulness and meditation have been shown to improve focus and concentration by helping individuals manage distractions and maintain a clear mental state (Mrazek et al., 2013)
- A study on college students found that those who participated in a brief mindfulness intervention experienced improved focus, concentration, and working memory compared to a control group (Mrazek et al., 2013)

Increased Cognitive Flexibility
- Mindfulness practices can promote cognitive flexibility, enabling individuals to switch tasks more efficiently and adapt to changing demands, leading to increased productivity (Moore & Malinowski, 2009)
- A study on older adults found that those who practiced mindfulness meditation showed greater cognitive flexibility and less negative affect compared to a control group (Ortner et al., 2007)

Improved Time Management and Decision-Making
- Enhanced prioritization skills
- Mindfulness and meditation can help individuals develop better time management and prioritization skills by promoting clarity of thought and self-awareness (Ostafin et al., 2012)
- A study on business leaders found that those who engaged in mindfulness meditation experienced improved decision-making, time management, and prioritization skills compared to a control group (Reb et al., 2015)

Reduced Workplace Stress and Burnout
- Increased job satisfaction and well-being

- o Mindfulness and meditation have been shown to reduce workplace stress and burnout, leading to increased job satisfaction and overall well-being (Hülsheger et al., 2013)
- o A study on healthcare professionals found that those who participated in a mindfulness-based intervention experienced reduced burnout, improved job satisfaction, and increased well-being compared to a control group (Krasner et al., 2009)

Enhanced Creativity and Innovation
- o Promotion of divergent thinking
- o Mindfulness and meditation can foster creativity and innovation by promoting divergent thinking and open-mindedness (Capurso et al., 2014)
- o A study on college students found that those who engaged in a brief mindfulness intervention experienced increased creativity and divergent thinking compared to a control group (Baird et al., 2014)

Improved Conflict Resolution and Communication Skills
- o Enhanced listening and empathy
- o Mindfulness practices can help individuals develop better listening and empathy skills, leading to improved conflict resolution and communication in both personal and professional settings (Lamothe et al., 2016)
- o A study on healthcare professionals found that those who participated in a mindfulness-based intervention experienced increased empathy, compassion, and improved communication with their patients compared to a control group (Krasner et al., 2009)

In summary, the productivity benefits of mindfulness and meditation include enhanced focus and concentration, improved time management and decision-making, reduced workplace stress and burnout, increased creativity and innovation, and improved conflict resolution and communication skills. By incorporating mindfulness and meditation practices into daily routines, individuals can boost their productivity, enhance their professional performance, and foster a more balanced, fulfilling work-life experience.

Practical Tips for Incorporating Mindfulness and Meditation into Daily Life

Establish a Regular Meditation Practice
- o Choose a Specific Time and Place
- o Set aside a dedicated time and space for your meditation practice, creating a routine that makes it easier to maintain consistency (e.g., meditate every morning in a quiet room)

Start with Short Sessions
- o Begin with short meditation sessions, such as 5 to 10 minutes, and gradually increase the duration as you become more comfortable with the practice

Utilize Guided Meditation Apps and Resources
- o Use guided meditation apps, online videos, or audio recordings to help you establish a consistent practice and explore different techniques

Practice Mindful Breathing Throughout the Day
- o Take mindful breaths during transitions
- o Use moments of transition throughout the day (e.g., before starting work, after lunch, or during a break) to practice mindful breathing, bringing awareness to each inhale and exhale

Use a Breath-Focused Anchor
- o When feeling stressed or overwhelmed, use your breath as an anchor to bring your focus back to the present moment and regain a sense of calm

Engage in Mindful Eating
- o Eat without distractions
- o Turn off electronic devices and avoid multitasking while eating to fully experience and savor your meal

Pay Attention to Hunger and Satiety Cues
- o Listen to your body's signals of hunger and fullness, eating slowly and mindfully to prevent overeating

Incorporate Mindfulness into Daily Activities
- o Practice mindful walking
- o When walking, bring your attention to the sensations in your body, the movement of your limbs, and the environment around you

Be Present During Routine Tasks
- o Choose routine tasks (e.g., brushing your teeth, washing dishes, or taking a shower) to practice mindfulness, focusing on the sensations and experiences of the activity

Cultivate Gratitude and Compassion
- o Keep a gratitude journal
- o Regularly record the things you are grateful for in a journal, fostering a greater appreciation for the positive aspects of your life

Practice Loving-Kindness Meditation
- o Incorporate loving-kindness meditation into your routine to develop compassion and empathy for yourself and others

Seek Out a Supportive Community
- o Join a local meditation group
- o Connect with others who share your interest in mindfulness and meditation by participating in a local group or attending meditation workshops and retreats

Share Your Experiences with Friends and Family
- o Encourage open discussions about mindfulness and meditation with your friends and family members, creating a supportive environment for your practice

By incorporating these practical tips into your daily life, you can establish a consistent mindfulness and meditation practice that promotes mental health, physical well-being, emotional balance, and increased productivity. With commitment and persistence, you can reap the numerous benefits that mindfulness and meditation have to offer.

Summary & Conclusion

Integrating mindfulness and meditation into one's daily routine offers numerous advantages that can considerably improve one's mental health, physical health, emotional equilibrium, and productivity. Individuals can harness the transformative power of mindfulness and meditation by establishing a regular meditation practice, practicing mindful breathing, engaging in mindful eating, incorporating mindfulness into daily activities, cultivating gratitude and compassion, and seeking a supportive community.

The proven benefits of mindfulness and meditation include reduced anxiety and depression, improved cardiovascular health, enhanced immune function, better sleep quality, reduced chronic pain, healthier weight management, increased emotional intelligence, enhanced self-compassion, improved emotional regulation, increased positive emotions and life satisfaction, decreased loneliness, greater resilience, enhanced focus and concentration, improved time management, and d

By incorporating mindfulness and meditation into daily life, people can enhance their overall well-being, leading to more fulfilling, balanced, and vibrant lives. Consistent practice and a dedication to personal development and self-discovery are the keys to unleashing these benefits. Remember, as you embark on this journey, that the transformative power of mindfulness and meditation is within your reach, and that the positive effects on your life can be profound and long-lasting.

Section IV. Coping with Stress and Anxiety

Chapter 21:
Understanding Stress and Anxiety and Their Impact on Mental Health

Introduction: Understanding the Impacts

Stress and anxiety are ubiquitous aspects of the human experience, serving as natural reactions to the numerous challenges and uncertainties we encounter in our daily lives. In moderation, these emotional responses can be adaptive, helping us to navigate difficult situations, solve problems, and protect ourselves from potential harm. However, when stress and anxiety become excessive or chronic, they can have significant detrimental effects on our mental health, physical health, emotional well-being, and productivity.

In today's fast-paced, high-pressure world, many individuals struggle with elevated levels of stress and anxiety. This chapter aims to provide a comprehensive understanding of the nature of stress and anxiety, their underlying causes, and the ways in which they impact various aspects of our lives. By gaining a deeper understanding of these emotional experiences, readers will be better equipped to recognize the warning signs of excessive stress and anxiety, as well as to develop effective strategies for managing and reducing these emotions in order to lead a more balanced and fulfilling life.

This chapter will begin by examining the science of stress and anxiety, including their physiological components and common triggers. Next, we will delve into the impact of stress and anxiety on mental health, exploring the connections between chronic stress, anxiety disorders, and depression. We will then discuss the ways in which stress and anxiety affect physical health, including their impact on the immune system and sleep patterns.

Subsequent sections will explore the effects of stress and anxiety on emotional well-being, highlighting their role in emotional regulation and the social consequences of these emotions. We will also examine the impact of stress and anxiety on productivity, addressing the ways in which these emotions can affect work performance and the financial costs associated with stress-related health issues and lost productivity.

Finally, we will provide practical tips and recommendations for managing stress and anxiety, focusing on mindfulness and meditation, exercise and physical activity, social support and connection, and time management and prioritization. By incorporating these strategies into daily routines, readers can improve their mental health and overall well-being while minimizing the detrimental effects of stress and anxiety.

The Science of Stress and Anxiety

Defining Stress and Anxiety

Stress is the body's natural response to a perceived peril or challenge, eliciting a variety of physiological and psychological responses designed to help us manage with the current situation. Depending on the duration and intensity of the stressor, stress can manifest as either acute (short-term) or chronic (long-term).

In contrast, anxiety is a sensation of unease, concern, or dread that can develop in response to real or perceived threats. While stress is typically a reaction to an external event or circumstance, anxiety is frequently the result of internal thoughts, beliefs, or perceptions regarding future events or circumstances.

Both tension and anxiety activate the body's stress response, a series of physiological changes that prepare the body for action. This response, known as the "fight, flight, or freeze" response, is coordinated by the sympathetic nervous system and the hypothalamic-pituitary-adrenal (HPA) axis, resulting in the release of stress hormones such as cortisol and adrenaline.

Causes of Anxiety and Stress

Stress and anxiety can be provoked by a variety of external and internal factors. Work-related constraints, relationship conflicts, financial difficulties, and traumatic events are frequent external causes of stress and anxiety. Personal beliefs, thought patterns, and coping styles, as well as genetic predispositions to anxiety disorders, can be internal sources of stress and anxiety.

Chronic stress can be caused by ongoing exposure to stressors or ineffective coping with life's challenges. When the body's stress response is repeatedly or persistently activated, it can have a variety of deleterious effects on physical and mental health.

The Physiological Basis of Anxiety and Stress

The body's stress response is activated in response to a perceived threat or challenge, resulting in a series of physiological changes designed to prepare us for action. The stimulation of the sympathetic nervous system causes an increase in heart rate, blood pressure, and respiration. This is accompanied by the release of stress hormones like cortisol and adrenaline, which mobilize energy reserves and heighten alertness.

Cortisol, also known as the "stress hormone," plays an essential role in modulating numerous physiological functions, such as metabolism, immune system function, and inflammatory responses. Cortisol levels follow a diurnal pattern, peaking in the morning and progressively declining throughout the day under normal conditions. However, chronic stress can disrupt this natural cadence, resulting in elevated cortisol levels and an array of adverse health effects.

The rapid physiological changes associated with the fight-or-flight response are caused by adrenaline, an additional essential stress hormone. It temporarily boosts vitality and alertness by increasing heart rate, blood pressure, and glucose release into the circulation. While these changes can be advantageous in the short term, chronic adrenaline exposure can contribute to a variety of health problems, including hypertension, cardiac disease, and anxiety disorders.

The Brain's Role in Stress and Anxiety

The brain plays a central role in the tension and anxiety experience. The amygdala, a small almond-shaped structure located deep in the brain, processes and interprets emotional information, particularly in relation to fear and prospective threats. When the amygdala detects a threat, it transmits signals to other regions of the brain, including the hypothalamus, which triggers the stress response.

The prefrontal cortex, the brain's location for higher-order cognitive functions like decision-making and emotion regulation, also plays a significant role in stress and anxiety. When functioning optimally, the prefrontal cortex regulates the amygdala's stress response, enabling more adaptive coping mechanisms. However, chronic stress or anxiety can impair the prefrontal cortex, leading to difficulties in emotion regulation and an increased susceptibility to anxiety disorders and depression.

The hippocampus, which is responsible for memory formation and retrieval, is another essential brain structure involved in stress and anxiety. Chronic stress can impede hippocampal function, thereby impairing memory and learning abilities. In addition, protracted exposure to stress hormones, particularly cortisol, can result in structural changes in the hippocampus, exacerbating cognitive difficulties and increasing the risk of mood disorders.

Personal Variations in Stress and Anxiety

Not everyone reacts the same way to tension and anxiety. Variations in how individuals experience and manage with stress and anxiety can be influenced by genetic, personality, and environmental factors.

An individual's susceptibility to anxiety disorders is significantly influenced by their genetics. Several alleles, notably those involved in the regulation of neurotransmitters such as serotonin and dopamine, have been associated with an increased risk of developing anxiety disorders, according to research.

An individual's experience and response to stress and anxiety can also be affected by their personality. In response to challenging situations, individuals with high levels of neuroticism, a personality trait characterized by emotional instability and a propensity to experience negative emotions, are more likely to experience stress and anxiety.

Environmental factors, such as early life experiences and social support, can also influence the stress response and coping skills of an individual. By altering the brain's stress response, adverse childhood experiences, such as maltreatment or neglect, can increase the risk of developing anxiety disorders later in life. In contrast, robust social support networks and positive coping strategies can help to mitigate the negative mental health effects of stress and anxiety.

By understanding the various factors that contribute to individual differences in stress and anxiety, we can devise interventions and strategies to assist individuals in better managing these emotions and reducing their impact on mental and physical health.

The Connection Between Stress, Anxiety, and Mental Health

Chronic tension and anxiety can have detrimental effects on mental health, increasing the likelihood of developing anxiety disorders, depression, and other mood disorders. Prolonged activation of the body's stress response can result in dysregulation of neurotransmitter systems such as serotonin and dopamine, which play crucial roles in mood regulation and the experience of pleasure and reward.

In addition, chronic tension and anxiety can impair the function of brain regions including the prefrontal cortex and hippocampus, resulting in difficulties with emotional regulation, decision-making, and memory formation. These cognitive impairments may exacerbate preexisting mental health problems or contribute to the emergence of new disorders.

Anxiety, Stress, and Anxiety Disorders

Anxiety disorders are the most prevalent mental health condition, influencing millions of individuals around the globe. They include generalized anxiety disorder, panic disorder, social anxiety disorder, and specific phobias, among others. Although the precise causes of anxiety disorders are complex and multifactorial, chronic stress is regarded as a significant contributor.

Prolonged exposure to stress can increase amygdala activity, resulting in heightened anxiety and terror responses. This elevated anxiety can become ingrained over time, leading to the development of anxiety disorders. Moreover, chronic stress can disrupt the normal functioning of the HPA axis, resulting in hormonal imbalances that exacerbate anxiety symptoms.

Anxiety, Stress, and Depression

Stress, anxiety, and depression have a complex and bidirectional relationship. By modifying neurotransmitter systems, impairing brain function, and contributing to negative thought patterns and behaviors, chronic stress and anxiety can increase the risk of developing depression.

In contrast, individuals with depression frequently experience elevated levels of tension and anxiety as a result of the difficulties and restrictions imposed by their depressive symptoms. This can result in a vicious cycle in which tension and anxiety exacerbate depressive symptoms, thereby further impairing mental health and well-being.

Stress and the Worsening of Existing Mental Health Disorders
Chronic tension and anxiety can exacerbate existing mental health conditions in addition to contributing to the development of new mental disorders. In response to stress, for instance, individuals with bipolar disorder may experience more frequent or severe mood episodes, whereas those with schizophrenia may experience increased paranoia or hallucinations.

In addition, chronic tension and anxiety can reduce the efficacy of treatments for mental health disorders, such as psychotherapy and medication. This can make it more difficult to manage symptoms and attain recovery.

The Influence of Resilience on Stress and Anxiety's Effects on Mental Health
Resilience, or the capacity to adapt and manage effectively in the face of adversity, can play a crucial role in mitigating the negative psychological effects of stress and anxiety. Individuals with greater resilience are frequently better able to manage tension and anxiety, thereby decreasing their risk of developing mental health disorders or experiencing exacerbations of existing conditions.

Multiple strategies and interventions, such as cognitive-behavioral therapy, mindfulness-based practices, and the development of strong social support networks, can foster resilience. By cultivating resilience, individuals can better safeguard their mental health and maintain their well-being in the midst of life's inevitable stresses and challenges.

Stress, Anxiety, and the Immune System
Chronic tension and anxiety can have serious effects on the immune system, impairing the body's ability to battle infections and cure wounds. When the stress response is activated, the body diverts resources away from non-essential functions, such as immune system function, in order to prioritize more pressing requirements. However, sustained activation of the stress response can impair the immune system and increase susceptibility to disease.

In addition, elevated cortisol levels caused by protracted stress can inhibit the immune system's inflammatory response, resulting in a diminished capacity to fight off pathogens and repair wounds. This can result in increased susceptibility to infections, delayed wound recovery, and a higher risk of developing autoimmune disorders and other immune-related conditions.

Anxiety, Stress, and Cardiovascular Wellness
Chronic stress and anxiety can have a negative effect on cardiovascular health, increasing the risk of developing hypertension, heart disease, and stroke. The

increased heart rate and blood pressure that accompany the stress response impose additional strain on the cardiovascular system. This can result in blood vessel injury, the development of atherosclerosis, and an increased risk of heart attack and stroke over time.

In addition, chronic stress and anxiety can lead to unfavorable lifestyle choices, such as inadequate diet, physical inactivity, and substance abuse, which further increase the risk of cardiovascular disease. By effectively managing stress and anxiety, individuals can reduce their risk of developing these significant conditions and improve their cardiovascular health overall.

Anxiety, Stress, and Sleep
Stress, anxiety, and slumber have a complex and bidirectional relationship. Stress and anxiety can have a significant impact on the quantity and quality of sleep, resulting in difficulty falling asleep, remaining asleep, and obtaining restorative sleep. This can have a variety of deleterious effects on physical health, including impaired cognitive function and compromised immune function.

Poor sleep, on the other hand, can exacerbate tension and anxiety, as it reduces the body's ability to effectively manage stressors and recuperate from daily challenges. This can result in a pernicious cycle in which stress and anxiety impede sleep, leading to further stress and anxiety and a variety of adverse health effects.

Anxiety, Stress, and Digestive Health
Irritable bowel syndrome (IBS), peptic ulcers, and gastroesophageal reflux disease (GERD) are just a few of the digestive disorders that can be caused by chronic stress and anxiety. The stress response can alter the balance of gut flora, impede digestive processes, and increase inflammation in the gastrointestinal tract, causing abdominal pain, bloating, diarrhea, and constipation, among other symptoms.

In addition, stress and anxiety can lead to unhealthy eating behaviors, such as gorging or ingesting high-fat, high-sugar foods, which can exacerbate digestive issues and contribute to the development of obesity and related health conditions.

By managing stress and anxiety effectively, individuals can improve their digestive health and reduce their risk of developing gastrointestinal disorders and other health problems associated with poor digestive function.

Emotional Regulation and Stress
Emotional well-being and resiliency in the face of life's challenges depend on one's ability to effectively regulate emotions. Chronic tension and anxiety can impede a person's ability to regulate their emotions, resulting in increased emotional reactivity, mood fluctuations, and a diminished ability to manage with adversity.

Chronic stress can impair the prefrontal cortex, which plays a central role in emotional regulation, making it more difficult to control and modulate emotional responses. This can have a variety of negative effects on emotional health, including an increased susceptibility to negative emotions like wrath, sorrow, and frustration.

Consequences of Stress and Anxiety on Society
An individual's capacity to establish and sustain healthy relationships with others may be negatively affected by stress and anxiety. High levels of tension and anxiety can result in social withdrawal, irritability, and diminished empathy, making it more difficult to communicate with others and form mutually beneficial relationships.

In addition, stress and anxiety can lead to maladaptive coping strategies, such as substance abuse, which can further impair social functioning and harm relationships. By effectively managing tension and anxiety, individuals can cultivate healthier social interactions and more supportive relationships.

Personal Worth and Self-Compassion
Chronic tension and anxiety can have a detrimental effect on self-esteem and self-compassion, resulting in increased self-criticism, self-doubt, and feelings of inadequacy. Individuals exposed to persistent stressors may develop negative beliefs about their capacity to manage, which can undermine their confidence and sense of self-worth.

Self-compassion, which entails treating oneself with kindness, understanding, and nonjudgment, can counteract the negative effects of tension and anxiety on one's self-esteem. By cultivating self-compassion, individuals can develop a more supportive and nurturing relationship with themselves, thereby enhancing emotional health and stress resistance.

Emotional Benefits of Reducing Stress
Managing tension and anxiety effectively can have numerous positive effects on emotional health. Individuals can experience more positive emotions, such as pleasure, contentment, and gratitude, by reducing tension and anxiety. In addition, effective stress management can boost emotional resilience, making it simpler to deal with future stressors and obstacles.

Reducing tension and anxiety can also enhance social functioning, resulting in healthier relationships, increased social support, and a stronger sense of belonging and connection with others. In turn, this can increase emotional well-being and overall life satisfaction.

By understanding how tension and anxiety affect emotional well-being, individuals can take measures to more effectively manage these emotions, thereby fostering greater emotional equilibrium, resilience, and life satisfaction.

Cognitive Function and Decision-Making

Chronic tension and anxiety can have significant effects on cognitive function and decision-making, impairing a person's ability to function effectively in their personal and professional lives. Prolonged tension can impair the prefrontal cortex's function, resulting in difficulties with duties requiring focus, planning, problem-solving, and decision-making.

In addition, anxiety and tension can contribute to cognitive distortions such as catastrophizing, black-and-white thinking, and overgeneralization, which can further impair decision-making and problem-solving skills. By effectively managing stress and anxiety, individuals can maintain optimal cognitive function and make more informed, rational decisions throughout the day.

Inspiration and Objective Pursuit

Stress and anxiety can also have a negative effect on motivation and goal pursuit, making it more difficult for individuals to remain goal-focused and engage in productive behaviors. High levels of stress and anxiety can result in feelings of overabundance, exhaustion, and hopelessness, which can impede motivation and progress toward personal and professional objectives.

In addition, chronic stress and anxiety can contribute to maladaptive coping strategies such as procrastination, which can further hinder productivity and goal achievement. Individuals can maintain motivation, remain focused on their goals, and increase their overall productivity by reducing their tension and anxiety levels.

Imagination and Innovation

Chronic tension and anxiety often have a negative impact on creativity and innovation. Constant tension causes the brain to prioritize imminent hazards and problems, leaving less cognitive resources for creative thought and idea generation.

Moreover, high levels of anxiety can result in a dread of failure or negative evaluation, which can inhibit risk-taking and the exploration of new ideas or methods. Individuals can cultivate a more conducive mental environment for creativity and innovation by effectively managing tension and anxiety, thereby augmenting their ability to generate novel ideas and problem-solving strategies.

Balanced Work-Life and Stress Management

Chronic tension and anxiety can also disrupt work-life balance, resulting in an increased risk of work-related exhaustion and a diminished capacity to completely engage in personal and family activities. Individuals can maintain a healthier work-life balance by effectively managing their tension and anxiety, ensuring they have the mental and physical resources to devote to both their personal and professional lives.

By incorporating stress management strategies, such as regular exercise, relaxation techniques, and sustaining social connections, individuals can better manage personal and professional demands, resulting in increased productivity and overall life satisfaction.

Managing tension and anxiety effectively is crucial for maintaining productivity in both the personal and professional realms. By comprehending how stress and anxiety influence cognitive function, motivation, creativity, and work-life balance, individuals can reduce their stress levels and improve their overall productivity and well-being.

Practical Tips for Managing Stress and Anxiety
Mindfulness and Meditation
Mindfulness and meditation have been shown to reduce levels of tension and anxiety by fostering relaxation and increasing self-awareness. By practicing mindfulness, individuals can cultivate a nonjudgmental, present-moment awareness of their thoughts, feelings, and bodily sensations, enabling them to more effectively identify and manage tension and anxiety as they arise. Meditation, a practice that frequently integrates mindfulness, can also help individuals cultivate a sense of calm and concentration, thereby reducing the daily effects of stress and anxiety.

Physical Exercise and Activity
Regular physical activity is another effective tension and anxiety management strategy. It has been demonstrated that exercise reduces stress hormone levels, increases the production of mood-enhancing endorphins, and improves overall mental and physical health. Regular physical activity, such as strolling, jogging, swimming, or yoga, can mitigate the negative mental health effects of stress and anxiety.

Management of Time and Priorities
Effective time management and prioritization can also aid in tension and anxiety management by reducing feelings of being overwhelmed and enhancing a sense of control. Individuals can more effectively manage their time and reduce the tension associated with unmanageable burdens and competing demands by setting realistic goals, separating tasks into smaller stages, and prioritizing activities based on importance and deadlines.

Social Support
Strong social support networks are essential for stress and anxiety management. By connecting with friends, family, and coworkers, individuals can share their experiences, receive emotional support, and obtain valuable insights and coping strategies for managing stress and anxiety. Engaging in social activities and maintaining regular contact with supportive individuals can help to mitigate the negative mental health effects of stress and anxiety.

Optional Healthy Lifestyles

Maintaining a healthy lifestyle, including a balanced diet, sufficient sleep, and stress-relieving activities, can assist individuals in managing stress and anxiety more effectively. A diet abundant in whole foods, fruits, vegetables, lean proteins, and healthy lipids can help to stabilize mood and provide the body with the nutrients required to manage stress. As sleep deprivation can exacerbate stress symptoms and impede cognitive function, ensuring adequate sleep is also crucial for managing stress and anxiety.

Professional Assistance

If tension and anxiety become overwhelming or impede daily functioning, it may be advantageous to seek professional assistance. Mental health professionals, such as therapists and counselors, can provide invaluable guidance and support in the development of effective stress and anxiety management strategies. In some instances, medication may be recommended for the management of tension and anxiety symptoms.

By incorporating these practical guidelines into their daily lives, individuals can manage tension and anxiety more effectively, thereby enhancing their mental health, physical health, emotional well-being, and overall productivity.

Summary & Conclusion: Embracing a Holistic Approach

It is impossible to exaggerate the effects of stress and anxiety on mental health, physical health, emotional well-being, and productivity. By comprehending the intricate relationship between stress, anxiety, and various facets of our lives, we can better appreciate the significance of addressing these issues and employing a holistic approach to stress and anxiety management.

In this chapter, the physiological and psychological mechanisms underlying tension and anxiety have been examined. We have also discussed the numerous effects of tension and anxiety on mental health, physical health, emotional well-being, and productivity, highlighting the significance of effectively managing these emotions for overall success and well-being.

In addition, we have provided guidelines and strategies for coping with tension and anxiety, such as mindfulness and meditation, exercise and physical activity, time management and prioritization, social support, healthy lifestyle choices, and when necessary, seeking professional assistance. By incorporating these techniques into our daily lives, we can not only reduce the negative effects of tension and anxiety, but also increase our resilience, contentment, and overall life satisfaction.

Understanding and managing tension and anxiety are crucial to promoting mental health, physical health, emotional well-being, and productivity, respectively. By adopting a holistic approach to managing tension and anxiety, we can cultivate a life that is healthier, more balanced, and more fulfilling.

Chapter 22:
Effective Stress Management Techniques & Strategies for Coping with Anxiety

Introduction:
Strategies for Coping with Anxiety

In today's fast-paced and demanding world, stress and anxiety are ubiquitous emotions. Chronic tension and anxiety can have detrimental effects on mental health, physical health, emotional well-being, and productivity, resulting in a diminished quality of life. This chapter seeks to provide an exhaustive overview of effective stress management techniques and strategies for managing with anxiety, as well as pertinent research, examples, and practical advice for improving mental health.

The significance of stress management and anxiety reduction in fostering resilience, personal development, and overall well-being cannot be emphasized. By obtaining a deeper comprehension of stress and anxiety, their triggers, and their effects, individuals can develop a stress management plan that is tailored to their specific needs and circumstances. Through the incorporation of evidence-based techniques and strategies, readers will learn how to effectively manage tension and reduce anxiety, thereby enhancing their mental health, physical health, emotional well-being, and productivity.

This chapter will examine the numerous benefits of stress management and anxiety reduction in various aspects of life, such as improved focus and lucidity, increased emotional resilience, improved sleep quality, and increased motivation and creativity. In addition, the chapter will explore various techniques and strategies for contending with anxiety, including Cognitive Behavioral Therapy (CBT), Mindfulness-based stress reduction (MBSR), deep breathing exercises, and progressive muscle relaxation. Each section of the chapter will provide real-world examples and research studies demonstrating the efficacy of these techniques, as well as practical suggestions for incorporating them into daily life.

By the end of this chapter, readers will have a comprehensive comprehension of the significance of effective stress management and anxiety reduction in their lives, as well as the tools and knowledge required to make long-lasting, positive changes for their mental health and overall well-being.

Definitions and Differences between Stress and Anxiety

Stress is a normal response to external demands or challenges, frequently manifesting as physical, emotional, and cognitive responses. It is a crucial adaptive mechanism that enables individuals to deal with difficult circumstances, such as meeting deadlines or confronting life-threatening events. However, chronic or overwhelming stress can result in negative consequences.

Anxiety, on the other hand, is a pervasive sensation of disquiet, concern, or dread that may or may not have a clear cause. Anxiety can persist even in the absence of external triggers, whereas stress typically originates in response to specific external stimuli. Anxiety is a normal human emotion, but it can become problematic when it is excessive, persistent, or out of proportion with the circumstances.

Causes and Stimuli

Numerous factors, including work demands, financial concerns, relationship issues, and health problems, can induce stress and anxiety. Other frequent catalysts include significant life changes, environmental factors, and individual beliefs. Identifying the causes of tension and anxiety is essential for developing effective coping strategies and mitigating their negative effects.

Influences on Psychological Health, Physical Health, Emotional Well-Being, and Productivity

Chronic tension and anxiety can have negative effects on many facets of a person's existence, including:

- **Mental Health:** Stress and anxiety can increase the likelihood of developing mental health disorders such as depression, anxiety disorders, and substance misuse.
- **Physical Health:** Chronic stress has been linked to a variety of physical health problems, including cardiac disease, gastrointestinal issues, and impaired immune function. In addition, anxiety can worsen or contribute to physical symptoms such as migraines, muscle tension, and fatigue.
- **Emotional Well-Being:** Persistent stress and anxiety can result in emotional exhaustion, lowered self-esteem, and decreased life satisfaction overall. In addition, they can inhibit the growth of healthy coping mechanisms and emotional resilience.
- **Productivity:** Excessive stress and anxiety can impair cognitive functions like attention, memory, and problem-solving, resulting in decreased productivity, poor decision-making, and increased absenteeism.

The first step in developing an effective stress management plan is to comprehend the complexities of stress and anxiety. By recognizing the distinctions between these emotions, identifying their causes and triggers, and recognizing their effects on various aspects of life, individuals can proactively address these obstacles and work toward a healthier, more balanced existence.

Improved Focus and Clarity

Effective stress management can improve cognitive function, resulting in enhanced concentration and mental lucidity. When tension levels are under control, individuals are able to think more effectively, concentrate better, and process information more efficiently. This enhanced cognitive function can result in improved decision-making and problem-solving skills.

Enhanced Emotional Toughness

By learning how to effectively manage stress, individuals can increase their emotional resilience. Emotional resilience is the capacity to adapt to and manage adversity, trauma, or duress. Individuals can cultivate a more balanced emotional state through the use of stress management techniques, allowing them to face life's challenges with greater ease and adaptability.

Reduced Risk of Psychological Disorders

Chronic tension and anxiety have been associated with an increased risk of mental health conditions such as depression, anxiety disorders, and substance misuse. Effective stress management can assist in mitigating these risks by reducing the intensity and duration of stress and anxiety, thereby promoting improved mental health overall.

Real-World Illustrations and Scientific Studies

Numerous studies have demonstrated the positive effects of effective stress management on mental health. Hoge et al. (2013) found that mindfulness-based stress reduction (MBSR) significantly reduced anxiety and depressive symptoms in participants with generalized anxiety disorder. Mortberg et al. (2007) reported in Behaviour Research and Therapy that cognitive-behavioral stress management interventions substantially reduced stress and enhanced mental health in people with social anxiety disorder.

Tips for Integrating Stress Management into Everyday Activities

To maximize the psychological health benefits of stress management, consider incorporating the following daily practices:

- o Develop a daily mindfulness practice, such as meditation or deep breathing exercises, to enhance present-moment awareness and alleviate tension.
- o Participate in regular physical activity, as research demonstrates that exercise has both immediate and long-term stress-relieving effects.
- o Make sleep a priority and establish a regular sleep schedule, as adequate sleep is essential for maintaining mental health and coping with stress.

- Establish reasonable objectives and divide duties into smaller, more manageable steps to avoid feeling overburdened.
- To reduce tension, practice effective time management and organizational skills, such as creating to-do lists and setting priorities.

By incorporating these stress management techniques into your daily life, you can enjoy the mental health benefits of enhanced focus and clarity, increased emotional resilience, and a decreased risk of mental health disorders.

Reduced Risk of Stress-Related Illnesses

Numerous health concerns, including heart disease, hypertension, diabetes, and obesity, have been linked to chronic stress. Individuals can reduce their risk of developing these stress-related illnesses by managing stress effectively. Techniques for managing stress can lower blood pressure, reduce inflammation, and encourage healthier lifestyle choices, all of which contribute to improved physical health as a whole.

Enhanced Immune System Performance

It has been demonstrated that chronic stress weakens the immune system, making individuals more susceptible to infection and disease. Effective stress management can improve immune system function by decreasing the production of stress hormones such as cortisol and increasing the release of endorphins, the body's natural analgesics and mood enhancers. Consequently, individuals who practice stress management are better able to fend off infections and maintain their overall health.

Better Sleep Quality

Stress and anxiety can exacerbate existing health problems and contribute to the development of new ones if sleep quality is poor. By effectively managing stress, individuals can improve the quality and duration of their slumber, allowing the body to recover and repair itself more efficiently. A sufficient amount of sleep is essential for maintaining physical health because it strengthens the immune system, regulates hormones, and promotes tissue growth and repair.

Real-World Illustrations and Scientific Studies

Multiple studies have demonstrated the positive effects of stress management on physical health. A 2011 study by Gulliksson et al. found that individuals who participated in a stress management program had a significant reduction in their risk of cardiovascular events such as heart attacks and strokes. Another study published in the Journal of Psychosomatic Research discovered that a mindfulness-based stress reduction (MBSR) program led to significant improvements in sleep quality among chronic insomnia patients (Ong et al., 2014).

Tips for Integrating Stress Management into Everyday Activities

To maximize the physical health benefits of stress management, consider implementing the following daily practices:

- o Participate in regular physical activity, such as walking, swimming, or yoga, to reduce tension and enhance physical health in general.
- o Employ relaxation techniques, such as progressive muscle relaxation and deep breathing exercises, to reduce blood pressure and muscle tension.
- o Establish a regular sleep schedule and develop a soothing bedtime routine to improve sleep quality.
- o Maintain a healthy diet by consuming nutrient-dense foods, such as fruits, vegetables, whole cereals, and lean proteins, which can aid the body's ability to deal with stress.
- o Consider seeking professional assistance, such as therapy or counseling, in order to develop individualized stress management strategies and enhance overall physical health.

By incorporating these stress management techniques into your daily life, you can enjoy the physical health benefits of a reduced risk of stress-related illnesses, enhanced immune function, and improved sleep quality.

Increased Self-Awareness and Emotional Intelligence

Developing self-awareness and emotional quotient is a common element of effective stress management techniques. By increasing their awareness of their emotions, thought patterns, and triggers, individuals can gain a deeper understanding of how stress affects their emotional health. This increased self-awareness can result in enhanced emotional regulation, self-compassion, and communication skills, all of which contribute to greater emotional well-being.

Improved Interpersonal Connections

Chronic anxiety and stress can strain interpersonal relationships by causing irritability, social withdrawal, and diminished empathy. By effectively managing stress, individuals can enhance their communication skills, become more empathetic listeners, and cultivate healthier, more supportive relationships with friends, family, and coworkers. In turn, improved interpersonal relationships can result in increased social support and tension relief.

Greater Life Satisfaction Overall

When tension levels are under control, individuals frequently experience greater life satisfaction overall. Effective stress management can result in improved mental and physical health, enhanced emotional well-being, and enhanced resilience, all of which contribute to a more balanced, satisfying existence. Individuals can regain a sense of control over their lives and experience greater contentment and happiness by proactively addressing stress.

Real-World Examples and Scientific Studies

Several studies have demonstrated the positive effects of effective stress management on emotional health. A study published in the Journal of Behavioral Medicine found that participants in a mindfulness-based stress reduction (MBSR) program experienced significant improvements in psychological well-being, including decreased anxiety, depression, and perceived stress. Dunkel-Schetter et al. (1991) found that a cognitive-behavioral stress management intervention enhanced relationship satisfaction and decreased stress levels among infertile couples.

Tips for Integrating Stress Management into Everyday Activities

Consider incorporating the following daily practices into your regimen to maximize the emotional well-being benefits of stress management:

- Develop a daily mindfulness practice, such as meditation or journaling, to foster self-awareness and emotional savvy.
- Devote time to pastimes and activities that bring you pleasure and relaxation, as these can help reduce tension and improve your emotional health.
- Strengthen your social ties by spending quality time with friends and family, joining societies or organizations, and volunteering for causes that are meaningful to you.

- o Practicing gratitude and concentrating on the positive aspects of your life can help alter your perspective and alleviate tension.
- o Consider obtaining professional assistance, such as therapy or counseling, to develop individualized stress management strategies and enhance emotional health.

By incorporating these stress management techniques into your daily routine, you can experience the emotional well-being benefits of increased self-awareness, improved interpersonal relationships, and greater life satisfaction overall.

Improved Cognitive Function and Decision Making

Effective stress management can enhance cognitive function, including memory, concentration, and problem-solving abilities. By reducing levels of tension, individuals are able to think more effectively and make better decisions, thereby boosting their overall productivity.

Enhanced Inspiration and Creativity
Chronic stress can inhibit motivation and impede innovation. By effectively managing stress, individuals can regain their motivation, passion, and creative energy. This renewed motivation can result in greater task engagement, increased creativity, and enhanced problem-solving, all of which contribute to enhanced productivity.

Time Management and Prioritization Improvements
Developing effective time management and prioritization skills is a common component of techniques for stress management. Individuals can reduce feelings of being overwhelmed and increase their productivity by learning to manage their time and set attainable objectives. Establishing priorities and breaking down duties into smaller, more manageable stages can assist individuals in maintaining focus and achieving their objectives more effectively.

Real-World Illustrations and Scientific Studies
Numerous studies have demonstrated that effective stress management increases productivity. For instance, according to a study published in the Journal of Occupational Health Psychology, participants who underwent a stress management intervention demonstrated significant improvements in job satisfaction, job performance, and overall productivity (Richardson & Rothstein, 2008). (Van der Klink et al., 2001) found that a cognitive-behavioral stress management program led to increased productivity and decreased stress levels among employees in a high-stress work environment.

Tips for Integrating Stress Management into Everyday Routines
To maximize the benefits of stress management on productivity, consider incorporating the following daily practices:

- o Develop a daily mindfulness practice to enhance your ability to focus, concentrate, and make sound decisions.
- o Establish attainable objectives and divide duties into smaller, more manageable stages to reduce feelings of being overwhelmed and increase productivity.
- o Employ effective time management strategies, including the creation of to-do lists, the establishment of priorities, and the allocation of time for pauses and relaxation.

- o Participate in regular physical activity to reduce tension, increase vitality, and enhance overall productivity.
- o Cultivate a healthy work-life balance by establishing limits, taking pauses, and engaging in relaxing activities.

By incorporating these stress management techniques into your daily life, you can enjoy the productivity benefits of enhanced cognitive function, increased motivation, and improved time management and prioritization.

Effective Techniques and Strategies for Coping with Anxiety

Cognitive-Behavioral Therapy (CBT)
Cognitive-behavioral therapy (CBT) is a well-researched and effective method for anxiety management. CBT focuses on identifying and challenging maladaptive thoughts and beliefs, as well as developing healthy coping behaviors in order to manage anxiety. Individuals can better manage their anxiety and lessen its impact on their daily lives by learning to recognize and modify detrimental thought patterns.

Observance and Meditation
Mindfulness practices, such as meditation, have been shown to reduce anxiety by fostering awareness of the present moment and nonjudgmental acceptance of one's thoughts and emotions. Individuals can develop a greater comprehension of their anxiety triggers and learn to respond to them more effectively by cultivating mindfulness.

Deep Breathing Workouts
By activating the body's relaxation response, deep breathing exercises, such as diaphragmatic breathing or the 4-7-8 breathing technique, can help alleviate anxiety. These exercises involve gradual, steady breathing, which can help lower pulse rate and blood pressure and promote relaxation.

Progressive Muscle Relaxation (PMR) is a Muscle Relaxation Technique
Progressive muscle relaxation (PMR) is a technique that entails systematically contracting and relaxing the body's numerous muscle groups. By focusing on the physical sensations of tension and relaxation, individuals can increase their awareness of their bodily responses to anxiety and develop the ability to counteract these responses using relaxation techniques.

Exposure Treatment
Exposure therapy is an effective method of anxiety management, especially for those with phobias or social anxiety. This strategy involves progressively and methodically exposing the individual to the anxiety-provoking situation, allowing them to confront their anxieties and develop new coping strategies.

Real-World Illustrations and Scientific Studies
Multiple studies have demonstrated that these techniques and strategies for managing with anxiety are effective. A meta-analysis published in the Journal of Consulting and Clinical Psychology found that CBT was highly effective in treating various anxiety disorders, with significant improvements in anxiety symptoms, functioning, and quality of life. Hoge et al. (2013) found in a study published in JAMA Internal Medicine that mindfulness meditation significantly reduced anxiety symptoms in participants with generalized anxiety disorder.

Tips for Implementing Anxiety Management Techniques into Everyday Routines
Consider incorporating the following practices into your daily routine to effectively manage anxiety:

- Seek professional assistance, such as therapy or counseling, to develop personalized anxiety management strategies and to acquire evidence-based techniques, such as cognitive behavioral therapy (CBT) and exposure therapy.
- Establish a daily mindfulness practice, such as meditation or deep breathing exercises, to aid in anxiety reduction and relaxation.
- Participate in regular physical activity, as research indicates that exercise has both immediate and long-term anxiety-relieving effects.
- Practice proper sleep hygiene and adhere to a regular sleep schedule to promote overall mental health and anxiety management.
- Establish a solid support network by connecting with friends, family, or support groups to share experiences and coping strategies.

By incorporating these techniques and strategies for anxiety management into your daily life, you can effectively contend with anxiety and enhance your mental health and well-being as a whole.

Summary & Conclusion

Effective stress management and anxiety coping strategies play a crucial role in promoting mental health, physical health, emotional well-being, and productivity. By understanding the nature of stress and anxiety and implementing evidence-based strategies to manage them, individuals can experience numerous benefits, such as improved focus and clarity, increased emotional resilience, decreased risk of mental and physical health disorders, increased motivation and creativity, and improved interpersonal relationships.

Numerous stress management and anxiety coping techniques, such as cognitive-behavioral therapy, mindfulness meditation, deep breathing exercises, progressive muscle relaxation, and exposure therapy, have been shown to be effective by research and real-world examples. By incorporating these practices into daily routines, individuals can not only better manage their tension and anxiety, but also enhance their quality of life as a whole.

To obtain the benefits of stress management and anxiety coping strategies, it is essential to practice them consistently and to seek professional assistance when necessary. Individuals can navigate the challenges of life with greater ease, resilience, and well-being if they develop a personalized stress management and anxiety reduction strategy. We can strive toward improved mental health and a more balanced, fulfilling existence by adopting these techniques and strategies.

Chapter 23:
Coping with Anxiety

Introduction:
The Ubiquity & Complexity of Anxiety

Anxiety is a natural and ubiquitous human emotion that everyone experiences to varying degrees throughout their lives. It is a natural response to stress and uncertainty that serves an essential evolutionary function by alerting us to potential hazards and motivating us to act. Anxiety can be beneficial in moderation, assisting us in navigating challenging situations, preparing for significant events, and enhancing performance in a variety of contexts. However, anxiety can substantially impair mental health, physical health, emotional well-being, and productivity when it becomes chronic, debilitating, and disproportionate to the situation.

Anxiety is becoming increasingly prevalent in today's fast-paced and complicated world. According to the World Health Organization (WHO), anxiety disorders are the most prevalent mental health condition worldwide, afflicting millions of people. Furthermore, the ongoing COVID-19 pandemic has exacerbated many people's anxiety and tension, making it more essential than ever to develop effective coping strategies.

This chapter seeks to provide a comprehensive comprehension of anxiety and its impact on various aspects of life, as well as evidence-based coping strategies and practical advice. The chapter is divided into five primary sections, each of which delves into a distinct aspect of anxiety management, and is supported by scientific research, real-world examples, and expert advice. The sections discuss comprehending anxiety and its effects, cognitive-behavioral techniques for managing anxiety, lifestyle modifications to reduce anxiety, developing emotional resilience, and seeking professional assistance when necessary.

At the conclusion of this chapter, readers will have a better comprehension of the complexity of anxiety and its consequences, as well as the tools and strategies necessary to effectively contend with anxiety and improve their mental health. Individuals can take proactive measures toward leading more fulfilling, balanced, and anxiety-free lives when armed with this knowledge.

Understanding Anxiety and Its Impact

The Nature of Anxiety

Anxiety is a complex and multifaceted emotional reaction to perceived threats, uncertainty, or stress. Anxiety comprises a variety of emotional, cognitive, and physiological responses, including feelings of disquiet, concern, and fear, as well as physical symptoms such as an accelerated heartbeat, rapid respiration, and muscle tension. Anxiety can manifest in numerous ways, including generalized anxiety disorder (GAD), social anxiety disorder, panic disorder, and phobias.

In daily life, anxiety functions as an adaptive mechanism, preparing the body to respond to potential threats and allowing individuals to perform better under duress. However, excessive anxiety can interfere with daily functioning and contribute to chronic psychological and physical health problems.

The Reasons for Anxiety

Biological, environmental, and individual experiences can all contribute to the development of anxiety. Among the leading factors of apprehension are:

- **Genetic Predisposition:** A A familial history of anxiety disorders may increase an individual's risk for developing anxiety, indicating a genetic component.
- **Brain Chemistry:** Neurotransmitter imbalances, such as serotonin and norepinephrine, are frequently associated with anxiety disorders.
- **Environmental Factors:** Chronic tension, exposure to traumatic events, and living in a high-pressure environment can all contribute to the onset of anxiety.
- **Personality Traits:** Certain personality qualities, such as perfectionism or heightened sensitivity to criticism, may predispose individuals to anxiety.
- **Life Experiences:** Personal experiences, such as childhood adversity or a history of maltreatment, can increase the risk of developing anxiety.

Physical and Psychological Effects of Anxiety

When anxiety becomes chronic or unmanageable, it can have extensive effects on a person's mental and physical health, as well as their well-being as a whole. Among the most important effects of anxiety are:

- **Stress Response and Its Effects on The Body:** Chronic anxiety can lead to protracted activation of the stress response, which can cause a variety of physical symptoms including migraines, digestive problems, muscle tension, and sleep disturbances. This can increase the likelihood of developing cardiovascular disease, diabetes, and chronic pain over time.
- **Anxiety and Mental Health Disorders:** Persistent anxiety can contribute to the development of other mental health disorders, including depression, OCD, and PTSD.
- **Impaired Relationships and Work Performance:** Excessive anxiety can hinder the maintenance of healthy relationships and the attainment of

personal or professional objectives. Anxious individuals may have difficulty with social interactions, concentration issues at work, or perfectionism that impedes progress and productivity.

Understanding the complex nature, causes, and effects of anxiety is essential for the development of effective coping strategies and the pursuit of appropriate treatment. By increasing self-awareness and recognizing the signs of anxiety, individuals can take proactive measures to address their anxiety and reduce its negative effects on their lives.

Cognitive-Behavioral Techniques for Managing Anxiety

Cognitive-behavioral therapy (CBT) is a psychological treatment based on empirical evidence that focuses on identifying and altering maladaptive thought patterns and behaviors that contribute to anxiety. CBT techniques are widely acknowledged as effective tools for anxiety management and have been demonstrated to produce long-lasting improvements in symptoms. This section will examine some of the most important CBT techniques for anxiety management.

Recognizing and Countering Negative Thoughts

Learning to recognize and modify distorted thought patterns that contribute to anxiety is a central component of CBT. Catastrophizing, black-and-white reasoning, and overgeneralization are examples of prevalent cognitive distortions associated with anxiety. Individuals can challenge these negative beliefs by:

- **Recognizing Distorted Thought Patterns:** Developing self-awareness and recognizing common cognitive distortions can assist people in recognizing when their beliefs contribute to anxiety.
- **Employ the ABC Cognitive Restructuring Model:** This paradigm involves identifying the activating event (A), investigating the beliefs (B), and assessing the consequences (C) of these beliefs. By analyzing and challenging irrational beliefs, people can develop more rational and realistic thought patterns, thereby reducing anxiety.
- **Utilize Thought Diaries:** Keeping a thought diary can assist individuals in monitoring and analyzing their negative thoughts, evaluating the evidence supporting or contradicting them, and developing alternative, more balanced perspectives.

Exposure Treatment

Exposure therapy is a CBT technique that entails confronting anxiety-provoking situations in a gradual and controlled manner in order to reduce fear and avoidance. By repeatedly exposing themselves to feared situations, individuals can learn that their anxiety is frequently unwarranted and gradually reduce their emotional response. Exposure therapy can be administered in numerous methods, including:

- **Systematic Desensitization:** This technique entails constructing a hierarchy of anxiety-provoking situations, from the least anxiety-provoking to the most difficult. Individuals progressively expose themselves to each situation while exercising anxiety-reducing relaxation techniques.

- o **In-vivo Exposure:** This form of exposure involves confronting anxiety-provoking situations in real life, allowing individuals to gain confidence and reduce anxiety through repeated exposure.
- o **Imaginal Exposure:** Imaginal exposure can be used in situations where in-vivo exposure is not feasible or secure. To reduce fear and anxiety, this technique entails vividly envisioning and confronting anxiety-provoking scenarios.

Relaxation Techniques

Incorporating relaxation techniques into anxiety management can help counteract anxiety's physiological symptoms and improve overall health. Some effective relaxation techniques include:

- o **Deep Breathing Exercises:** Slow, controlled respiration can assist in regulating the body's tension response and alleviating anxiety symptoms. Regular practice of techniques such as diaphragmatic breathing and the 4-7-8 breathing method can be used to manage anxiety.
- o **Progressive Muscle Relaxation (PMR)** entails systematically tensing and relaxing various muscle groups to reduce physical tension and promote relaxation. By routinely practicing PMR, individuals can increase their awareness of the body's stress response and learn to release tension more effectively.
- o **Mental Imagery and Guided Visualization:** Creating tranquil and peaceful mental images through mental exercises can help reduce anxiety and promote serenity. There are numerous formats for guided imagery exercises, including audio recordings, smartphone applications, and written narratives.

Individuals can develop the skills and tools necessary to effectively contend with anxiety, lessen its influence on their lives, and enhance their overall mental health by incorporating cognitive-behavioral techniques into their anxiety management strategies.

Lifestyle Changes to Reduce Anxiety

Positive behavioral adjustments can have a substantial impact on anxiety levels and mental health as a whole. Individuals can develop resilience against anxiety and improve their well-being by incorporating healthy behaviors and routines into their daily lives. This section will discuss important lifestyle modifications that can help reduce anxiety.

Physical Exercise and Activity

Regular exercise has been shown to have numerous mental health benefits, including the reduction of anxiety. Physical activity may facilitate:

- o **Release Endorphins:** Physical activity stimulates the release of endorphins, which are natural mood boosters that can aid in reducing anxiety and enhancing general well-being.
- o **Improve Sleep:** Regular exercise can contribute to improved sleep quality, which is essential for anxiety management.
- o **Increase Self-Confidence:** Regular physical activity can increase self-esteem and self-confidence, resulting in decreased apprehension.

Tips for Incorporating Physical Activity into Daily Routines Include:

- o **Selecting Pleasurable Activities:** Selecting physical activities that are pleasurable and enduring is essential for sustaining long-term exercise habits.
- o **Setting Realistic Goals:** Setting Realistic objectives Establishing fitness objectives that are attainable can help individuals remain motivated and prevent feelings of overabundance and anxiety.
- o **Including Physical Activity in Everyday Life:** Simple adjustments, such as taking the stairs instead of the escalator, can contribute to an increase in daily physical activity.

Diet and Nutrition

A balanced and nutritious diet is essential for anxiety management. The following dietary factors can help reduce anxiety:

- o **Eating a Variety of Whole Foods:** A diet rich in fruits, vegetables, whole cereals, lean proteins, and healthy lipids promotes overall mental health and reduces anxiety.
- o **Restricting Processed and Sugary Foods:** Processed foods and sugar can contribute to fluctuations in blood sugar and temperament, which can exacerbate anxiety. Reducing consumption of these foods may aid in anxiety management.
- o **Incorporating Foods That Reduce Anxiety:** Certain nutrients, including those high in omega-3 fatty acids, magnesium, and antioxidants, have been associated with decreased anxiety. The consumption of these substances may alleviate anxiety symptoms.

Sleeping and Relaxing

Quality sleep is essential for anxiety management and overall mental health maintenance. Developing healthy sleep habits can aid in enhancing sleep quality and decreasing anxiety. Some sleep hygiene recommendations include:

- o **Establishing a Consistent Sleep Schedule:** Consistently going to bed and rising up at the same time each day can help regulate the body's internal clock and improve sleep quality.

- ○ **Establishing a Relaxing Bedtime Routine:** Engaging in tranquil activities, such as reading or taking a warm bath, can help communicate to the body that it is time to sleep and facilitate the transition into rest.
- ○ **Limiting Exposure to Screens and Technology:** Limiting screen time, particularly before bedtime, can help reduce mental stimulation and promote tranquility.

In addition to adequate rest, incorporating relaxation techniques into daily life can aid in anxiety management. Such techniques as deep breathing, progressive muscle relaxation, and mindfulness meditation can aid in reducing anxiety and promoting overall health.

Individuals can considerably reduce their anxiety levels and enhance their mental health as a whole by making lifestyle modifications in areas such as exercise, nutrition, and sleep. These modifications may require time and effort, but the long-term benefits for anxiety management and general health make them worthwhile investments.

Developing Emotional Resilience

Emotional resilience is the capacity to adapt to and manage difficult emotions, such as anxiety, tension, and adversity. Emotional resilience is essential for the management of anxiety and maintenance of overall mental health because it enables individuals to navigate challenging situations more effectively and recover from setbacks. This section will discuss techniques for cultivating emotional resilience and incorporating them into daily life.

Mindfulness and Self-Compassion Practice

Mindfulness and self-compassion are effective strategies for enhancing emotional resilience and reducing anxiety. By cultivating nonjudgmental self-awareness and self-compassion, individuals can better manage their emotions and develop healthier coping mechanisms. Some examples of mindfulness and self-compassion practices include:

- ○ **Mindfulness Meditation:** Regular mindfulness meditation can help individuals develop the capacity to observe their thoughts and emotions without judgment or reactivity. This can be accomplished through guided meditations, applications, or simply setting aside time every day for silent reflection.
- ○ **Self-Compassion Exercises:** Engaging in self-compassion exercises, such as loving-kindness meditation or composing a compassionate letter to oneself, can assist individuals in developing a more compassionate and supportive relationship with themselves.
- ○ **Practicing Gratitude:** Concentrating on positive experiences and expressing gratitude for them can assist in diverting attention away from negative thoughts and feelings, thereby promoting emotional resilience.

Developing Social Links

- **Engaging in Group Activities:** Strong social connections are essential for fostering emotional resiliency and overcoming anxiety. During difficult circumstances, social support can provide a sense of belonging, validation, and encouragement. Participating in Group Activities: Joining organizations, participating in team sports, or attending community events can assist individuals in meeting new people and fostering social connections.
- **Reaching Out to Friends and Family:** Maintaining regular contact with friends and family can strengthen existing relationships and provide a support system during times of tension or anxiety.
- **Seeking Support from Mental Health Professionals or Support Groups**: Connecting with others who have had similar experiences can provide valuable insights, advice, and motivation.

Establishing Realistic Objectives and Fostering a Growth Mindset
Creating a sense of purpose and motivation by establishing attainable and significant objectives can cultivate emotional resilience. Individuals can approach challenges with a more optimistic and adaptable attitude if they cultivate a growth mindset, or the belief that abilities and intellect can be developed through dedication and hard work. Techniques for establishing objectives and fostering a growth mindset include:

- **Setting SMART Objectives:** Setting SMART (Specific, Measurable, Attainable, Relevant, and Time-Bound) objectives can assist individuals in defining their goals and monitoring their progress.
- **Breaking Large Objectives into Smaller Steps:** Dividing long-term objectives into smaller, more manageable tasks can make them seem less daunting and more attainable.
- **Embracing Challenges and Learning from Setbacks:** Viewing challenges as opportunities for growth and learning can aid in the development of emotional resiliency and decrease anxiety surrounding failure.

By emphasizing the development of emotional resilience through mindfulness, self-compassion, strong social connections, and goal-setting, individuals can better manage anxiety and navigate inevitable challenges and stresses. Developing emotional resilience is a continuous process that requires persistence and commitment, but the positive effects on mental health and well-being are substantial and long-lasting.

Seeking Professional Help
Although self-help strategies and lifestyle modifications can be effective in managing anxiety, professional assistance may be required for more severe or persistent anxiety issues. Seeking professional assistance can provide individuals with additional resources, guidance, and support to better manage their anxiety and enhance their

mental health as a whole. This section will discuss the significance of seeking professional assistance and will enumerate essential measures.

Understanding When to Seek Professional Assistance

It is essential to recognize when anxiety has become unmanageable and is negatively affecting daily functioning, interpersonal relationships, and overall health. The following are indicators that it may be time to seek professional assistance:

- o   Persistent, excessive, or irrational anxiety that impairs daily functioning o Panic attacks or extreme terror in specific situations
- o   Avoidance of social situations or activities because of anxiety o A substantial decline in work or school performance
- o   Difficulty managing relationships or sustaining social connections
- o   The emergence of problematic coping strategies, such as substance abuse

Choosing an Appropriate Mental Health Professional

Selecting the appropriate mental health professional is a crucial step in obtaining anxiety treatment. A variety of practitioners, including psychologists, psychiatrists, clinical social workers, and licensed counselors, can provide support and treatment. Consider the following factors when selecting a mental health professional:

- o   **Licensing and Qualifications:** Ensure that the mental health professional is licensed and possesses the necessary credentials.
- o   **Specialization in Anxiety Disorders:** Seek out a professional who specializes in anxiety disorders or has experience treating patients with similar issues.
- o   **Compatibility and Rapport:** It is essential to find a mental health professional with whom one feels comfortable discussing personal concerns and issues. This may necessitate meeting with multiple professionals prior to locating the ideal match.

Examining Treatment Alternatives

There are a variety of evidence-based treatment options available for anxiety disorders, and the approach that is most suitable for an individual will depend on his or her specific requirements and preferences. Examples of common treatments for anxiety include:

- o   **CBT:** CBT is a widely recognized and effective treatment for anxiety disorders, as mentioned previously. It emphasizes the recognition and modification of negative thought patterns and behaviors that contribute to anxiety.
- o   **Medication:** In some instances, medication may be prescribed to assist with anxiety management. Antidepressants, beta-blockers, and anti-anxiety medications are some of the medications commonly used to treat anxiety disorders. It is necessary to discuss the potential benefits and hazards of a medication with a healthcare professional.

- o **Alternative and Complementary Therapies:** In addition to conventional treatments, some individuals may find anxiety alleviation through alternative therapies such as acupuncture, massage, and botanical supplements. Prior to incorporating these options into a treatment plan, it is essential to consult with a healthcare professional.

Seeking professional assistance for anxiety is an essential component of taking charge of one's mental health and well-being. Individuals can develop more effective strategies to manage their anxiety and lead healthier, more fulfilling lives by recognizing when to seek assistance, locating the right mental health professional, and investigating appropriate treatment options.

Summary & Conclusion

Anxiety is a pervasive and complex issue that impacts millions of people worldwide. Effective anxiety management necessitates a multifaceted strategy that addresses both the cognitive and behavioral aspects of this mental health challenge, as well as the broader lifestyle factors that contribute to overall health.

This chapter has examined various evidence-based strategies for managing anxiety, including comprehending anxiety and its impact, employing cognitive-behavioral techniques, making lifestyle changes, developing emotional resilience, and seeking professional assistance when necessary. Individuals can better manage anxiety and enhance their mental health, physical health, emotional well-being, and productivity by employing a holistic approach that incorporates these strategies.

Developing an effective plan for anxiety management is a personal and ongoing process, as the requirements and circumstances of each individual are unique. It is essential to maintain patience, compassion, and persistence in the face of obstacles and setbacks, as well as to be adaptable in one's approach.

In conclusion, contending with anxiety requires commitment, self-awareness, and the willingness to seek support from others, whether through professional assistance or personal relationships. Individuals can cultivate a greater sense of control and empowerment by actively managing their anxiety, ultimately leading to a more balanced, gratifying, and resilient existence.

Chapter 24:
How to Develop a Personalized Stress and Anxiety Management Plan

Introduction:
Setting up a Plan

Stress and anxiety are pervasive in contemporary life, impacting people of all ages, origins, and occupations. Chronic stress and anxiety can have negative effects on our mental health, physical health, emotional well-being, and overall productivity, despite the fact that a certain amount of stress can be motivating and energizing. Developing a personalized stress and anxiety management plan is not only a proactive approach to maintaining optimal well-being, but also an essential strategy for preventing exhaustion, enhancing resilience, and enhancing the quality of life overall.

This chapter will provide a comprehensive guide to help you comprehend the nature of stress and anxiety, identify your unique stressors and triggers, and develop a personalized plan that incorporates evidence-based techniques for stress management and reduction. The chapter will also emphasize pertinent research, real-world examples, and practical advice to equip you with the tools and knowledge necessary to implement stress management strategies in your daily life.

You will be well on your way to developing a personalized stress and anxiety management plan that empowers you to take charge of your mental health, promotes your physical and emotional well-being, and ultimately improves your quality of life.

Understanding Stress and Anxiety
Defining Stress and Anxiety

Differences and Similarities

- **Stress:** Stress is a natural response to either positive (eustress) or negative (distress) external pressures or demands. It entails the physiological and psychological responses of the body to situations requiring adaptation or change.
- **Anxiety** is a sensation of disquiet, anxiety, or apprehension about a future event or situation that is frequently accompanied by physical symptoms. Anxiety can arise without a specific cause, unlike tension, which is typically precipitated by an external factor.

Frequent Symptoms and Origins

- **Symptoms:** Stress and anxiety can manifest in a variety of ways, including physical (e.g., migraines, muscle tension), emotional (e.g., irritability, sorrow), cognitive (e.g., difficulty concentrating, rapid thoughts), and behavioral (e.g., social disengagement, appetite changes) symptoms.
- **Causes:** Common causes of stress include demands at work, relationship conflicts, financial concerns, and health concerns. Anxiety can be caused by similar factors, as well as genetic predisposition, brain chemistry, or underlying mental health disorders.

Stress and Anxiety's Effects on Mental and Physical Health

Consequences on Mental Health

- Chronic stress and anxiety can contribute to the development or exacerbation of mental health disorders like depression, anxiety disorders, and post-traumatic stress disorder (PTSD).

Consequences on Physical Health

- o Prolonged tension and anxiety can negatively impact the immune system, increase the risk of cardiovascular diseases, cause digestive issues, and disrupt sleep patterns, among other health issues.
- o Emotional Well-Being o Unmanaged stress and anxiety can result in emotional exhaustion, diminished resilience, and impaired emotional regulation, which in turn can reduce life satisfaction and contentment.

The Importance of Stress and Anxiety Management

Enhanced Mental Health

- o Effectively managing stress and anxiety can prevent the onset or deterioration of mental health problems, promote psychological well-being, and cultivate resilience in the face of life's challenges.

Enhanced Physical Health

- o Reducing stress and anxiety can reduce the risk of stress-related health problems, enhance immune function, and promote overall physical health.

Greater Emotional Well-Being

- o Appropriate management of stress and anxiety can result in enhanced emotional regulation, increased life satisfaction, and a more balanced and satisfying emotional experience.

Higher Productivity

- o Individuals can improve their focus, energy, and overall performance in various aspects of life, including work, relationships, and personal pursuits, by learning to effectively manage tension and anxiety.

Assessing Your Personal Stressors and Triggers

Identifying Sources of Stress and Anxiety

Work-Related Stressors

- o Examples of work-related stressors include tight deadlines, excessive workload, office politics, and job insecurity. It is essential to recognize the specific factors that contribute to work-related stress to develop targeted strategies for managing and reducing it.

Relationship Stressors

- o Relationship stressors can arise from conflicts with family members, romantic partners, friends, or colleagues. Identifying the root cause of these conflicts and working on effective communication and conflict resolution can help alleviate relationship-related stress.

Health-Related Stressors
- o Health-related stressors can include chronic illnesses, injuries, or concerns about one's general health and well-being. Seeking appropriate medical care and adopting a healthy lifestyle can help address these stressors.

Financial Stressors
- o Financial stressors can stem from debt, insufficient income, or concerns about financial security. Developing a realistic budget, addressing financial issues, and seeking professional advice can help mitigate financial stress.

Recognizing your Stress Triggers

Situational Triggers
- o Situational triggers are specific events or circumstances that provoke stress or anxiety. Examples include public speaking, social gatherings, or time-sensitive tasks. Identifying these triggers can help you develop targeted coping strategies.

Emotional Triggers
- o Emotional triggers are feelings or emotions that can exacerbate stress and anxiety, such as feelings of inadequacy, guilt, or anger. Recognizing these triggers and developing effective emotional regulation techniques can help you better manage stress and anxiety.

Cognitive Triggers
- o Cognitive triggers are thought patterns or beliefs that contribute to stress and anxiety. Examples include perfectionism, catastrophizing, or negative self-talk. Identifying these cognitive triggers and challenging irrational thoughts through cognitive-behavioral techniques can help reduce stress and anxiety.

Assessing your Stress Levels

Self-Assessment Tools
- o Various self-assessment tools, such as questionnaires, can help you evaluate your current stress and anxiety levels. Examples include the Perceived Stress Scale (PSS) and the Generalized Anxiety Disorder 7-item (GAD-7) scale.

Professional Assessment
- o If you're struggling to manage stress and anxiety or suspect an underlying mental health disorder, seeking professional help from a mental health provider, such as a psychologist or therapist, can provide further assessment and guidance on developing a personalized stress and anxiety management plan.

By understanding the nature of stress and anxiety, identifying your unique stressors and triggers, and assessing your stress levels, you can develop a targeted and personalized approach to managing and reducing stress and anxiety in your life.

Developing a Personalized Stress and Anxiety Management Plan

Setting Goals and Objectives

SMART Goals
- Establish Specific, Measurable, Achievable, Relevant, and Time-bound (SMART) goals for your stress and anxiety management plan. These goals should be tailored to your unique needs and focus on addressing your specific stressors and triggers.

Short-Term and Long-Term Goals
- Create a combination of short-term and long-term goals to ensure you're making immediate progress while also working towards lasting change. Short-term goals may include incorporating daily relaxation techniques, while long-term goals might involve building stronger social support networks or improving work-life balance.

Selecting Evidence-Based Stress Reduction Techniques

Cognitive-Behavioral Therapy (CBT)
- CBT is a proven psychological intervention that helps individuals identify and change maladaptive thought patterns and behaviors that contribute to stress and anxiety. You can work with a therapist trained in CBT or use self-help resources to incorporate CBT techniques into your stress management plan.

Mindfulness and Meditation
- Mindfulness and meditation practices, such as mindfulness-based stress reduction (MBSR) or loving-kindness meditation, have been shown to reduce stress and anxiety levels. Incorporate daily mindfulness exercises or meditation sessions into your routine to enhance relaxation and emotional regulation.

Physical Activity and Exercise
- Engaging in regular physical activity and exercise can help alleviate stress and anxiety by releasing endorphins, promoting relaxation, and improving overall well-being. Choose activities you enjoy, such as walking, swimming, or yoga, and aim for at least 150 minutes of moderate-intensity aerobic exercise per week.

Social Support
- o Strong social support networks can buffer against stress and anxiety by providing emotional, informational, and practical assistance. Prioritize nurturing existing relationships, building new connections, and seeking professional help if needed.

Creating a Daily Routine

Prioritizing Self-Care
- o Self-care activities, such as getting enough sleep, eating a balanced diet, and engaging in hobbies, can help reduce stress and anxiety levels. Incorporate self-care practices into your daily routine to maintain physical, emotional, and mental well-being.

Incorporating Stress-Reduction Techniques
- o Include stress-reduction techniques, such as meditation, physical activity, or relaxation exercises, into your daily routine. Regular practice can help you develop a consistent habit and ensure ongoing stress and anxiety management.

Setting Boundaries and Managing Time Effectively
- o Establish boundaries between work and personal life, learn to delegate tasks, and practice effective time management to prevent stress and anxiety from becoming overwhelming.

Tracking Progress and Making Adjustments

Journaling
- o Maintain a stress and anxiety journal to track your experiences, emotions, and progress. Journaling can help you identify patterns, recognize achievements, and make necessary adjustments to your stress management plan.

Periodic Self-Assessment
- o Regularly evaluate your stress and anxiety levels using self-assessment tools or through personal reflection. This process can help you gauge the effectiveness of your current strategies and identify areas for improvement.

Seeking Professional Guidance as Needed
- o If you're struggling to manage stress and anxiety or require additional support, consider seeking professional guidance from a mental health provider. They can help you refine your stress management plan and provide targeted interventions.

By setting SMART goals, selecting evidence-based stress reduction techniques, creating a daily routine that prioritizes self-care and incorporates stress-reduction practices, and regularly tracking progress and making adjustments, you can develop a personalized stress and anxiety management plan that effectively addresses your unique needs and challenges.

Real-Life Examples and Scientific Studies
The Benefits of Mindfulness and Meditation

Jon Kabat-Zinn's Mindfulness-Based Stress Reduction (MBSR) Program
Jon Kabat-Zinn, a pioneer in the field of mindfulness, developed the MBSR program to help individuals manage stress, pain, and illness. MBSR combines mindfulness meditation, body awareness, and gentle yoga to improve mental and physical well-being. Numerous individuals have reported significant stress reduction and improved quality of life after participating in the MBSR program.

Research on the Effectiveness of MBSR for Stress and Anxiety Reduction
Multiple scientific studies have demonstrated the efficacy of MBSR in reducing stress and anxiety. A meta-analysis of 29 studies revealed that MBSR effectively reduced stress levels and anxiety symptoms, with lasting effects observed in follow-up assessments (Goyal et al., 2014).

The Role of Physical Activity in Stress Management

The Stress-Buffering Effects of Exercise
Engaging in regular physical activity has been shown to buffer against the adverse effects of stress by improving mood, reducing anxiety, and promoting relaxation. For example, a study by Gerber et al. (2014) found that individuals with higher levels of physical activity experienced fewer symptoms of stress-related burnout.

Research on Exercise's Impact on Mental Health
Numerous studies have demonstrated the positive effects of exercise on mental health. A review of 49 studies found that exercise was associated with a significant reduction in anxiety symptoms (Stubbs et al., 2017). Furthermore, research has shown that exercise can help reduce depressive symptoms, enhance self-esteem, and improve cognitive function.

The Power of Social Support

Case Studies on the Benefits of Strong Social Networks
Real-life examples, such as the close-knit community of Roseto, Pennsylvania, have shown the protective effects of social support on health and well-being. Despite having similar risk factors for heart disease as neighboring towns, Roseto residents had lower rates of heart disease, which researchers attributed to the town's strong social bonds and community support (Wolf & Bruhn, 1979).

Research on the Relationship Between Social Support and Stress Reduction
Several scientific studies have demonstrated the link between strong social support networks and reduced stress and anxiety levels. A meta-analysis of 148 studies found that individuals with stronger social relationships had a 50% lower risk of premature mortality than those with weaker social connections (Holt-Lunstad et al., 2010). Furthermore, research has shown that social support can improve coping strategies, enhance psychological well-being, and reduce the negative effects of stress on physical health.

These real-life examples and scientific studies highlight the significant benefits of incorporating mindfulness and meditation, regular physical activity, and strong social support networks into your personalized stress and anxiety management plan. By integrating these evidence-based strategies, you can effectively manage stress and anxiety, promote overall well-being, and enhance your quality of life.

Practical Tips for Incorporating Stress Management into Your Daily Routine

Mindfulness and Meditation

Start Small: Begin with short meditation sessions of 5-10 minutes and gradually increase the duration as you become more comfortable with the practice.

Choose a Consistent Time and Place: Establish a specific time and place for your daily meditation practice to create a routine that is easy to follow and maintain.

Utilize Guided Meditation Apps and Resources: Use guided meditation apps, such as Headspace or Calm, or online resources to help you establish a consistent meditation practice and learn various techniques.

Physical Activity and Exercise

Make it Enjoyable: Choose physical activities that you enjoy, such as dancing, hiking, or team sports, to increase the likelihood that you will maintain a consistent exercise routine.

Break it Down into Manageable Sessions: If you have difficulty finding time for longer workouts, break your physical activity into shorter sessions throughout the day (e.g., three 10-minute walks).

Incorporate movement into your daily routine: Look for opportunities to incorporate more movement into your day, such as taking the stairs instead of the elevator, walking or biking to work, or doing stretching exercises during work breaks.

Social Support

Prioritize Quality over Quantity: Focus on nurturing a few close relationships rather than trying to maintain a large number of superficial connections.

Make Time for Social Activities: Schedule regular social activities, such as weekly dinners with friends or family, to ensure you maintain strong social connections.

Seek out New Connections: Join clubs, classes, or community groups that interest you to meet new people and expand your social network.

Time Management and Setting Boundaries

Create a Daily Schedule: Plan your day in advance, allocating specific time blocks for work, relaxation, and self-care activities. This can help you avoid feeling overwhelmed and ensure you make time for stress-reduction practices.

Practice Saying No: Learn to decline requests or invitations that may exacerbate stress or interfere with your self-care routines.

Establish Clear Boundaries: Set boundaries between work and personal life by designating specific times and spaces for each. For example, avoid checking work emails during personal time and create a dedicated workspace at home to minimize distractions.

Additional Stress-Reduction Techniques

Deep Breathing Exercises: Practice deep breathing exercises, such as diaphragmatic breathing or the 4-7-8 technique, throughout the day to promote relaxation and stress relief.

Progressive Muscle Relaxation (PMR): Regularly practice PMR, a technique that involves tensing and relaxing various muscle groups, to release physical tension and promote relaxation.

Gratitude Journaling: Develop a habit of writing down three things you're grateful for each day to cultivate a more positive mindset and reduce stress.

By incorporating these practical tips into your daily routine, you can effectively manage stress and anxiety, enhance your overall well-being, and enjoy a more balanced and fulfilling life.

Summary & Conclusion

For optimal mental health, physical health, emotional well-being, and productivity, it is crucial to develop a personalized stress and anxiety management plan. By comprehending the nature of stress and anxiety, identifying your unique stressors and triggers, and evaluating your stress levels, you can develop a targeted strategy for managing stress and anxiety in your life. Incorporating evidence-based stress reduction techniques, such as mindfulness and meditation, physical activity, and social support, as well as practical stress management strategies into your daily routine can substantially improve your overall health.

Real-world examples and scientific research demonstrate the efficacy of these techniques for reducing stress and anxiety and promoting overall health. You can develop a personalized stress and anxiety management plan that addresses your unique needs and challenges by setting SMART goals, selecting evidence-based stress reduction techniques, establishing a daily routine that prioritizes self-care, and regularly monitoring progress and making adjustments.

Managing tension and anxiety is an essential component of a balanced and healthy lifestyle. You can cultivate resilience, better your emotional well-being, and enhance your overall quality of life by devising a personalized stress management plan and adopting a proactive approach. Keep in mind that stress management is an ongoing process, and it is essential to adapt and modify your strategies as your needs and circumstances change.

Chapter 25:
Managing Chronic Stress and Anxiety

Introduction:
Chronic Stress and Anxiety – What is it?

In today's high-pressure, fast-paced society, chronic tension and anxiety are an unfortunate reality for many people. With increasing demands from work, family, and social life, it can be difficult to maintain a healthy balance, frequently resulting in chronic stress and anxiety. Chronic exposure to stressors can have significant negative effects on mental health, physical health, emotional well-being, and productivity. While short-term stress can be adaptive and help us meet challenges, chronic exposure to stressors can have significant negative effects on mental health, physical health, emotional well-being, and productivity.

This chapter will explore the complexities of chronic stress and anxiety in an effort to provide a comprehensive comprehension of these conditions and their effects on various aspects of life. It will also emphasize the need for a proactive approach to personal well-being by emphasizing the significance of self-awareness and self-care in managing chronic tension and anxiety.

To help readers better comprehend and address these issues, the chapter will cover:

- o The definitions and causes of chronic stress and anxiety, distinguishing these two related but distinct concepts, and investigating the factors that contribute to their development.
- o The effect of protracted stress and anxiety on mental health, including a discussion of the diverse psychological consequences and the role of social support in mitigating these effects.
- o The effects of chronic stress and anxiety on physical health, including the stress response, the functioning of the immune system, and the long-term health consequences.
- o The effects of chronic stress and anxiety on emotional well-being and interpersonal relationships, as well as strategies for maintaining emotional resilience and wholesome relationships with others.
- o The impact of chronic tension and anxiety on productivity and work-life balance, as well as the significance of organizational culture in aggravating or mitigating these problems.
- o Tips and strategies for managing chronic tension and anxiety, including evidence-based techniques and modifications to daily routines, that can assist

readers in taking charge of their mental health and enhancing their overall well-being.

This chapter seeks to equip readers with the knowledge and tools necessary to effectively manage and alleviate chronic stress and anxiety by providing a comprehensive understanding of these conditions supported by scientific research, real-world examples, and practical advice. Individuals can achieve a healthier, more balanced, and more fulfilling existence through increased self-awareness and proactive self-care.

Understanding Chronic Stress and Anxiety

Chronic stress is a person's continual, long-term response to a variety of stressors. It is caused by recurrent or protracted exposure to stressors. In contrast, anxiety refers to the feelings of concern, apprehension, or disquiet that can result from the anticipation of future events or perceived threats. Although tension and anxiety are closely related, they are distinct concepts that can manifest and affect people in various ways.

Some common causes of chronic stress and anxiety include:

- o Work-related stressors, including unreasonable deadlines, excessive burden, lack of control, and job insecurity.
- o Relationship-related stressors, such as conflicts with family, colleagues, or romantic partners, and feeling unsupported or alone.
- o Financial stressors, such as accumulating debt, job loss, or persistent financial difficulties.
- o Stressors related to health, such as chronic illness, disability, or injury.
- o Life adjustments and transitions, such as relocating, beginning a new job, getting married, or having a child.

It is essential to acknowledge that individual distinctions play a significant role in how tension and anxiety manifest in individuals. An individual's susceptibility to chronic stress and anxiety, as well as their coping mechanisms, can be influenced by personality traits, genetic predispositions, and upbringing.

Influence on Mental Health

Chronic stress and anxiety can have significant consequences for mental health. Some potential consequences include:

- o Greater likelihood of depression and anxiety disorders: Prolonged tension can cause or exacerbate mental health disorders such as melancholy and generalized anxiety disorder.

- o Chronic tension and anxiety can impair cognitive functioning, such as memory, focus, and decision-making skills. This may manifest as forgetfulness, concentration difficulties, or indecisiveness.
- o Substance abuse as a coping mechanism: Some people may use alcohol, drugs, or other detrimental coping mechanisms to mitigate their tension and anxiety, which can ultimately exacerbate mental health issues and create additional problems.
- o The moderating effect of social support on mental health outcomes: Strong social support networks can help mitigate the negative mental health effects of chronic stress and anxiety. The development and maintenance of supportive relationships are essential for overall health.

Understanding the causes and effects of chronic stress and anxiety on mental health is essential for the development of effective management and relief strategies. Individuals can take proactive measures to reduce their tension and anxiety levels, thereby enhancing their mental health and well-being, if they are aware of the contributing factors and potential consequences.

The Effects on Physical Health

Chronic stress and anxiety can have significant, both immediate and long-term, effects on physical health. This section will examine the physiological stress response, the immune system, and the potential health problems that can result from protracted stress and anxiety.

Stress Response and Immune Function

Our bodies initiate the stress response, also known as the "fight or flight" response, in response to stressors. This physiological response involves the release of stress hormones, such as cortisol and adrenaline, which cause various changes in the body, such as an increased heart rate, elevated blood pressure, and increased vigilance. Chronic activation of this response can have detrimental effects on the body, despite the fact that its short-term activation can be beneficial.

The immune system is particularly affected by chronic stress. Stress can cause increased inflammation and a compromised immune response, making individuals more susceptible to infection and disease. In addition, chronic stress can exacerbate preexisting conditions such as autoimmunity and allergies. Additionally, stress can disturb the equilibrium between the sympathetic and parasympathetic nervous systems, resulting in long-term imbalances in the body's regulatory mechanisms.

Long-Term Repercussions

On physical health, the long-term effects of chronic stress and anxiety can be severe and far-reaching. Some possible health problems include:

- o **Enhanced Cardiovascular Disease Risk:** Chronic stress has been associated with an increased risk of cardiac disease, hypertension, and heart attacks or strokes. Over time, the chronic elevation of stress hormones and high blood pressure can damage blood vessels and the heart. Additionally, tension can contribute to the development of atherosclerosis, a condition characterized by the accumulation of plaque in the arteries, which restricts blood flow and increases the risk of heart-related issues.
- o **Digestive Disorders:** Prolonged stress can cause or exacerbate digestive disorders such as irritable bowel syndrome (IBS), ulcers, and gastroesophageal reflux disease (GERD). The effects of stress on gastrointestinal motility include diarrhea, constipation, and abdominal discomfort. Additionally, it can alter the intestinal microbiome, which is essential for digestion, immune function, and overall health.
- o **Sleep Disturbances and Sleep Disorders:** Chronic tension and anxiety can disrupt normal sleep patterns, resulting in insomnia and other sleep disorders. Inadequate sleep quality can exacerbate stress and contribute to a variety of other physical and mental health issues. Lack of sleep has been associated with obesity, type 2 diabetes, and impaired immune function.
- o **Musculoskeletal Issues:** Chronic stress can cause muscle tension and discomfort, especially in the neck, shoulders, and back. This tension can contribute to chronic pain conditions such as tension headaches, migraines, and temporomandibular joint disorder (TMJ).
- o **Hormonal Imbalances:** Prolonged stress can disrupt the normal functioning of the endocrine system, resulting in hormonal imbalances that can affect many aspects of health, such as metabolism, growth, and reproductive function.

Understanding the effects of chronic tension and anxiety on physical health is essential for taking preventative measures to alleviate these conditions. Individuals can prioritize self-care and stress management techniques to safeguard their physical health in addition to their mental health if they are aware of the potential health consequences. Individuals can achieve a healthier, more balanced existence by promoting a holistic approach to well-being that includes both mental and physical health.

Emotional Well-Being and Relationships
Chronic tension and anxiety can have a substantial impact on emotional health and interpersonal relationships. This section will examine how stress and anxiety affect emotional regulation and resilience, as well as the impact on relationships and the significance of social support.

Regulation of Emotions and Resilience
Emotional regulation is the capacity to manage and respond to one's emotions effectively. Chronic tension and anxiety can interfere with emotional regulation,

making it challenging to navigate emotional experiences and maintain emotional stability. As a result, individuals may experience more frequent and intense emotional swings, which can have a negative impact on their overall health.

Emotional resiliency is essential for managing with chronic tension and anxiety. Emotional resilience is the capacity to adapt to and recover from emotional difficulties and stressors. Among the strategies for enhancing emotional resilience are:

- **Emotional Intelligence:** Developing emotional intelligence can assist individuals in comprehending and controlling their emotions. This includes the capacity to recognize, express, and regulate one's emotions in a healthy manner, as well as to understand the emotions of others.
- **Mindfulness:** Mindfulness practice can help individuals become more aware of their emotions, thoughts, and bodily sensations, enabling them to respond more effectively to stressors. Mindfulness techniques, such as meditation or deep breathing, can facilitate emotional regulation by cultivating a nonjudgmental awareness of the present moment.
- **Self-Compassion:** Cultivating self-compassion involves treating oneself with tenderness, acceptance, and understanding, particularly during difficult circumstances. Individuals who practice self-compassion are better able to manage their emotions and recover from stressors.

Interpersonal Connections

Chronic tension and anxiety can significantly affect interpersonal relationships, such as alliances, family dynamics, and romantic partnerships. Some potential consequences include:

- **Relationship Satisfaction and Stability**: Excessive levels of stress and anxiety can impair relationships, resulting in decreased satisfaction and a greater likelihood of conflict. This can erode the stability and endurance of relationships over time.
- **Communication:** Anxiety and stress can interfere with effective communication, making it difficult for individuals to articulate their needs, concerns, and emotions. This can result in misunderstandings, unresolved issues, and an increase in relationship tension.
- **Social Withdrawal:** Chronic tension and anxiety can cause individuals to disengage from social interactions, resulting in isolation and loneliness. This can exacerbate stress levels and have detrimental effects on mental health.

It is crucial to prioritize effective communication and social support to maintain healthy relationships under duress. Among the strategies employed to accomplish this result are:

- **Active Listening:** To practice active listening, give the speaker your undivided attention, reflect on their words, and ask clarifying questions. This can help cultivate empathy and understanding in relationships.
- **Assertive Communication:** Express your thoughts, feelings, and needs in a clear, direct, and respectful manner, while remaining receptive to the viewpoints of others. Effective assertive communication can help resolve conflicts and maintain healthy relationship boundaries.
- **Construction and Maintenance of Social Support Networks:** Develop and maintain robust relationships with family, colleagues, and other supportive people. To strengthen your social support network, engage in social activities, join societies or organizations, and seek professional assistance if necessary.

Understanding the effects of chronic stress and anxiety on emotional health and interpersonal relationships is necessary for taking proactive measures to manage and mitigate these conditions. Individuals can navigate the challenges of stress and anxiety while maintaining healthy relationships with others if they cultivate emotional resilience and prioritize effective communication and social support.

Productivity and Work-Life Balance

The effects of chronic tension and anxiety on productivity and work-life balance can be substantial. This section will examine how tension and anxiety can impact performance, the significance of organizational culture, and methods for maintaining a healthy work-life balance.

Effect on Efficiency

Chronic tension and anxiety have a variety of deleterious effects on productivity and performance, including:

- o **Decreased Focus and Concentration:** High levels of tension and anxiety can make it difficult to maintain focus and concentration, resulting in decreased productivity and increased error likelihood.
- o **Procrastination:** Stress and anxiety can contribute to procrastination because individuals may feel overburdened by tasks or avoid tasks that cause anxiety.
- o **Impaired Decision-Making**: Chronic stress can impair cognitive functions such as decision-making, which may result in subpar decisions or indecision in the workplace.
- o **Burnout:** Stress can contribute to burnout, which is characterized by emotional exhaustion, cynicism, and diminished personal accomplishment. Burnout can substantially diminish both productivity and health.

Organizational Culture's Role

Employees' chronic tension and anxiety are either exacerbated by or mitigated by organizational culture. A supportive and healthful work environment can help employees better manage stress, whereas a noxious or high-pressure environment can exacerbate these issues. Among the variables that can impact organizational culture are:

- **Leadership Styles:** Effective leaders cultivate open communication, trust, and a supportive environment, which reduces employee tension and anxiety.
- **Workload and Expectations:** Organizations should strike a balance between challenging and manageable duties, and set reasonable expectations to prevent excessive stress.
- **Flexibility:** Offering employees flexible work options, such as remote work or flexible hours, can help them achieve a better work-life balance and more effectively manage stress.
- **Recognition and Rewards:** Recognizing employees' efforts and accomplishments can promote a positive work environment and reduce tension.

Strategies for Maintaining a Balanced Work-Life

Achieving a healthy work-life equilibrium is necessary for coping with chronic tension and anxiety. Some strategies for maintaining this equilibrium include:

- **Time Management:** Prioritize tasks, establish realistic objectives, and establish a daily routine to effectively manage time and reduce tension. Incorporate pauses and recreational activities to maintain productivity.
- **Establishing Boundaries:** Establish boundaries between work and personal life, such as avoiding work-related activities during personal time and establishing a dedicated workstation at home if working remotely.
- **Self-Care:** Prioritize self-care by engaging in regular physical activity, consuming a healthy diet, obtaining sufficient rest, and participating in activities that promote relaxation and well-being.
- **Seek Support:** Discuss your burden and stress levels with your supervisors and coworkers. If necessary, seek professional assistance, such as therapy or counseling.

Understanding the effects of chronic stress and anxiety on productivity and work-life balance is necessary for taking preventative measures to manage and alleviate these conditions. Individuals can improve their overall well-being and productivity by implementing strategies to improve performance and maintain a healthy balance between work and personal life. In addition, organizations play a crucial role in nurturing a supportive work environment that enables employees to more effectively manage stress.

Practical Tips and Strategies for Managing Chronic Stress and Anxiety

It is essential to effectively manage chronic tension and anxiety in order to maintain overall health, productivity, and healthy relationships. This section will provide advice and strategies for coping with tension and anxiety in a variety of life contexts.

Stress Reduction Techniques

Individuals can integrate a variety of stress reduction techniques into their daily lives to manage chronic stress and anxiety:

- **Mindfulness Meditation:** Mindfulness meditation practice can increase self-awareness, emotional control, and relaxation. Set aside time daily for mindfulness practices such as deep breathing, body assessments, and guided meditations.
- **Progressive Muscle Relaxation (PMR)** is a technique that involves tensing and relaxing various muscle groups in order to reduce physical tension and promote relaxation. Regular practice can aid in tension and anxiety management.
- **Exercise:** Regular physical activity can reduce stress hormones, improve mood, and enhance mental health overall. Aim for at least 150 minutes of moderate-intensity aerobic exercise or 75 minutes of vigorous-intensity aerobic exercise per week, in addition to two or more days per week of strength-training activities.
- **Time in Nature:** It has been shown that spending time in natural environments reduces tension and anxiety. To obtain the benefits of nature, incorporate outdoor activities such as walking, hiking, and horticulture into your daily routine.

Psychological and Cognitive Strategies

Individuals can challenge and reframe negative thought patterns and beliefs that contribute to tension and anxiety by employing cognitive and emotional strategies:

- **Cognitive Restructuring:** Recognize and challenge irrational thoughts and beliefs that contribute to anxiety and tension. Replace negative notions with more realistic and balanced options.
- **Gratitude Practice:** Cultivate an attitude of gratitude by ruminating on and expressing appreciation for the positive aspects of your life on a regular basis. This can help divert attention away from stressors and foster a more positive outlook.
- **Cultivate a Growth Mindset:** Instead of viewing difficulties and setbacks as insurmountable obstacles, view them as opportunities for development and learning. The development of a growth mindset can aid in the development of resilience and the reduction of anxiety.

Social Assistance and Interaction

Strong social support and effective communication are crucial for stress and anxiety management:

- **Communicate with Friends and Family**: Share your emotions and experiences with dependable friends and family members to gain support, advice, and comprehension.
- **Join a Support Group:** Joining a support group can help you connect with others confronting similar challenges, fostering a sense of belonging and understanding.
- **Develop Assertiveness:** Practice communicating your needs, thoughts, and emotions in a direct and polite manner. Assertiveness can aid in stress management and foster healthy relationships.

Professional Assistance

Seeking professional assistance can be a crucial step in the management of chronic stress and anxiety:

- **Therapy or Counseling:** Consult a mental health professional, such as a psychologist, counselor, or therapist, to develop coping strategies and address underlying causes of stress and anxiety.
- **Medication:** In some cases, anxiety symptoms may be treated with medication. Consult a medical expert to determine if medication is appropriate for your condition.

By incorporating these tips and techniques into daily routines, individuals can effectively manage chronic tension and anxiety, resulting in enhanced mental health, physical health, emotional well-being, and productivity. It is essential to keep in mind that each individual's experience with stress and anxiety is unique, and that discovering the most effective strategies may require trial and error. Consistency and dedication to self-care are essential for managing chronic stress and anxiety effectively.

Summary & Conclusion

The Chronic tension and anxiety are ubiquitous obstacles that can affect a person's mental health, physical health, emotional well-being, interpersonal relationships, and productivity, among others. It is crucial to recognize the far-reaching effects of these conditions and take proactive measures to effectively manage them. This chapter has provided an in-depth analysis of the effects of chronic tension and anxiety, as well as suggestions and techniques for overcoming these obstacles.

Key takeaways from this chapter include:

- Understand the nature and causes of chronic tension and anxiety, as well as their intricate interaction with mental and physical health.
- Recognize the effects of chronic stress and anxiety on physical health, including the stress response, the immune system, and the possibility of long-term health consequences.
- Understand the significance of emotional regulation, resilience, and effective communication in maintaining emotional well-being and healthy relationships in the face of chronic stress and anxiety.
- Recognize the impact of organizational culture and work-life balance on productivity and stress management, and employ strategies to maintain a healthy work-life balance.
- Incorporate into daily routines stress reduction techniques, cognitive and emotional strategies, social support, and professional assistance for managing chronic stress and anxiety.

In spite of the challenges posed by chronic tension and anxiety, individuals can achieve a healthier, more balanced existence by implementing these strategies and preserving a holistic approach to well-being. It is essential to remember that each individual's experience is unique, and discovering the most effective coping strategies may require patience and perseverance. Ultimately, a commitment to self-care and ongoing personal development can aid individuals in navigating the complexities of tension and anxiety and nurture a greater sense of well-being overall.

Chapter 26:
The Importance of Support in Coping with Stress and Anxiety

Introduction:
Importance of Support

In our modern, fast-paced society, stress and anxiety are common experiences. Combining personal, professional, and social obligations with the constant barrage of information can make us feel as though we are perpetually treading water in an ocean of uncertainty. In these tumultuous times, a solid support system is more vital than ever. Support from friends, family, and coworkers can be a vital lifeline, aiding us in navigating life's challenges and complexities. This chapter examines the significance of support in managing with tension and anxiety, highlighting the numerous ways in which it can improve mental health, physical health, emotional well-being, and productivity.

For a deeper understanding of the transformative force of support, we will investigate research and real-world examples of its positive effects. In addition, we will provide hints and recommendations on how to cultivate and sustain a strong support network, empowering you to improve your resilience and well-being as a whole. At the conclusion of this chapter, you will have gained valuable insights into the benefits of social support and learned strategies for incorporating it into your daily life, thereby nurturing a happier, healthier, and more fulfilling existence.

Mental Health Benefits of Social Support
Improved Stress Management
By providing a sounding board for concerns, providing advice, and sharing coping strategies, social support can help individuals navigate stressful situations. By interacting with others who understand and empathize with their challenges, individuals can obtain new insights and develop more effective stress management strategies. According to research, those with strong social connections are better equipped to deal with stress, resulting in improved mental health.

Reduced Risk of Depression and Anxiety
A strong support system can serve as a buffer against the development of anxiety and depression. Individuals are less likely to internalize negative emotions and succumb to feelings of hopelessness when they have someone to confide in and rely on during difficult circumstances. Consistently, research has shown that individuals with strong

social ties have a reduced risk of developing anxiety and depression, highlighting the importance of social support in maintaining mental health.

Improved Resilience

Resilience, or the capacity to overcome adversity, is an essential aspect of mental health. In times of difficulty, the encouragement, reassurance, and direction provided by friends, family, and coworkers can strengthen resilience. According to research, individuals with strong support networks are more likely to demonstrate resilience in the face of adversity because they have access to resources and emotional support that can help them surmount obstacles and persevere.

Promotion of Psychological Health

Not only does social support mitigate adverse mental health outcomes, but it can also actively promote mental health. Developing meaningful relationships with others promotes a sense of belonging, purpose, and shared identity. These relationships can be a source of happiness, humor, and positive experiences that contribute to an overall feeling of well-being and life fulfillment.

Tip: Make a concerted effort to cultivate and maintain social connections, even during hectic or trying times. Schedule regular catch-ups with friends and family, engage in shared pastimes or interests, and be open to forming new relationships to assist in constructing a solid support network.

Physical Health Benefits of Social Support

Boosted Immune System

Numerous studies have demonstrated that having strong social connections can improve immune system function. Interactions with others can trigger the release of hormones such as oxytocin, which has been associated with reduced inflammation and enhanced immune function. Therefore, individuals with a strong support system are less likely to become unwell and may recover more rapidly if they do become ill.

Reduction in Blood Pressure

Positive social interactions have been shown to reduce blood pressure, promoting cardiovascular health as a whole. The tranquil effect of supportive relationships can help regulate blood pressure. Strong social connections have been shown to reduce the risk of hypertension and other cardiovascular conditions.

Increased Lifespan

Strong support networks are associated with extended, healthier lives. Social support can motivate individuals to engage in healthful behaviors such as exercise, appropriate nutrition, and regular medical examinations. In addition, having access to essential resources and emotional support can contribute to an overall sense of well-being, which is associated with a longer life span.

Superior Sleep Quality

Quality sleep is essential for physical health and well-being as a whole. By reducing tension and anxiety, which are known to disrupt sleep, social support can positively affect sleep patterns. According to research, individuals with strong social ties are more likely to experience better sleep quality, which contributes to better physical health and vitality levels.

Tip: Prioritize time spent with friends and family members engaging in physical health-promoting activities, such as group exercise classes, outdoor athletics, and shared culinary experiences. By combining social engagement with health-promoting behaviors, you can simultaneously strengthen your support network and enhance your physical health.

Emotional Well-Being Benefits of Social Support

Enhanced Self-Esteem

Individuals can feel esteemed, appreciated, and respected when they receive support from others. This affirmation and acknowledgement can contribute to a heightened sense of self-worth and self-esteem. Individuals are better equipped to confront challenges and manage difficult emotions when they feel secure in their social connections.

Greater Life Contentment

Consistently, research has demonstrated that individuals with robust social networks report greater life satisfaction and contentment. Positive relationships can provide a sense of belonging, companionship, and life-enriching shared experiences. These connections enable people to derive greater meaning and satisfaction from their daily experiences, thereby contributing to their overall emotional health.

Enhanced Emotional Control

Emotional support from peers, family, and colleagues can assist individuals in more effectively processing and managing their emotions. Individuals can gain insight into their emotional experiences and develop healthier coping mechanisms if they have a secure space in which to express and examine their emotions. This improved emotional regulation may result in greater emotional stability and resilience.

Reduced Loneliness and Isolation Feelings

Loneliness and isolation, which are known to have negative effects on emotional health, can be mitigated with the assistance of social support. Individuals can feel more connected, understood, and supported by forging robust relationships with others. This sense of belonging can substantially enhance emotional health and reduce the risk of developing mental health issues associated with social isolation and loneliness.

Tip: Nurture supportive relationships and actively participate in social activities to cultivate emotional health. Maintain open and honest communication with family and friends, share your experiences and emotions, and offer support in exchange. Consider joining societies, groups, or organizations that align with your interests, as these can provide opportunities to forge new relationships and strengthen existing ones.

Productivity Benefits of Social Support

Increased Motivation and Engagement

Individuals' motivation and engagement in their personal and professional lives can be maintained with the aid of supportive relationships. Encouragement and acknowledgement from friends, family, and coworkers can provide the motivation necessary to undertake difficult tasks and maintain dedication to achieving objectives. According to studies, individuals with strong social support networks are more likely to be motivated, focused, and engaged in their endeavors.

Enhanced Problem-Solving Skills

Collaboration can result in the creation of innovative solutions and increased productivity. A diverse support network can provide access to a variety of perspectives, ideas, and experiences, which can be invaluable when tackling complex issues. Individuals are better suited to find innovative and effective solutions to problems when they consolidate their resources and expertise, thereby increasing their productivity and efficiency.

Reduced Fatigue

Burnout, which is characterized by emotional depletion, cynicism, and diminished personal accomplishment, can have negative effects on productivity and happiness. A robust support network can help prevent fatigue by providing emotional and practical support during difficult circumstances. According to research, individuals with strong social ties are less likely to experience exhaustion because they are more likely to receive the support necessary to manage stress and maintain a healthy work-life balance.

Enhanced Choice-Making

As it enables individuals to seek advice and input from others, social support can also contribute to more effective decision-making. Individuals can make better-informed decisions that are more likely to result in positive outcomes by engaging in discussions and evaluating diverse perspectives. A supportive network can also assist individuals in gaining confidence in their decision-making skills, thereby boosting productivity even further.

Promote open communication, team-building activities, and peer recognition to foster a supportive work environment. Actively solicit the feedback and input of coworkers, and be receptive to collaboration and the exchange of ideas. Maintain a healthy balance outside of work by scheduling regular social activities and spending time with family and friends, as these relationships can provide much-needed emotional support and encouragement.

Summary & Conclusion

Accepting Assistance for a Healthier and Happier Life

The importance of support in today's complex and demanding world cannot be emphasized. As discussed throughout this chapter, having a strong support system is essential for contending with tension and anxiety, as well as promoting mental health, physical health, emotional well-being, and productivity. The advantages of social support extend far beyond mundane comfort; they can transform how we navigate obstacles, interact with others, and pursue our objectives.

By cultivating relationships with friends, family, and coworkers, we can establish a network of support that helps us maintain resilience in the face of adversity, promotes healthier behaviors, and enables us to realize our maximum potential. As the foundation of our well-being and a significant contributor to our overall life satisfaction, it is crucial to actively cultivate and maintain these relationships.

Incorporating the practical advice and suggestions presented in this chapter can assist you in establishing and maintaining a strong support network, allowing you to better manage tension and anxiety and ultimately lead a more fulfilling life. Embrace the transformative force of support in order to cultivate a happier, healthier, and more resilient existence.

Chapter 27:
Making Stress and Anxiety Management a Lifelong Habit

Introduction:
Creating a Lifelong Habit

Stress and anxiety have become an unfortunate component of many people's lives in today's fast-paced world. It is not uncommon for individuals to experience varying levels of tension and anxiety as a result of their demanding professions and personal obligations. Chronic stress and unmanaged anxiety can have detrimental effects on our overall health, despite the fact that some tension can be advantageous and help us perform under duress.

By comprehending the causes and effects of stress and anxiety and implementing effective management techniques, it is possible to make stress and anxiety management a lifelong practice. This enhances not only our quality of life, but also our mental health, physical health, emotional well-being, and productivity.

This chapter seeks to provide a comprehensive guide to the benefits of effective stress and anxiety management, with real-world examples, scientific studies, and suggestions for incorporating these techniques into one's daily life. The mental health benefits of tension and anxiety management will be discussed first, followed by the physical health, emotional well-being, and productivity benefits.

At the conclusion of this chapter, readers should have a deeper comprehension of the significance of stress and anxiety management as well as the tools and techniques necessary to develop a sustainable and effective approach to managing stress and anxiety throughout their lives.

Mental Health Benefits of Stress and Anxiety Management

Management of stress and anxiety is essential for maintaining and enhancing mental health. In this section, we will delve deeper into the mental health benefits of effective stress and anxiety management, with a focus on enhanced cognitive functioning and decreased risk for mental health disorders.

Enhanced Cognitive Performance

Chronic anxiety and tension can have a substantial impact on cognitive performance. Multiple cognitive functions, including memory, attention, and decision-making, may be impaired by excessive stress, according to research. This is because tension activates the body's "fight or flight" response, resulting in the release of stress hormones such as cortisol, which can impair the brain's ability to process information.

By effectively managing stress and anxiety, individuals can enhance their cognitive performance in multiple ways:

- **Mindfulness:** Mindfulness practices, such as meditation and deep breathing, have been shown to reduce tension and enhance attention, memory, and overall cognitive performance. Mindfulness enables individuals to remain present and attentive, thereby mitigating the detrimental effects of stress on cognitive processes.
- **Exercise:** Regular physical activity has been shown to reduce stress and anxiety while enhancing cognitive function. The increased blood supply to the brain as a result of exercise promotes the growth of new neurons and improves overall brain function.
- **Cognitive Restructuring:** This technique identifies and challenges negative thought patterns associated with tension and anxiety, replacing them with healthier, more rational alternatives. By fostering a more balanced and optimistic outlook on life, cognitive restructuring can enhance decision-making and problem-solving skills.

Reduced Risk of Psychological Disorders

Stress and anxiety that are not effectively managed can contribute to the development of mental health disorders like depression, anxiety disorders, and substance use disorders. By managing stress and anxiety effectively, individuals can reduce their risk of developing these mental health conditions.

One cannot exaggerate the significance of early intervention and prevention. Recognizing the symptoms of chronic stress and anxiety and taking proactive measures to manage them can prevent the development of more serious mental health issues. Among the healthful coping strategies that can reduce the risk of developing mental health issues are:

- o **Social Support:** By providing emotional support, a sense of belonging, and opportunities for relaxation and enjoyment, strong social connections can help reduce stress and anxiety. Encourage peers and family members to communicate openly and truthfully about their feelings and experiences.
- o **Self-Care:** Putting an emphasis on self-care, such as engaging in activities, getting enough sleep, and maintaining a healthy diet, can help individuals better manage stress and anxiety. Self-care activities improve overall health and resiliency, thereby decreasing the likelihood of developing mental health disorders.
- o **Professional Help:** In some instances, it may be beneficial for individuals to seek the assistance of a therapist or counselor. Therapy can provide helpful tools and techniques for coping with stress and anxiety, as well as addressing any underlying mental health issues.

By comprehending the mental health benefits of stress and anxiety management and incorporating effective techniques into daily life, individuals can reduce their risk of developing mental health disorders and enhance their cognitive functioning overall.

Physical Health Benefits of Stress and Anxiety Management

Effective tension and anxiety management can have numerous positive effects on physical health. In this section, we will examine how managing stress and anxiety can strengthen the immune system and reduce the risk of developing chronic diseases.

Stronger Immune System

Stress can have negative effects on the immune system. When the body is under duress, stress hormones such as cortisol are released, which can suppress immune function. This can increase a person's susceptibility to infections and diseases and delay the healing process.

Mentally Healthy: Mind Over Matter

The immune systems of individuals who employ stress management techniques tend to be stronger, according to research. The following are some guidelines for enhancing immune health through stress management:

- ○ **Regular Exercise:** Regular moderate exercise can help reduce tension and enhance immune function. Exercise stimulates the production of neurotransmitters, which are natural mood boosters, and improves blood circulation, which is necessary for optimal immune function.
- ○ **Balanced Diet:** Eating a diet rich in fruits, vegetables, lean proteins, and whole grains can help maintain a healthy immune system by supplying the body with the essential nutrients it needs to function correctly. In addition to stabilizing mood and energy levels, a balanced diet can reduce the impact of stress on the immune system.
- ○ **Quality Sleep:** For a robust immune system, adequate and consistent sleep is essential. Insomnia can elevate cortisol levels and impair immune function. Aim for 7 to 9 hours of sleep per night and adhere to a regular sleep schedule to support optimal immune health.

Reduced Risk of Chronic Disorders

Several health concerns, including cardiovascular disease, diabetes, and obesity, have been linked to chronic stress. By effectively managing stress and anxiety, individuals can lower their risk of developing these chronic diseases.

Evidence-based stress management and chronic disease risk reduction practices include:

- **Regular Physical Activity:** Exercise not only reduces tension and anxiety, but also helps maintain a healthy weight, lowers blood pressure, and enhances cardiovascular health. For optimal physical health, aim for at least 150 minutes of moderate-intensity exercise per week.
- **Social Support:** Having a strong social network aids in stress management and has been linked to improved physical health outcomes. Engage in regular social activities, maintain healthy relationships, and, when necessary, seek support from friends and family.
- **Relaxation Techniques:** Incorporating relaxation techniques into daily life, such as deep breathing exercises, progressive muscle relaxation, and meditation, can help reduce stress levels and the risk of developing chronic conditions. These practices can enhance emotional health, reduce blood pressure, and promote physical health in general.

Individuals can improve their immune system function and reduce their risk of developing chronic health conditions by comprehending the physical health benefits of stress and anxiety management and incorporating effective techniques into daily life.

Emotional Well-Being Benefits of Stress and Anxiety Management

Effectively managing tension and anxiety can lead to significant improvements in emotional health. This section will examine the positive effects of stress and anxiety management on emotional resilience and interpersonal relationships.

Enhanced Emotional Toughness

Emotional resilience is the capacity to adapt and recover from adversity, stress, and life's challenges. Stress and anxiety management play a crucial role in the development of emotional resilience because they endow individuals with the tools and skills required to navigate challenging situations and maintain emotional equilibrium.

Research has shown that those who employ stress management techniques are better equipped to deal with life's challenges and recover from setbacks more swiftly. The following are examples of emotional resilience-building strategies:

- **Mindfulness:** As stated previously, mindfulness practices such as meditation or deep breathing exercises can assist individuals in remaining present and attentive even during stressful situations. By cultivating mindfulness, people can cultivate greater emotional awareness and regulation, which contributes to emotional resilience.
- **Self-Compassion:** Self-compassion is the practice of being kind and understanding to oneself, especially during times of duress or failure. Individuals can develop a healthier relationship with themselves and navigate difficult emotions and experiences by cultivating self-compassion.
- **Emotional Regulation:** The ability to effectively regulate and express emotions is an essential component of emotional resilience. Individuals can process and regulate their emotions in a healthy manner by using techniques such as cognitive restructuring, journaling, or seeking support from friends and family.

Better Relationships

Anxiety and stress can negatively impact interpersonal relationships, leading to conflicts, misunderstandings, and emotional strain. By effectively managing tension and anxiety, individuals can improve their relationships with others and cultivate deeper bonds.

The following strategies for managing tension to enhance relationships:

- **Communication:** Open and trustworthy communication is essential for healthy relationships. Discussing feelings and experiences related to stress and anxiety can aid partners in understanding one another's requirements and collaborating to find solutions.
- **Empathy:** Developing empathy for your partner's experiences and emotions can contribute to the creation of a supportive and understanding environment, which can reduce tension and strengthen the relationship.
- **Establishing Boundaries:** Establishing and maintaining healthy boundaries can help individuals more effectively manage stress and anxiety in relationships. This may involve setting aside specific time for self-care, discussing the division of responsibilities, or seeking outside support from friends and family.

By comprehending the benefits of stress and anxiety management for emotional well-being and incorporating effective techniques into daily life, individuals can increase their emotional resilience and improve their relationships with others. This contributes to a greater sense of emotional equilibrium, satisfaction, and general well-being.

Productivity Benefits of Stress and Anxiety Management

Effectively managing tension and anxiety can result in substantial increases in both personal and professional productivity. In this section, we will examine the impact of tension and anxiety management on work productivity, innovation, and creativity.

Enhanced Work Productivity

By impairing concentration, decision-making, and time management, stress and anxiety can negatively impact workplace productivity. By effectively managing tension and anxiety, individuals can improve their work performance and achieve greater professional success. Techniques for reducing tension to improve workplace performance include:

- **Time Management:** Developing effective time management skills can help individuals feel more in control and less overburdened by their work-related responsibilities. To reduce tension and increase productivity, create a daily schedule, prioritize tasks based on importance and deadline, and break down larger tasks into smaller, more manageable steps.
- **Goal-Setting:** Setting realistic and attainable objectives can provide a sense of direction and motivation, thereby reducing tension and enhancing work performance. Establish both short-term and long-term objectives, and assess your progress regularly to maintain focus and motivation.
- **Prioritization:** Learning to prioritize tasks and allocate time and resources accordingly can aid in stress management and increase work productivity. When practicable, prioritize high-priority tasks and delegate or postpone low-priority tasks.

Successful entrepreneurs, high-performing athletes, and top executives are examples of real-world individuals who have improved their work productivity through stress and anxiety management. These individuals have been able to improve their concentration, motivation, and overall work performance by implementing effective stress management techniques.

Increased Originality and Creativity

An individual's capacity for innovation can be hindered by stress and anxiety, which can impair inventive thinking and problem-solving skills. By effectively managing tension and anxiety, individuals can cultivate a more creative and innovative mindset, leading to personal and professional development.

Research on the relationship between stress, anxiety, and creative thinking has revealed that individuals who practice stress management are better able to think creatively, find innovative solutions, and acclimate to new challenges. Among the techniques for fostering a creative mindset and managing tension are:

- **Brainstorming:** Individuals can generate new ideas and solutions by engaging in individual or group ideation sessions. Creating a relaxed, stress-free environment that encourages open communication and creative thinking can facilitate this process.
- **Reframing Challenges:** Learning to view challenges and setbacks as opportunities for growth and innovation can aid individuals in stress management and the development of a more creative mindset. By reframing challenges, individuals are able to concentrate on finding inventive solutions instead of feeling inundated by tension and anxiety.
- **Embracing Failure:** Individuals can manage tension and anxiety more effectively by accepting that failure is a natural part of the creative process. Individuals can cultivate an innovative mindset and enhance their adaptability to new challenges by embracing failure and learning from their errors.

By grasping the productivity benefits of stress and anxiety management and implementing effective techniques in daily life, individuals can improve their work efficiency and foster greater creativity and innovation. This can result in increased personal and professional development, as well as increased overall happiness and success.

Summary & Conclusion

Effectively managing tension and anxiety is essential for leading a balanced and fulfilling existence. By incorporating stress management techniques into daily routines, individuals can experience numerous benefits in multiple facets of their lives, such as improved mental health, enhanced physical health, greater emotional well-being, and increased productivity.

This chapter has examined the significance of stress and anxiety management and provided real-world examples, scientific studies, and practical suggestions for incorporating these techniques into daily life. By understanding the mental health benefits, such as improved cognitive functioning and reduced risk of mental health disorders, the physical health benefits, such as a stronger immune system and lower risk of chronic conditions, the emotional well-being benefits, such as enhanced emotional resilience and improved relationships, and the productivity benefits, which include increased work efficiency and greater creativity and innovation, individuals can develop a well-rounded approach.

In conclusion, making tension and anxiety management a lifelong practice is essential for overall health and achievement. By implementing the techniques and advice presented in this chapter, individuals can establish a solid foundation for effectively managing tension and anxiety, leading to a healthier, happier, and more productive existence.

Section IV. Building Strong Relationships

Chapter 28:
Importance of Healthy Relationships for Mental Health

Introduction:
Healthy Relationship Building

The basis of human existence is the capacity to establish and maintain relationships with others. We rely on our relationships with family, peers, and society to develop and thrive from the instant of our birth. These relationships continue to define our experiences, influence our decisions, and affect our mental health as we progress through life. In this context, stable relationships are essential for our mental and physical health, emotional stability, and productivity.

This chapter examines the significance of cultivating and sustaining healthy relationships and how they can contribute to enhanced mental health in greater depth. We will discuss the various aspects of healthy relationships that contribute to mental health, supported by pertinent research, real-world examples, and helpful hints. By understanding the vital role that healthy relationships play in our lives, readers can gain valuable insights and recommendations for nurturing stronger connections that promote mental health.

The chapter is divided into sections, each of which emphasizes a particular aspect of the significance of healthy relationships. We will examine the evidence supporting the connection between healthy relationships and mental health, physical health, emotional well-being, and productivity. In addition, we will offer guidelines and suggestions that readers can use to foster and maintain healthy relationships, thereby enhancing their mental health and overall quality of life.

At the conclusion of this chapter, readers will have a thorough comprehension of the various ways in which beneficial relationships contribute to mental health and well-being. With this knowledge and practical advice, readers will be better equipped to forge stronger relationships with others and actively work to improve their mental health through the power of healthy relationships.

The Impact of Healthy Relationships on Mental Health

Reducing Stress and Anxiety
Healthy relationships provide emotional support and a sense of security, which significantly reduces levels of stress and anxiety. When people feel understood and

valued, stress hormones such as cortisol are reduced. Cohen and Wills (1985) found that social support not only aids individuals in coping with stress, but also protects them from the detrimental impacts of stress on mental health.

Increasing One's Self-Esteem and Confidence

Positive relationships foster a sense of belonging and self-worth, resulting in increased self-esteem and confidence. Individuals are more likely to have a positive self-image and to feel confident in their abilities when they are encircled by supportive and compassionate people. According to a study by Orth et al. (2018), individuals with stable relationships tend to have higher self-esteem, which contributes to better mental health.

Defense Against Depression

The buffering effect of social support from stable relationships against depression. Strong social connections can provide individuals with a sense of purpose, companionship, and emotional support, thereby assisting them in navigating challenging situations and emotions. Teo et al. (2013) discovered that people with strong social ties are less likely to develop depression and recover more rapidly if they do.

Increasing Adaptation Mechanisms

Individuals can develop more effective coping mechanisms when they have healthy relationships. Individuals with strong social support are more likely to seek assistance and advice from their network when confronted with adversity, thereby enhancing their ability to cope with stressors. Thoits's (2011) research highlights the significance of social support in promoting adaptive coping strategies, which leads to improved mental health outcomes.

Developing a Sense of Purpose and Significance

A person's existence can be imbued with purpose and significance through the cultivation of healthy relationships. The relationships we form with others motivate us to participate in meaningful activities, take care of ourselves, and positively impact our communities. According to a study conducted by Steger et al. (2006), having a sense of purpose and meaning in life is associated with improved mental health and well-being.

Promoting Positive Lifestyle Decisions

Healthy relationships can encourage positive lifestyle decisions, such as regular exercise, a balanced diet, and good sleep hygiene. Social support from peers and family can motivate, encourage, and hold individuals accountable for making healthier decisions. Umberson & Montez (2010) highlight the significance of social relationships in shaping health behaviors, which can have a significant effect on mental health.

By comprehending the various ways in which healthy relationships contribute to mental health, individuals can prioritize cultivating strong social connections to improve their overall wellbeing.

The Impact of Healthy Relationships on Physical Health

Boosting Immune System Function

Strong social ties have been associated with enhanced immune system function, resulting in greater physical health and well-being. When people have robust social networks, they tend to have lower levels of inflammation and stronger immune responses, which protects them from a variety of diseases. Uchino (2006) discovered that individuals with strong social connections had stronger immune responses than those with weaker social connections, demonstrating the power of healthy relationships to promote physical health.

Increasing Heart Health

As social support helps reduce stress and its associated risk factors for heart disease, healthy relationships can contribute to improved cardiovascular health. Holt-Lunstad et al. (2010) found that people with strong social ties have reduced rates of heart disease and are less likely to die from cardiovascular events. These findings emphasize the significance of nurturing healthy relationships for optimal heart health maintenance.

Enhancing Pain Management

An individual's ability to effectively manage and bear with chronic pain can be enhanced by his or her relationships. Having a strong support system can increase pain tolerance, decrease pain perception, and promote positive coping mechanisms. Gatchel et al. (2007) discovered that people with greater social support experienced less pain and were better able to manage their chronic pain conditions.

Promoting Healthier Conduct

Social connections can influence the lifestyle decisions of individuals, encouraging healthful behaviors such as regular exercise, balanced nutrition, and abstinence from smoking and excessive alcohol consumption. Christakis and Fowler (2007) demonstrated that individuals are more likely to adopt healthy behaviors when their social networks also engage in these behaviors, highlighting the importance of healthy relationships in determining physical health.

Enhanced Sleep Quality

Strong social connections can provide a sense of safety and security, thereby reducing tension and fostering relaxation, which can improve sleep quality. According to a study by Troxel et al. (2010), individuals with higher levels of social support slept better, which is crucial for optimal physical health and well-being.

Increasing Lifespan

Strong social connections are associated with increased longevity, as healthy relationships can reduce the risk of untimely mortality from a variety of causes. A meta-analysis by Holt-Lunstad et al. (2015) found that individuals with strong social relationships had a 50% greater chance of survival than those with weaker connections, highlighting the importance of healthy relationships in promoting physical health and extending life expectancy.

Individuals can prioritize cultivating and sustaining strong social connections in order to improve their overall well-being and longevity by recognizing the numerous ways in which healthy relationships contribute to physical health.

The Impact of Healthy Relationships on Emotional Well-Being

Emotional Regulation and Resilience

Individuals can better regulate their emotions and develop resilience to stressors when they have healthy relationships. When individuals have strong social connections, they are more likely to express their emotions and seek emotional support, which enables them to deal with life's challenges more effectively. According to a study by Bonanno and Burton (2013), social support improves an individual's capacity to deal with stress, resulting in increased emotional well-being and resiliency in the face of adversity.

Compassion and Sympathy

Nurturing healthy relationships can increase self- and other-awareness and compassion. Individuals with strong social connections are more likely to experience and exhibit empathic concern, which can strengthen emotional attachments and improve emotional health. According to a study by Batson et al. (2007), strong social connections foster empathic concern and compassionate actions, which contribute to better emotional health.

Emotional Intelligence

Emotional intelligence, which is the capacity to recognize, comprehend, and manage one's own and others' emotions, can be fostered by healthy relationships. Emotional intelligence is essential for effective communication, the resolution of conflicts, and the maintenance of solid social connections. According to a study by Lopes et al. (2004), individuals with greater emotional intelligence tend to have more gratifying and fruitful relationships, resulting in greater emotional well-being.

Establishing Faith and Safety

Healthy relationships are based on trust and safety, allowing people to express their emotions without fear of rejection or criticism. This sense of safety and acceptance allows individuals to develop a secure attachment style, which is linked to greater emotional stability and relationship satisfaction. A study conducted by Mikulincer and Shaver (2007) revealed that individuals with secure attachment styles experience more positive emotions and are better equipped to manage negative emotions, resulting in enhanced emotional well-being.

Developing Positive Emotions and Contentment
By providing affection, support, and companionship, healthy relationships can promote positive emotions and joy. Diener and Seligman (2002) discovered that those with strong social connections reported greater levels of contentment, life satisfaction, and positive emotions than those with weaker connections. By cultivating healthy relationships, individuals can cultivate a more positive emotional state and enjoy greater well-being in general.

Reducing Isolation and Loneliness
Loneliness and isolation, which have been linked to a variety of detrimental mental and emotional health outcomes, can be mitigated by sustaining healthy relationships. According to a study conducted by Cacioppo et al. (2006), individuals who reported higher levels of loneliness had more depressive symptoms and lower overall well-being. By nurturing strong social connections, individuals can reduce feelings of isolation and enhance their emotional health.

Individuals can prioritize cultivating and sustaining strong social connections as a means to improve their emotional health and overall life satisfaction by comprehending the numerous ways in which healthy relationships contribute to emotional well-being.

The Impact of Healthy Relationships on Productivity
Enhancing Work Performance
By offering support, encouragement, and motivation, healthy relationships can have a positive effect on work performance. Individuals are more likely to be concentrated, engaged, and confident in their abilities when they feel supported by their social network, resulting in increased productivity. Greenhaus et al. (2003) discovered that employees with strong work-family relationships reported greater job satisfaction, dedication, and performance.

Enhanced Problem-Solving and Determination
By fostering open communication, collaboration, and diverse perspectives, healthy relationships can improve the problem-solving and decision-making skills of individuals. Strong social connections can facilitate more effective problem-solving in both personal and professional contexts, leading to improved outcomes and increased productivity. According to a study by Reagans and Zuckerman (2001), diverse social networks contributed to enhanced problem-solving and decision-making.

Reducing Absenteeism and Presenteeism
By fostering physical and mental health, healthy relationships can reduce work absenteeism and presenteeism by promoting physical and mental health. When

people have strong social connections, they are less likely to experience illness and exhaustion, resulting in a reduction in absenteeism. Moreover, healthy relationships can increase engagement and concentration, thereby reducing absenteeism. According to a study by Grawitch et al. (2017), employees with high levels of social support reported reduced levels of absenteeism and greater job satisfaction.

Fostering Innovation and Creativity

By creating a supportive atmosphere that encourages individuals to express their ideas and take risks, healthy relationships can stimulate creativity and innovation. People are more likely to think creatively and investigate new ideas when they feel supported and valued by their social network. Individuals with diverse social networks are more likely to generate innovative ideas and solutions, according to a study by Perry-Smith (2006).

Promoting Professional Development and Growth

Strong social connections can contribute to professional growth and development by providing opportunities for networking, mentorship, and constructive criticism. Healthy relationships can assist individuals in expanding their knowledge, skills, and expertise, resulting in enhanced productivity and career advancement. According to a study by Seibert et al. (2001), employees with robust social networks reported greater access to resources and greater career success.

Improving Work-Life Balancing

By providing emotional support, tension relief, and time-management skills, healthy relationships can enhance work-life balance. When people maintain strong social connections, they are better able to prioritize their personal and professional responsibilities, resulting in increased productivity and overall life satisfaction. Kossek et al. (2011) discovered that individuals with a high work-life balance reported improved job performance, reduced stress levels, and greater job satisfaction.

Individuals can enhance their overall efficacy and success in both personal and professional endeavors by prioritizing the development and maintenance of strong social connections after recognizing the numerous ways in which healthy relationships contribute to productivity.

Practical Tips for Nurturing Healthy Relationships
Develop Effective Communication Skills

Clear and frank communication forms the basis of all healthy relationships. Developing effective communication skills, such as active listening, conveying oneself plainly, and making use of non-verbal signals, can assist individuals in establishing stronger relationships with others.

Focus on Quality Time

Spending quality time with friends, family, and romantic companions is essential for preserving and fostering healthy relationships. Make an effort to schedule regular catch-ups, engage in meaningful dialogues, and participate in bond-strengthening shared activities.

Employ Compassion and Emotional Support

Empathy is the capacity to comprehend and experience another's emotions. Practicing empathy by providing emotional support, validating emotions, and displaying genuine concern for the well-being of others can contribute to the development of healthy relationships.

Confront the Conflict Constructively

Conflict is an inevitable aspect of any relationship, but how it is handled makes all the difference. Approach conflicts with a problem-solving mentality, utilizing transparent communication and a willingness to compromise. Obtain the assistance of a mediator or counselor, if necessary, to address and resolve any underlying issues.

Participate in Joint Activities

Participate in activities that are enjoyed by both parties to create shared experiences and strengthen connections. These activities can range from pastimes, sports, and group excursions to volunteer work and collaborative initiatives.

Establish Sound Boundaries

Maintain a balance between one's own requirements and those of others by establishing clear boundaries within relationships. Respect one another's boundaries and communicate candidly about acceptable and objectionable behavior in the relationship.

Exhibit Admiration and Gratitude

Regularly expressing gratitude and appreciation reinforces positive emotions and strengthens relationships. Simple acts of compassion, verbal expressions of gratitude, and considerate actions can go a long way towards fostering healthy relationships.

Cultivate Emotional Intelligence

Developing emotional intelligence can assist individuals in better comprehending, managing, and responding to their own and others' emotions. Enhance emotional intelligence and relationship quality through the practice of self-awareness, self-control, empathy, and social skills.

Maintain a Network of Support

Develop a diverse network of encouraging friends, family members, and coworkers who can offer encouragement, advice, and emotional support during difficult times. Having a diversity of relationships can assist individuals in navigating various aspects of life and maintaining their overall health.

Invest in Your Own Development

Personal development and self-improvement can foster healthier relationships. By investing in their own emotional, mental, and physical health, individuals are able to bring their best selves to their relationships, thereby nurturing stronger ties and greater satisfaction.

Individuals can actively foster and maintain healthy relationships that contribute to enhanced mental health, physical health, emotional well-being, and productivity by implementing the aforementioned suggestions.

Summary & Conclusion

We have examined the multifaceted impact of healthy relationships on mental health, physical health, emotional well-being, and productivity throughout this chapter. We have also provided suggestions for cultivating and sustaining robust social relationships. The presented research and examples highlight the crucial role that healthy relationships play in promoting overall well-being and life satisfaction.

Healthy relationships are essential to our well-being because they provide us with support, companionship, and a sense of belonging, all of which enrich our lives. It is impossible to exaggerate the impact of healthy relationships on various aspects of our existence. They not only contribute to our physical health and productivity, but also improve our mental and emotional health. As a result, it is crucial for people to prioritize establishing and maintaining strong social connections throughout their lives.

In conclusion, wholesome relationships are essential to a satisfying existence. Individuals can experience numerous benefits, including enhanced mental health, physical health, emotional well-being, and productivity, by cultivating strong connections. Individuals can foster and maintain healthy relationships, which will ultimately improve their overall quality of life, by implementing the practical advice provided in this chapter. As we gain a deeper appreciation for the significance of healthy relationships, we can recognize the positive influence they have on our lives.

Chapter 29:
Strategies for Improving Communication and Building Strong, Supportive Relationships

Introduction:
Strategies for Improving Communications

In today's fast-paced and interconnected society, the ability to communicate effectively and cultivate strong, supportive relationships is more crucial than ever before. Healthy communication is essential for establishing meaningful relationships with others, as it forms the basis of our social interactions. Nurturing positive relationships with friends, family, colleagues, and romantic partners can have a significant impact on our mental health, physical health, emotional well-being, and productivity as we navigate the complexities of life.

In this chapter, we will examine a variety of techniques that can help you improve your communication skills and cultivate enduring, mutually beneficial relationships. By comprehending the essential components of effective communication and implementing these strategies on a daily basis, you will be better able to navigate both personal and professional relationships. In addition, you will acquire an understanding of the significance of active listening, emotional intelligence, assertiveness, conflict resolution, and relationship building. This chapter seeks to serve as an exhaustive aid for anyone wishing to improve their interpersonal skills and strengthen their relationships with others.

As you read this chapter, consider how these strategies can be incorporated into your daily life and the potential benefits they may have for your mental health and well-being as a whole. The journey to improved communication and stronger relationships is a lifelong process, and we hope that the insights and tools presented in this chapter will serve as valuable resources in your pursuit of personal development and fulfillment.

Active Listening
The Importance of Active Listening
- **Enhances Empathy and Understanding:** Active listening allows you to put yourself in the speaker's shoes, better understand their perspective, and respond empathetically. This fosters a deeper connection and improves the overall quality of communication.

- o **Helps to Prevent Misunderstandings:** By paying close attention to the speaker's words and nonverbal cues, active listening minimizes the likelihood of misinterpretation, resulting in fewer misunderstandings and conflicts.
- o **Builds Trust and Rapport:** Active listening demonstrates that you value and respect the speaker's thoughts and feelings, contributing to increased trust and rapport between you and the speaker.

Strategies for Active Listening
- o **Give Your Full Attention to the Speaker:** Make eye contact, turn off or put away distractions, and face the speaker. This communicates that you are genuinely interested in understanding their message.
- o **Avoid Interrupting:** Allow the speaker to finish their thoughts before interjecting or asking questions. Interruptions can disrupt the speaker's train of thought and make them feel unheard or dismissed.
- o **Reflect on the Speaker's Feelings and Thoughts:** As you listen, try to identify the emotions and thoughts underlying the speaker's words. This will help you gain a deeper understanding of their perspective and respond more empathetically.
- o **Clarify Your Understanding Through Summarizing and Asking Questions:** After the speaker has finished, briefly summarize what you understood from their message and ask any clarifying questions. This demonstrates that you have been listening attentively and provides an opportunity to correct any misconceptions.

Practical Tips for Practicing Active Listening
- o **Practice Mindfulness:** Mindfulness exercises, such as meditation, can help you develop greater focus and attentiveness, which are essential for active listening.
- o **Develop Patience:** Active listening requires patience, as it involves giving the speaker ample time to express themselves. Practicing patience in everyday situations will make it easier to apply this skill during conversations.
- o **Seek Feedback:** Ask friends or family members for feedback on your listening skills and identify areas for improvement. This will help you recognize your strengths and weaknesses as a listener and guide your personal growth in this area.

Overcoming Common Listening Barriers
- o **Mental Distractions:** Be aware of your own thoughts and feelings that may be causing internal distractions. Gently bring your focus back to the speaker if you find yourself drifting away.
- o **Preconceived Notions:** Recognize and set aside any biases, assumptions, or judgments you may have about the speaker or the topic being discussed. This will enable you to listen with an open mind and respond more objectively.
- o **Emotional Reactions:** If you find yourself reacting emotionally to the speaker's words, take a moment to acknowledge your emotions, and then

refocus on the speaker's message. This will prevent your emotions from clouding your understanding of their perspective.

Active Listening in Different Contexts

- o **Personal Relationships:** Active listening is crucial for fostering healthy connections with friends and family. By genuinely engaging in conversations, you demonstrate that you care about the other person's thoughts and feelings, which can strengthen your bonds.
- o **Workplace Interactions:** In professional settings, active listening helps you better understand colleagues' ideas, concerns, and perspectives, leading to improved collaboration and decision-making.
- o **Conflict Resolution:** Active listening is a vital tool in resolving conflicts, as it allows you to understand each party's viewpoint and facilitates constructive dialogue.

Benefits of Active Listening on Mental Health

- o **Reduced Stress and Anxiety:** Active listening enables you to address and resolve misunderstandings or conflicts more effectively, thereby reducing stress and anxiety associated with interpersonal difficulties.
- o **Enhanced Self-Esteem:** As your active listening skills improve, you will likely feel more confident in your ability to navigate social situations and foster meaningful connections with others.
- o **Improved Emotional Well-Being:** Active listening promotes empathy and understanding, which can lead to more satisfying relationships and a greater sense of connectedness, ultimately contributing to enhanced emotional well-being.

In conclusion, active listening is a crucial skill for improving communication and building strong, supportive relationships. By honing your active listening abilities, you can foster deeper connections, prevent misunderstandings, and create a more empathetic and understanding environment in both personal and professional settings. Practicing active listening in your daily life can lead to significant benefits for your mental health, emotional well-being, and overall quality of life.

Emotional Intelligence

The Role of Emotional Intelligence in Communication
- **Helps to Recognize and Manage Emotions:** Emotional intelligence allows you to identify and regulate your emotions, as well as understand the emotions of others. This enhances your ability to communicate effectively, as emotions can significantly impact the way you convey and interpret messages.
- **Contributes to Effective Decision-Making and Problem-Solving:** Emotionally intelligent individuals can separate emotions from facts, enabling them to make more informed decisions and resolve conflicts efficiently.
- **Fosters Healthy Relationships:** Emotional intelligence promotes empathy, compassion, and understanding, which are essential for building and maintaining strong, supportive relationships.

Developing Emotional Intelligence
- **Practice Self-Awareness:** Cultivate an awareness of your emotions by regularly checking in with yourself and acknowledging your feelings. Recognize the triggers that elicit strong emotional responses and reflect on how your emotions impact your thoughts, behaviors, and communication.
- **Cultivate Empathy:** Develop empathy by actively listening to others, putting yourself in their shoes, and considering their emotions and perspectives. This will help you become more understanding and compassionate in your interactions.
- **Develop Effective Coping Mechanisms:** Learn healthy ways to manage your emotions, such as deep breathing, meditation, or seeking social support. This will help you regulate your emotional responses and maintain balance during challenging situations.

Emotional Intelligence and Mental Health
- **Improved Self-Regulation:** Developing emotional intelligence enables you to manage your emotions more effectively, reducing the risk of impulsive actions or harmful emotional outbursts.
- **Enhanced Stress Management:** Emotionally intelligent individuals are better equipped to handle stress and adversity, as they can identify and utilize appropriate coping strategies.
- **Increased Emotional Well-Being:** Emotional intelligence promotes self-awareness, empathy, and effective communication, which contribute to greater satisfaction in personal and professional relationships.

Practical Tips for Improving Emotional Intelligence
- **Keep a Feelings Journal:** Regularly writing about your emotions can help you become more aware of your feelings and identify patterns or triggers.

- o **Practice Active Listening and Empathy**: Engage in conversations with others, and genuinely try to understand their emotions and perspectives. This will help you develop greater empathy and emotional intelligence.
- o **Seek Feedback from Others:** Ask friends, family members, or colleagues for their insights on how you handle emotions and communicate. Use this feedback to identify areas for improvement and guide your personal growth in emotional intelligence.

In summary, emotional intelligence plays a crucial role in effective communication and the development of strong, supportive relationships. By focusing on improving your emotional intelligence, you can enhance your interpersonal skills, make better decisions, and foster healthier connections with others. Investing in your emotional intelligence can yield significant benefits for your mental health, emotional well-being, and overall quality of life.

Assertiveness

Assertiveness and Its Benefits
- **Allows for Honest Communication:** Assertiveness enables you to express your thoughts, feelings, and needs openly and honestly, leading to more effective and genuine communication.
- **Protects Personal Boundaries:** Being assertive allows you to set and maintain healthy boundaries, ensuring that your rights and needs are respected by others.
- **Enhances Self-Esteem:** Assertive communication promotes a sense of self-worth and confidence, as you take responsibility for your emotions, thoughts, and actions.

Tips for Practicing Assertiveness
- **Use "I" Statements:** Frame your thoughts, feelings, and needs using "I" statements, such as "I feel," "I need," or "I think." This allows you to communicate assertively without placing blame or making accusations.
- **Avoid Aggressive or Passive Language:** Strive for a balanced communication style that is neither aggressive nor passive. Aggressive language can be confrontational and disrespectful, while passive language may result in your needs being overlooked.
- **Stand Up for Your Rights and Needs Respectfully:** Assertiveness involves standing up for yourself in a respectful and non-confrontational manner. Clearly communicate your needs and boundaries while considering the rights and feelings of others.

Overcoming Barriers to Assertiveness
- **Address Negative Self-Talk:** Be aware of any internal dialogue that undermines your self-confidence or prevents you from asserting yourself. Replace these thoughts with positive affirmations and self-compassionate statements.
- **Develop Self-Awareness:** Understand your needs, values, and boundaries, and become more aware of situations where you may need to assert yourself.
- **Practice in Low-Stakes Situations:** Begin practicing assertiveness in less challenging scenarios, such as expressing your preferences or standing up for yourself in minor disagreements. This will help you build confidence and prepare for more difficult situations.

Assertiveness in Different Contexts
- **Personal Relationships:** Assertive communication is essential for maintaining healthy relationships with friends and family. By clearly expressing your needs and boundaries, you can build stronger connections based on mutual respect and understanding.

- **Workplace Interactions:** Assertiveness in professional settings helps you advocate for your ideas, negotiate effectively, and navigate difficult conversations or conflicts.
- **Conflict Resolution:** Assertiveness is a key skill in resolving conflicts, as it allows you to communicate your needs and perspectives while respecting the rights and feelings of others.

Benefits of Assertiveness on Mental Health

- **Reduced Stress and Anxiety:** Assertiveness helps you address and resolve conflicts or difficulties, reducing the stress and anxiety associated with unresolved issues or unmet needs.
- **Enhanced Self-Esteem and Confidence:** As your assertiveness skills improve, you will likely feel more confident in your ability to navigate social situations and advocate for your needs and rights.
- **Improved Emotional Well-Being:** Assertive communication promotes a sense of empowerment and self-respect, contributing to greater overall emotional well-being.

In conclusion, assertiveness is a vital skill for effective communication and building strong, supportive relationships. By practicing assertiveness, you can openly and honestly express your needs, protect your boundaries, and foster a greater sense of self-worth and confidence. Developing assertiveness can have significant benefits for your mental health, emotional well-being, and overall quality of life.

Conflict Resolution
The Importance of Conflict Resolution

- **Maintains Healthy Relationships:** Effectively resolving conflicts can help maintain and even strengthen relationships by addressing issues, promoting understanding, and fostering a sense of mutual respect.
- **Reduces Stress and Anxiety:** Unresolved conflicts can lead to increased stress and anxiety. By addressing conflicts in a timely and constructive manner, you can alleviate these negative emotions and promote emotional well-being.
- **Enhances Personal and Professional Growth:** Conflict resolution can provide valuable learning experiences and opportunities for personal and professional growth, as it allows you to develop critical problem-solving, communication, and interpersonal skills.

Strategies for Conflict Resolution

- **Identify the Underlying Issue:** Before attempting to resolve a conflict, ensure you have a clear understanding of the root cause. This will allow you to address the core problem, rather than just the symptoms.
- **Practice Active Listening:** Listen attentively and empathetically to the other person's perspective. This will help you gain a better understanding of their needs and concerns, and facilitate a more constructive dialogue.

- o **Communicate Assertively:** Use assertive communication techniques, such as "I" statements, to express your thoughts, feelings, and needs. This allows you to convey your perspective without being aggressive or confrontational.
- o **Seek Compromise or Collaboration:** Aim for a resolution that addresses the needs and concerns of both parties. This may involve finding a compromise or working collaboratively to develop a mutually satisfactory solution.

Tips for Managing Emotions During Conflict Resolution
- o **Remain Calm and Composed:** Take deep breaths or practice other relaxation techniques to help you maintain your composure during difficult conversations.
- o **Recognize and Manage Emotional Triggers:** Be aware of any factors that may cause you to become emotionally reactive during conflicts. Develop strategies for managing these triggers to ensure you remain calm and focused during the resolution process.
- o **Use Timeouts if Necessary:** If emotions become too heated during conflict resolution, take a brief timeout to regain your composure and refocus on the issue at hand.

Conflict Resolution in Different Contexts
- o **Personal Relationships:** Effective conflict resolution is crucial for maintaining healthy connections with friends and family. By addressing conflicts constructively, you can preserve and even strengthen these relationships.
- o **Workplace Interactions:** In professional settings, conflict resolution helps maintain a positive work environment and promotes collaboration, creativity, and effective decision-making.
- o **Group Dynamics:** Conflict resolution is essential for maintaining harmony and productivity within groups, teams, or organizations. By addressing conflicts proactively, you can prevent issues from escalating and ensure that everyone's needs and concerns are considered.

Benefits of Conflict Resolution on Mental Health
- o **Reduced Stress and Anxiety:** Effectively resolving conflicts can alleviate the stress and anxiety associated with unresolved issues, leading to improved mental health and well-being.
- o **Enhanced Self-Esteem and Confidence:** Developing conflict resolution skills can boost your confidence in your ability to navigate challenging situations and maintain healthy relationships.
- o **Greater Emotional Well-Being:** By addressing conflicts and fostering a sense of understanding and mutual respect, you can promote emotional well-being for yourself and those around you.

In conclusion, conflict resolution is a critical skill for improving communication and building strong, supportive relationships. By learning to effectively navigate and resolve conflicts, you can maintain healthy connections, reduce stress and anxiety, and promote personal and professional growth. Investing in conflict resolution skills can have significant benefits for your mental health, emotional well-being, and overall quality of life.

Building Supportive Relationships

The Value of Supportive Relationships
- o **Enhances Emotional Well-Being**: Supportive relationships provide a sense of belonging, acceptance, and understanding, which are essential for emotional well-being.
- o **Promotes Resilience:** Having a strong support network can help you navigate challenges and setbacks more effectively, fostering resilience in the face of adversity.
- o **Encourages Personal Growth:** Supportive relationships offer opportunities for personal growth, as they provide a safe environment for self-expression, feedback, and learning.

Key Components of Supportive Relationships
- o **Trust:** Trust is the foundation of any supportive relationship. It is essential for open communication, emotional vulnerability, and the establishment of healthy boundaries.
- o **Empathy and Understanding:** Supportive relationships are characterized by a deep sense of empathy and understanding between individuals. This fosters emotional connection and promotes compassionate communication.
- o **Mutual Respect:** In a supportive relationship, both parties respect each other's thoughts, feelings, and boundaries, creating an environment of acceptance and appreciation.

Strategies for Building Supportive Relationships
- o **Be Approachable and Open:** Display a welcoming demeanor, and be open to engaging in conversations and sharing your thoughts and feelings with others.
- o **Show Genuine Interest:** Ask questions and actively listen to others, demonstrating that you value their thoughts and experiences.
- o **Offer Support and Encouragement:** Be there for others during both good times and challenging periods, offering encouragement, understanding, and assistance when needed.
- o **Be Reliable and Consistent:** Fulfill your commitments and follow through on promises, establishing yourself as a dependable and trustworthy individual.

Cultivating Supportive Relationships in Different Contexts
- o **Personal Relationships:** Foster supportive connections with friends and family members by spending quality time together, engaging in meaningful conversations, and offering emotional support and encouragement.

- **Workplace Interactions:** Build supportive professional relationships by collaborating effectively, offering assistance when needed, and providing constructive feedback and encouragement to colleagues.
- **Community Involvement:** Engage in community activities, clubs, or organizations to establish new supportive relationships and contribute to a sense of belonging and connectedness.

Benefits of Supportive Relationships on Mental Health
- **Reduced Stress and Anxiety:** Supportive relationships can provide emotional support and practical assistance during difficult times, helping to alleviate stress and anxiety.
- **Increased Sense of Belonging:** Supportive relationships contribute to a greater sense of belonging and connectedness, which are fundamental to emotional well-being and mental health.
- **Enhanced Self-Esteem:** Being part of a supportive network can boost your self-esteem and confidence, as you feel valued and appreciated by others.

In conclusion, building supportive relationships is a vital aspect of improving communication and promoting overall mental health. By cultivating connections characterized by trust, empathy, and mutual respect, you can foster a sense of belonging, resilience, and personal growth. Investing in supportive relationships can have significant benefits for your mental health, emotional well-being, and overall quality of life.

Real-Life Examples, Scientific Studies, and Practical Tips

Real-Life Examples
- **Example 1:** A couple facing communication difficulties attends couples' therapy, where they learn active listening and assertiveness techniques. As a result, they develop a deeper understanding of each other's needs and feelings, leading to a stronger, more supportive relationship.
- **Example 2:** A manager in a workplace adopts an emotionally intelligent leadership style, fostering open communication, empathy, and understanding among team members. This results in increased collaboration, job satisfaction, and overall team performance.

Scientific Studies
- **Study 1:** A study by James J. Gross and Oliver P. John (2003) found that individuals with higher emotional intelligence experienced greater success in their personal and professional lives, as well as better mental health and well-being.
- **Study 2:** A meta-analysis by Hülsheger, U. R., Alberts, H. J., Feinholdt, A., & Lang, J. W. (2013) indicated that mindfulness-based interventions, which can improve active listening and emotional intelligence, were associated with reduced stress, anxiety, and depression.

Practical Tips
- **Tip 1:** Set aside dedicated time for meaningful conversations with friends, family members, or colleagues. Use this time to practice active listening, emotional intelligence, and assertive communication techniques.
- **Tip 2:** Participate in workshops, courses, or therapy sessions focused on communication and relationship-building skills. These resources can help you develop your active listening, emotional intelligence, assertiveness, and conflict resolution abilities.
- **Tip 3:** Engage in mindfulness practices, such as meditation or yoga, to enhance your self-awareness, emotional intelligence, and ability to remain calm and focused during challenging conversations or conflicts.

Incorporating these real-life examples, scientific studies, and practical tips into your daily routine can help you improve your communication skills and foster strong, supportive relationships. By focusing on active listening, emotional intelligence, assertiveness, and conflict resolution, you can enhance your mental health, emotional well-being, and overall quality of life.

Summary & Conclusion

Integral to our mental health, emotional well-being, and overall quality of life are effective communication and supportive relationships. By focusing on essential skills such as active listening, emotional intelligence, assertiveness, and conflict resolution, we can improve our interpersonal relationships and cultivate a sense of belonging, resiliency, and personal growth.

Real-world instances, scientific studies, and useful hints all demonstrate the importance of investing in our communication skills and cultivating supportive relationships. Taking the time to cultivate these skills, whether through dedicated dialogues, seminars, or mindfulness practices, can yield significant benefits in our personal and professional lives.

Prioritizing the development of effective communication strategies and establishing strong, supportive relationships can have a significant impact on our mental health and well-being. We can create a more fulfilling and gratifying existence for ourselves and those around us by cultivating relationships characterized by trust, empathy, and mutual regard. Embrace the path of personal development and self-improvement, and you will obtain the benefits of enhanced communication and healthier relationships.

Chapter 30:
Tips for Managing Conflict in Relationships

Introduction:
Hints and Tips

Every relationship, whether romantic, familial, or platonic, will inevitably experience conflict. As individuals with varying histories, beliefs, and values, disagreements and misunderstandings are inevitable. Conflict can be uncomfortable and difficult at times, but it is essential to recognize that it is not inherently negative. In fact, when conflict is managed effectively, it can lead to individual development, heightened understanding, and enhanced communication.

This chapter seeks to provide readers with practical tips and strategies for managing conflict in relationships, emphasizing the potential benefits of effective conflict resolution on multiple facets of life, including mental health, physical health, emotional well-being, and productivity. Individuals can transform their relationships into sources of support, growth, and resiliency if they comprehend the underlying causes of conflict and develop the necessary skills to navigate it.

Throughout this chapter, we will examine several techniques and principles that are fundamental to effective conflict management, including active listening, empathy, communication skills, emotional regulation, and conflict resolution approaches. Real-world examples, scientific studies, and useful advice will be provided to illustrate the significance of these concepts and assist readers in incorporating them into their everyday lives.

Our ultimate objective is to equip readers with the skills and knowledge necessary to approach conflict with confidence and competence, thereby transforming potential obstacles into opportunities for personal and relational development. By investing in these skills and employing a proactive approach to conflict resolution, individuals can increase their personal and professional satisfaction and well-being.

Understanding Conflict and Its Effects on Mental Health
Defining Conflict and Its Common Causes
Conflict can be defined as a disagreement or divergence of opinion among individuals resulting from divergent beliefs, values, requirements, or expectations. Miscommunication, unmet needs, contrasting priorities, and external stressors are

common sources of conflict in relationships. It is essential to acknowledge that conflict is a natural component of human interaction and, when handled effectively, can serve as a catalyst for positive change and development.

Psychological Consequences of Unresolved Conflict

Unresolved conflict can be detrimental to a person's mental health. It can result in increased tension, anxiety, and depression, as well as frustration, impotence, and resentment. Over time, these negative emotions can erode trust and emotional closeness, resulting in deteriorating relationships. In addition, unresolved conflict can lead to rumination and mental exhaustion, which impairs cognitive functioning and overall health.

How Effective Resolution of Conflict Can Improve Mental Health

Conflict resolution can have numerous positive effects on mental health. Individuals can reduce tension and negative emotions, foster comprehension, and generate a sense of closure by addressing disagreements in an open and constructive manner. Effective conflict resolution can also improve self-awareness and emotional intelligence, as it requires comprehending one's own needs and emotions in addition to those of the other party. Successful conflict management can ultimately result in stronger, more resilient relationships, providing individuals with a vital source of support and connection, which is essential for maintaining mental health.

Active Listening and Empathy

The importance of Active Listening in Conflict Resolution

Active listening is a crucial component of conflict resolution because it enables individuals to completely comprehend and value the perspective of the other party. By attentively hearing, individuals can identify the underlying issues and emotions at the core of the conflict, thereby nurturing a more empathetic and productive dialogue. Active listening involves not only hearing the words spoken but also observing nonverbal indicators, such as body language and tone of voice. This attentiveness demonstrates respect and genuine interest, thereby contributing to the creation of an environment conducive to open communication.

Developing Compassion for Another's Perspective

Empathy is the capacity to comprehend and share another person's emotions and experiences. Empathy is essential for conflict resolution because it enables people to approach disagreements with an open mind and a willingness to see the situation from the other person's perspective. By putting themselves in the other person's position, individuals can obtain a greater understanding of their needs, concerns, and emotions, enabling them to respond with more compassion and knowledge. Developing empathy also counteracts defensiveness and blame, fostering a more collaborative and solution-oriented approach to conflict resolution.

Tips for Improving Active Listening and Empathy Abilities

Consider the following practical suggestions for enhancing active listening and empathy:

- **Be Present:** Provide the other individual with your undivided attention by eliminating distractions, sustaining eye contact, and adopting an open and attentive posture.
- **Reflect and Clarify:** Restate what the other person has said in your own words to ensure comprehension and demonstrate that you are attentive. Ask open-ended inquiries to elicit additional explanation and elaboration.
- **Validate Emotions:** Recognize the other person's emotions without judgment, even if you disagree with their viewpoint. Validate their experience and express comprehension of their emotions.
- **Exhibit Patience:** Allow the other person to finish speaking before interjecting. Allow them ample time to articulate their thoughts and emotions, and resist the impulse to offer solutions or defenses.
- **Cultivate Curiosity:** Approach disagreements with an inquisitive mindset, seeking to learn and comprehend the other person's viewpoint as opposed to demonstrating them incorrect.
- **Practice Empathy Daily:** Engage in daily activities that promote empathy, such as reading fiction, engaging in a variety of social interactions, and practicing compassion-focused mindfulness meditation.

Effective Communication Techniques

Utilizing "I" statements to communicate emotions and requirements During a conflict, "I" statements are an effective means of communicating one's emotions and requirements. By using "I" statements, individuals can express their viewpoints without assigning fault or making accusations. This approach promotes constructive dialogue by fostering a more open and non-confrontational atmosphere. To compose an effective "I" statement, individuals must express their emotions, characterize the specific situation or behavior, and explain how it has affected them. As an alternative to the statement, "You never listen to me," one could say, "I feel unheard when you interrupt me during our conversations."

Avoiding Accusatory and Combative Language

The use of accusatory and defensive language can exacerbate conflict and impede effective communication. To avoid this, individuals should concentrate on expressing their own emotions and requirements rather than disparaging or attacking others. As previously stated, this can be accomplished by using "I" statements and avoiding absolute language such as "always" and "never." Moreover, individuals should be receptive to feedback and willing to acknowledge their own contributions to the conflict, thereby demonstrating accountability and nurturing trust.

Identifying Shared Ground and Pursuing Compromise

Frequently, conflict resolution requires finding common ground and cooperating to find mutually gratifying solutions. Individuals should focus on shared objectives, values, or concerns and be willing to make concessions or compromises to facilitate this process. Enhance collaborative problem-solving by generating multiple solutions, weighing the advantages and disadvantages of each option, and selecting a course of action that strikes a balance between the needs and interests of both parties. By approaching conflict with a cooperative mindset, individuals can cultivate a sense of partnership and unity, thereby paving the way for relationships that are stronger and more resilient.

Practical tips for improving communication during conflict:

- **Take a Break:** If emotions are running high, take a brief break to calm down and consolidate your thoughts before resuming the conversation.
- **Select the Appropriate Time and Place:** Choose a time and location that permits a focused, uninterrupted conversation, avoiding public spaces and times when either party is anxious or exhausted.
- **Be Concise and Clear:** Communicate your thoughts and emotions clearly and concisely, avoiding excessive detail or digressions that may confound or overwhelm the other person.
- **Employ Nonverbal Communication:** Be mindful of body language, facial expressions, and tone of voice, ensuring that your nonverbal signals are congruent with your message and convey courtesy and candor.
- **Engage in Active Listening:** As previously discussed, active listening is essential for effective communication during conflict. Ensure that you employ active listening techniques during challenging conversations.
- **Remain Solution-Focused:** Instead of ruminating on past grievances or designating blame, maintain the conversation's focus on finding solutions and reaching a resolution.

Managing Emotions During Conflict
Recognizing and Regulating Emotional Responses
Emotions can significantly influence how individuals perceive and respond to conflict. It is essential to recognize and comprehend one's emotional responses in order to better manage and control them during conflicts. By developing greater self-awareness and emotional sensitivity, individuals can prevent their emotions from dominating a conversation and leading to unproductive or detrimental results. Emotional regulation entails recognizing emotions without becoming overwhelmed by them, allowing for more deliberate responses in conflict.

The Importance of Mindfulness in Conflict Resolution
Mindfulness can be a useful technique for regulating emotions during conflict. By practicing mindfulness, individuals can cultivate greater self-awareness and emotional control, allowing them to approach disagreements with a level head. Being mindful

entails being present in the moment, observing one's thoughts and emotions without judgment, and embracing them as they are. By cultivating a mindful approach to conflict, individuals can avoid impulsive or defensive responses, thereby promoting more constructive and compassionate communication.

Techniques for Maintaining Calm and Concentration During Challenging Conversations

To effectively manage emotions during conflict, individuals must remain composed and focused. Here are some practical strategies for maintaining decorum and emotional equilibrium during challenging conversations:

- **Practice Deep Breathing:** Deep, leisurely inhalation can assist in regulating emotions and promoting relaxation, thereby counteracting the physiological effects of stress and anxiety. Take a few moments to inhale through your nostril and exhale through your mouth prior to and during a difficult conversation.
- **Center Yourself:** Grounding techniques can assist in restoring awareness to the present moment and diminishing emotional intensity. Examples of grounding techniques include concentrating on the sensation of your feet on the floor, holding a small object, or performing a brief mindfulness exercise.
- **Pause and Reflect:** Take brief interruptions during the conversation to consolidate your thoughts and evaluate your emotional state. This can help prevent impulsive responses and permit more deliberate responses.
- **Use Positive Self-Talk:** Encourage yourself with positive affirmations, reminding yourself of your ability to handle difficult situations and the significance of resolving conflicts in a healthy way.
- **Establish Boundaries:** To protect your emotional well-being, recognize your limits and establish boundaries during conflict. This may involve establishing guidelines for respectful communication or pausing the conversation if it becomes contentious.
- **Seek Assistance:** Reach out to friends, family, or mental health professionals for guidance and assistance in managing emotions during conflict. Sharing your experiences and seeking advice can help you develop resiliency and enhance your ability to regulate your emotions.

Conflict Resolution Styles and Strategies

The Five Conflict Resolution Styles

There are five (5) primary conflict resolution methods, each with its own advantages and disadvantages based on the circumstances. Understanding these styles and when to employ them can enhance one's ability to effectively navigate conflicts:

1. **Avoidance:** This style involves avoiding or disregarding conflict, frequently in the hope that it will go away or resolve itself. While avoidance can be useful in

situations where emotions are high or the issue is minor, it can also lead to unresolved issues and a breakdown in communication.

2. **Accommodation:** Accommodation is the act of prioritizing the requirements and preferences of another individual over one's own. This style can be advantageous for maintaining harmony and nurturing benevolence, but it can also result in feelings of resentment or a lack of assertiveness.

3. **Competition:** Competitive approach to conflict entails pursuing one's own interests and objectives at the expense of those of others. This style can be effective when decisive action is required, but it can also harm relationships and impede collaboration.

4. **Compromise:** Compromise involves finding a middle ground where both parties make concessions to reach a solution that is mutually acceptable. This approach can be advantageous for swiftly resolving conflicts and maintaining relationships, but it can also result in suboptimal outcomes if the compromise does not address the underlying issues.

5. **Collaboration:** Collaboration is a cooperative strategy that strives to resolve the requirements and interests of all involved parties. This style emphasizes problem-solving and frank communication to discover mutually beneficial solutions. Collaboration can be time-consuming, but it frequently results in stronger relationships and more long-lasting solutions.

Selecting the Conflict Resolution Style Most Appropriate for Each Situation

The appropriate approach of conflict resolution is determined by variables such as the nature of the conflict, the personalities involved, and the desired result. It is essential to evaluate each circumstance on its own merits and adapt one's approach accordingly. For instance, collaboration may be the best strategy for resolving a conflict with a close acquaintance or family member, whereas a compromise may be more appropriate in a professional environment where both parties must reach an agreement quickly.

Integrating Assertiveness and Cooperation

Often, effective conflict resolution requires striking a balance between assertiveness (expressing one's own needs and interests) and cooperation (considering the needs and interests of others). Achieving this equilibrium can aid in ensuring that both parties feel heard and valued, thereby promoting a more positive and fruitful conversation. As discussed in previous sections, individuals can exercise skills such as active listening, empathy, and assertive communication to achieve this balance.

Practical Advice Regarding the Selection and Implementation of Conflict Resolution Styles:

- **Assess the Situation:** Consider factors such as the nature of the conflict, your relationship with the other party, and the desired outcome prior to deciding on a conflict resolution style.
- **Be Adaptable:** Recognize that different conflict resolution styles may be required in various situations. Be willing to adjust your strategy as necessary.

- o **Contemplate Past Events**: Learn from past conflicts by analyzing the strategies that worked and those that failed. Consider these insights as you approach future conflicts.
- o **Solicit Feedback:** Solicit feedback from trusted family members, acquaintances, and coworkers regarding your conflict resolution manner and areas for improvement.
- o **Create a Conflict Resolution Toolkit for Yourself**: Equip yourself with a variety of techniques and strategies for conflict resolution, allowing you to choose the most appropriate approach for each circumstance.
- o **Practice, Practice, Practice:** Conflict resolution, like any other talent, requires exercise. Seize opportunities to engage in challenging dialogues and employ a variety of conflict resolution techniques, reflecting on your experiences to refine your approach over time.

The Impact of Conflict Management on Physical Health and Emotional Well-Being

The Connection Between Conflict Management and Physical Health

The manner in which individuals manage interpersonal conflict has a significant bearing on their physical health. Chronic unresolved conflict can result in protracted stress, which can contribute to a variety of health problems, including hypertension, heart disease, sleep disturbances, and a compromised immune system. In contrast, effective conflict management can reduce tension levels and promote relaxation and well-being overall. By resolving conflicts in a constructive and wholesome manner, individuals can reduce the negative effects of conflict on their physical health.

Relationship between Emotional Health and Conflict Resolution

Emotional health is closely related to an individual's capacity to effectively manage conflict. Unresolved conflict can result in frustration, wrath, and resentment, which can have a negative effect on emotional health. On the other hand, effectively resolving conflicts can cultivate sentiments of satisfaction, empowerment, and self-efficacy, thereby enhancing emotional health. In addition, effective conflict resolution skills can enhance the character of one's relationships, thereby providing an essential source of emotional support and connection.

Conflict Management's Role in Personal Development and Self-Awareness

Conflict management is not only necessary for sustaining healthy relationships, but it can also promote personal development and self-awareness. By engaging in constructive conflict resolution, individuals can gain insight into their own needs, emotions, and communication styles, as well as a greater appreciation for others. This enhanced self-awareness can assist individuals in recognizing their strengths and areas for development, thereby nurturing personal growth and emotional intelligence.

Conflict Management Strategies for Promoting Physical and Emotional Health:

- o **Make Self-Care a Priority:** Participate in regular self-care activities, such as exercise, relaxation techniques, and maintaining a healthy diet, to promote overall health and well-being during times of conflict.
- o **Cultivate Emotional Intelligence:** Cultivate your emotional intelligence by practicing self-awareness, empathy, and emotional regulation, which will enable you to manage conflict more effectively and contribute to your emotional well-being.
- o **Focus on the Positives:** After resolving a conflict, ruminate on the positive aspects of the experience, such as the lessons learned, personal development, and strengthened relationships.
- o **Establish a Support Network:** Create a network of friends, family members, and/or professionals who can provide support, guidance, and encouragement during difficult times.
- o **Practice Forgiveness**: By practicing forgiveness and letting go of resentment, you can facilitate emotional restoration and enhance your well-being.
- o **Engage in Mindfulness and Meditation:** Incorporate mindfulness and meditation practices into your daily regimen to aid in stress management, enhance self-awareness, and promote emotional well-being.

Conflict Management and Productivity

The Impact of Conflict on Productivity
Whether in personal or professional relationships, conflict can have a significant impact on productivity. Unresolved conflict can result in an increase in tension, a decrease in motivation, and a collapse in communication, all of which can reduce productivity. In addition, conflict can occupy valuable time and resources, hindering a person's ability to concentrate on their objectives and priorities. Effective conflict management, on the other hand, can help maintain a positive and collaborative environment, allowing individuals to work more efficiently and accomplish their goals.

Importance of Efficient Conflict Resolution in Boosting Productivity
Effective conflict management and resolution can increase productivity in a variety of ways:

- o **Improved Communication:** Constructive conflict resolution encourages open and honest communication, which helps individuals better understand one another's needs, expectations, and points of view. This comprehension can facilitate more efficient collaboration and decision-making, thereby increasing productivity.
- o **Stronger Relationships**: Effective conflict management can strengthen relationships by nurturing a sense of unity and cultivating trust. Strong relationships in the workplace can lead to increased cooperation, collaboration,

and a more cohesive team dynamic, all of which contribute to greater productivity.

o **Personal Development and Growth:** As discussed previously, engaging in effective conflict resolution can lead to personal development and self-awareness. This personal development can enhance a person's emotional intelligence, problem-solving skills, and communication abilities, which are all valuable assets for boosting productivity.

o **Reduced Stress and Fatigue:** Conflict management can help reduce stress and prevent fatigue, allowing individuals to maintain their concentration, vitality, and motivation.

Effective Conflict Management: Tips for Increasing Productivity

o **Address Conflicts Promptly:** Rather than allowing conflicts to persist and escalate, address them as they arise. This proactive approach can prevent conflicts from requiring an inordinate amount of time and effort.

o **Specify Precise Expectations:** Establish explicit guidelines and expectations for communication and conflict resolution in both personal and professional relationships. This clarity can aid in preventing misunderstandings and expedite problem-solving.

o **Encourage Open Dialogue:** Cultivate a culture of open dialogue and feedback in which people feel secure expressing their thoughts, concerns, and ideas. This transparency can lead to enhanced collaboration and increased output.

o **Develop Conflict Resolution Abilities**: Constantly hone your conflict resolution abilities, including active listening, empathy, and assertive communication. These abilities can be valuable assets for conflict management and productivity maintenance.

o **Focus on Solutions:** During conflicts, keep the conversation focused on finding solutions and resolving the issue, as opposed to ruminating on past grievances or assigning blame.

After resolving a conflict, take the time to ruminate on the experience and identify any lessons learned or areas for improvement. This introspection can assist individuals in becoming more competent at resolving conflicts in the future, ultimately leading to increased productivity.

Summary & Conclusion

Effectively managing conflict in relationships is crucial for promoting mental health, physical health, emotional well-being, and productivity, as stated in the conclusion. Individuals can develop the skills and strategies necessary to resolve disagreements in a constructive and healthy manner if they comprehend the nature of conflict and its impacts on various aspects of life.

Mentally Healthy: Mind Over Matter

The importance of active listening and empathy, effective communication techniques, managing emotions during conflict, understanding and employing various conflict resolution methods, and the influence of conflict management on overall well-being and success are among the key insights from this chapter. Individuals can improve their conflict resolution skills, as well as their relationships and overall quality of life, by incorporating these concepts and techniques into their daily lives.

To promote effective conflict management, it is essential to remain open to learning and development, continually refining one's skills and adapting to new circumstances. This ongoing process of self-improvement and personal development can assist individuals in navigating the complexities of interpersonal relationships, ultimately resulting in increased emotional intelligence, resilience, and success in a variety of spheres of life.

Chapter 31:
The Role of Empathy in Building Strong Relationships

Introduction:
The Role of Empathy

Empathy is a potent and indispensable human capacity that enables us to communicate with others on a profoundly emotional level. It involves our capacity to comprehend and share the sentiments of others, allowing us to put ourselves in their position and sense their emotions. Empathy involves not only experiencing compassion for others but also effectively communicating that understanding. In a world that is becoming more interconnected and diverse, empathy is more vital than ever for establishing meaningful relationships.

This chapter explores the multifaceted function of empathy in various aspects of life, such as mental health, physical health, emotional well-being, and productivity. We will begin by discussing the significance of empathy in mental health and its impact on emotional comprehension, emotional regulation, and psychological well-being. Then, we will examine the function of empathy in physical health, focusing on its relationship to stress reduction and immunity.

Next, we will examine the influence of empathy on emotional health, with a focus on its contributions to resilience, coping, and relationship satisfaction. Following this, we will investigate the effect of empathy on productivity, with a particular focus on cooperation, collaboration, and leadership. We will provide evidence from scientific research and real-world examples throughout the chapter to illustrate the significance of empathy in these areas.

Finally, the chapter will provide practical advice and guidelines for cultivating empathy and incorporating it into daily life. By employing these strategies, readers can improve their empathic abilities and cultivate more satisfying relationships in their personal and professional lives. In conclusion, we will recapitulate the key points and insights, highlighting the importance of empathy in our daily lives and interpersonal relationships.

The Importance of Empathy in Mental Health
Understanding Emotions

- o **Decoding Emotional Signals**: Empathy enables us to accurately interpret the emotions of others by decoding their verbal and non-verbal cues. This skill is crucial for effectively navigating interpersonal relationships and understanding the emotional landscape of social situations.

- o **Emotional Validation:** Validating others' emotions through empathy is essential for building trust and rapport in relationships. When people feel heard and understood, they are more likely to open up, share their experiences, and develop deeper connections.

Emotional Regulation

- o **Self-Awareness:** Empathy helps us to become more self-aware and better understand our own emotions. This increased self-awareness is a key component of emotional intelligence and allows us to manage our emotions more effectively.
- o **Supporting Others:** By empathizing with others, we can help them regulate their emotions and navigate difficult situations. This support not only strengthens relationships but also contributes to our own sense of self-efficacy and satisfaction in helping others.

Decreased Loneliness and Isolation

- o **Social Connection:** Empathic connections foster a sense of belonging and social connection, reducing feelings of loneliness and isolation. These connections are vital for mental health, as prolonged loneliness has been linked to depression, anxiety, and other psychological issues.
- o **Research:** A study by Cacioppo et al. (2006) found that loneliness is associated with increased morbidity and mortality. Cultivating empathy and forming strong relationships can counteract these negative effects.

Psychological Well-Being

- o **Self-Worth and Self-Esteem:** Empathy can lead to increased feelings of self-worth and self-esteem, as we experience the satisfaction of connecting with others and providing support. This boost in self-esteem can contribute to overall psychological well-being.
- o **Empathy and Mental Health Disorders:** Research suggests that empathy can play a protective role in certain mental health disorders. For example, a study by Gleichgerrcht et al. (2013) found that high levels of empathy were associated with lower levels of depression and anxiety in medical students.
- o **Buffering Against Stress:** Empathy can help buffer against the negative effects of stress by fostering social support and emotional understanding. This support can prevent the onset of mental health issues or aid in their recovery.

By understanding and validating emotions, regulating our own emotions, decreasing loneliness, and fostering psychological well-being, empathy plays a critical role in promoting mental health. Cultivating empathy in our relationships not only enhances our connections with others but also supports our own emotional and psychological health.

The Role of Empathy in Mental Health
Stress Reduction

- o **Sharing Emotional Burdens:** Empathy allows us to share and alleviate the emotional burdens of others. By providing a supportive and understanding environment, we can help reduce stress levels for both ourselves and those around us.
- o **Emotional Regulation and Stress:** As empathy aids in emotional regulation, it can help us better manage stress. When we are more aware of our own emotions and can effectively regulate them, we are less likely to experience stress-related physical health issues.
- o **Research:** A study by Seppälä et al. (2014) found that people with high levels of empathy experienced lower stress levels and better overall health. Cultivating empathy can, therefore, contribute to stress reduction and improved physical health.

Social Support and Immunity

- o **Empathy and Social Support:** Empathy fosters a sense of social support, as it enables us to build strong connections with others. When we feel supported and understood, we are more likely to have better physical health.
- o **Immune Function:** Strong social support networks have been linked to improved immune function, which in turn can help protect us from illness and disease.
- o **Research:** A study by Uchino et al. (1996) found that individuals with strong social support networks had better immune function and lower levels of inflammation. By cultivating empathy and forming deep connections with others, we can bolster our immune systems and improve our physical health.

Pain Management

- o **Empathy and Pain Perception:** Empathy can help us understand and better manage pain, both in ourselves and others. By recognizing and validating the pain someone else is experiencing, we can provide appropriate support and care.
- o **Shared Pain Relief:** Research has shown that empathy can lead to shared pain relief. A study by Goldstein et al. (2016) found that when people experienced pain relief, their partners who were present and empathized with their pain also experienced relief.

Cardiovascular Health

- o **Empathy and Heart Health:** Empathy has been linked to better cardiovascular health, as it can help reduce stress levels, lower blood pressure, and promote overall well-being.
- o **Research:** A study by Varnum et al. (2012) found that people who reported higher levels of empathy had lower resting heart rates, suggesting a potential link between empathy and cardiovascular health.

In summary, empathy plays a significant role in physical health by reducing stress, fostering social support, improving pain management, and promoting cardiovascular health. By cultivating empathy, we can not only improve our mental health but also support our physical well-being.

Empathy and Emotional Well-Being
Resilience and Coping

- o **Emotional Support:** Empathy helps build resilience by providing emotional support during challenging times. When we face adversity, knowing that someone understands and shares our feelings can make it easier to cope with the situation.
- o **Problem-Solving:** Empathic understanding can facilitate problem-solving by encouraging open communication and the sharing of perspectives. This allows individuals to work together to find solutions to difficult situations, ultimately enhancing their resilience.
- o **Research:** A study by Zaki and Ochsner (2012) found that empathy can help promote resilience by fostering social bonds and providing emotional support during stressful times.

Improved Relationship Satisfaction

- o **Communication and Trust:** Empathy fosters open and honest communication, which leads to increased trust between individuals. This sense of trust is fundamental to relationship satisfaction.
- o **Conflict Resolution:** Empathy can aid in resolving conflicts by allowing individuals to understand each other's feelings and perspectives. This understanding helps to diffuse tension and promote collaborative solutions, ultimately contributing to more satisfying relationships.
- o **Research:** A study by Krok and Baker (2018) found that empathy was positively associated with relationship satisfaction in romantic couples, as well as in friendships and family relationships.

Emotional Balance

- **Emotional Attunement:** Empathy allows us to become more emotionally attuned to ourselves and others. This attunement can help us maintain a healthy emotional balance, as we are better able to recognize and respond to emotional cues.
- **Emotional Regulation:** Empathy contributes to emotional regulation by helping us understand and manage our own emotions, as well as the emotions of those around us. This skill is essential for maintaining emotional well-being.

Self-Compassion and Empathy

- **Empathy for Oneself:** Developing empathy for others can also lead to increased self-compassion. When we can understand and validate our own emotions, we are better equipped to manage and care for our emotional well-being.
- **Research:** A study by Neff et al. (2007) found that self-compassion was positively correlated with empathy, suggesting that cultivating empathy for others can contribute to greater self-compassion and emotional well-being.

In conclusion, empathy plays a crucial role in emotional well-being by fostering resilience, improving relationship satisfaction, promoting emotional balance, and enhancing self-compassion. By cultivating empathy in our relationships, we can support both our own emotional well-being and that of others, leading to a more fulfilling and emotionally healthy life.

The Impact of Empathy on Productivity
Teamwork and Collaboration

- **Understanding Diverse Perspectives**: Empathy allows us to appreciate and understand the diverse perspectives of our colleagues, fostering a collaborative environment where individuals can effectively work together. By empathizing with others, we can bridge gaps in communication and create a more inclusive and productive team dynamic.
- **Conflict Resolution:** Empathy plays a critical role in resolving conflicts within teams by enabling team members to understand each other's feelings and viewpoints. This understanding can lead to more constructive discussions and collaborative problem-solving, ultimately improving productivity.
- **Research:** A study by Goleman and Boyatzis (2008) found that teams with higher levels of empathy displayed better group problem-solving abilities and higher overall performance.

Leadership

- o **Inspirational Leadership:** Empathic leaders can inspire loyalty, trust, and commitment among their followers. By understanding and validating the emotions of their team members, leaders can create a supportive and motivating environment that encourages employees to excel.
- o **Effective Decision-Making:** Empathic leaders are better equipped to make informed decisions by taking into consideration the feelings, needs, and perspectives of their team members. This comprehensive approach to decision-making can lead to more effective and sustainable solutions.
- o **Real-Life Example:** Highly empathic leaders, like Nelson Mandela, were able to unite people and inspire change by demonstrating a deep understanding of and compassion for the experiences of others.

Customer Relations

- o **Understanding Customer Needs**: Empathy is crucial for understanding and addressing customer needs. By empathizing with customers, businesses can create products and services that better meet their needs, leading to increased customer satisfaction and loyalty.
- o **Improved Communication:** Empathy allows for more effective communication with customers, as it enables businesses to understand and address customer concerns and emotions. This can lead to stronger customer relationships and better problem-solving.
- o **Research:** A study by Gremler and Gwinner (2000) found that empathic communication was positively associated with customer satisfaction and loyalty.

Workplace Well-Being

- o **Employee Satisfaction:** Empathy can contribute to a more positive and supportive workplace culture, leading to higher levels of employee satisfaction. When employees feel understood and valued, they are more likely to be engaged and committed to their work.
- o **Reduced Burnout:** Empathy can help reduce burnout by fostering emotional support and understanding within the workplace. This support can help employees manage work-related stress, preventing burnout and its negative effects on productivity.
- o **Research:** A study by Konrath et al. (2016) found that empathy was associated with lower levels of burnout and higher levels of job satisfaction.

In summary, empathy has a profound impact on productivity by promoting teamwork, collaboration, effective leadership, customer relations, and workplace well-being. By cultivating empathy in professional environments, individuals and organizations can foster more productive, satisfied, and engaged workforces, leading to better outcomes and overall success.

Practical Tips on Cultivating Empathy

Active Listening

- o **Give your Full Attention:** When engaging with others, focus on what they are saying without interruption or distraction. This demonstrates that you genuinely care about their thoughts and feelings.
- o **Reflect and Paraphrase:** By reflecting and paraphrasing the speaker's words, you show that you are actively listening and trying to understand their perspective. This can lead to deeper connections and improved communication.

Perspective-Taking

- o **Put Yourself in Their Shoes:** Imagine yourself in the other person's situation and try to understand their emotions, thoughts, and experiences. This can help you appreciate their perspective and foster empathy.
- o **Ask Questions:** To better understand someone else's perspective, ask open-ended questions that encourage them to share their feelings and experiences.

Mindfulness

- o **Practice Self-Awareness:** Being mindful of your own emotions and thoughts can help you better understand and empathize with the emotions of others. Develop a daily mindfulness practice, such as meditation, to improve self-awareness.
- o **Be Present:** Stay present and focused during conversations, which allows you to be more in tune with the emotions and experiences of others.

Develop Emotional Intelligence

- o **Recognize and Manage Emotions:** Work on identifying and managing your own emotions to better empathize with others. This can involve journaling, practicing self-reflection, or seeking therapy.
- o **Educate Yourself:** Read books or take courses on emotional intelligence to increase your skills in understanding and managing emotions, both your own and those of others.

Engage in Empathy-Building Activities

- o **Read Fiction:** Reading fiction can help you practice empathy by allowing you to immerse yourself in the emotions, thoughts, and experiences of the characters. This can translate to better empathizing with people in real life.
- o **Watch Movies and Plays:** Similar to reading fiction, watching movies or plays can expose you to different perspectives and emotions, fostering empathy.

Volunteer and Help Others
- o **Engage in Volunteer Work or Community Service:** Participating in volunteer work or community service allows you to connect with people from different backgrounds and develop empathy. By understanding their experiences and emotions, you can broaden your empathic abilities.
- o **Acts of Kindness and Generosity:** Engaging in acts of kindness and generosity can help you better understand others' experiences and emotions. Small gestures of kindness can go a long way in fostering empathy and building stronger relationships.

Cultivate a Growth Mindset
- o **Acknowledge Biases:** Recognize and challenge your own biases and assumptions about others. Embrace the idea that you can learn from every person and situation, regardless of your initial perception.
- o **Be Open to Learning:** Be open to learning from others and developing your empathic abilities. Cultivating a growth mindset can help you become more empathetic over time.

By adopting these practical strategies, you can enhance your empathic abilities and ultimately build stronger, more meaningful relationships in your personal and professional life. Empathy is a skill that can be nurtured and developed with practice, and by making a conscious effort to cultivate it, you can experience the many benefits it offers.

Summary & Conclusion

This chapter examined the multifaceted function of empathy in fostering strong relationships, as well as its effects on mental health, physical health, emotional well-being, and productivity. Empathy is not only crucial for traversing our social world, but also a potent tool for fostering resilience, enhancing relationship satisfaction, promoting emotional balance, and cultivating self-compassion.

By cultivating empathy, we can create more inclusive, supportive, and effective teams, improve communication and collaboration, and enhance our personal and professional relationships. Furthermore, empathy plays a crucial role in promoting overall health and well-being, as it can reduce stress, enhance immune function, and even contribute to improved cardiovascular health.

In addition, we have provided suggestions for incorporating empathy into one's daily life, such as active listening, perspective-taking, mindfulness, emotional intelligence development, engaging in empathy-building activities, volunteering, and cultivating a growth mindset. By employing these strategies, we can improve our empathic abilities and reap the many benefits that empathy provides.

Empathy is a potent and transformative skill that can substantially enhance the quality of our relationships and our well-being as a whole. We can create a more compassionate, supportive, and productive world by investing in our empathic abilities and nurturing empathic connections with those around us. Experience the profound impact that empathy can have on your life and the lives of those around you by embracing its power.

Chapter 32:
Building Strong Relationships with Romantic Partners

Introduction:
Strong Relationships – The Importance

The character of our intimate relationships has a significant impact on our well-being as a whole. Strong and supportive relationships not only offer us companionship and affection, but also contribute to our mental health, physical health, emotional well-being, and productivity. In contrast, relationships characterized by conflict, mistrust, or inadequate communication can result in stress, anxiety, and other mental health problems. Consequently, it is essential to comprehend the factors that contribute to the formation of healthy relationships with romantic partners.

The purpose of this chapter is to provide readers with a comprehensive comprehension of the main factors that contribute to the formation of robust romantic relationships. The course will explore the significance of effective communication, trust, emotional intimacy, conflict resolution, and quality time spent together, supported by pertinent research, examples, and practical advice. By implementing these suggestions into their daily lives, readers will be able to strengthen their current relationships and establish healthier ones in the future.

This chapter will also examine the positive effects of healthy romantic relationships on mental health, physical health, emotional well-being, and productivity. Through the examination of real-world examples and scientific research, readers will gain insight into the transformative force of healthy partnerships in various aspects of their lives. The chapter will also provide readers with practical advice and suggestions for incorporating these key factors into their daily lives, thereby assisting them in cultivating satisfying and supportive romantic relationships.

Importance of Communication
Effective communication is the bedrock of any healthy relationship, enabling partners to comprehend one another's requirements, emotions, and perspectives. It promotes confidence, emotional closeness, and relationship satisfaction. Consistently, research has demonstrated that couples who communicate effectively are more likely to have healthier, longer-lasting relationships (Gottman, 1994). In addition, inadequate communication is frequently cited as the primary cause of relationship disruptions and discontent.

Types of Interaction

- o **Verbal Communication** is the use of spoken language to convey messages, ideas, and feelings. To ensure clarity and avoid misunderstandings, it is crucial to choose the appropriate words, tone, and tempo when communicating with your companion.

- o **Nonverbal Communication** consists of body language, facial expressions, and gestures that convey vital information about a person's emotions and goals. Partners who are cognizant of nonverbal communication can better comprehend one another's emotions and requirements.

- o **Listening:** Active and compassionate listening is an essential aspect of communication. It involves not only receiving and comprehending your partner's words, but also validating their emotions.

Obstacles to Successful Communication

- o **Emotional Barriers:** Previous experiences, insecurities, and unresolved conflicts can create emotional barriers, making it challenging for partners to communicate openly and honestly.
- o **Defensive Behaviors:** When one partner feels attacked or criticized, he or she may become defensive, hindering communication and problem-solving.
- o **Poor Listening Skills:** Interrupting, ignoring, or disregarding your partner's emotions can impede communication and lead to misunderstandings.

Tips for Improving Communication That Are Practical

- o **Active Listening:** Encourage frank and honest conversations by giving your companion your undivided attention, asking questions, and ruminating on what they say. Listen empathically to validate their emotions and facilitate comprehension.
- o **Assertiveness:** Express your feelings, needs, and boundaries without fear of rejection or disapproval and with respect. Focus on your own experience rather than accusing or criticizing your companion by using "I" statements.
- o **Emotional Intelligence:** Develop the ability to identify and control your own emotions, as well as to empathize with your partner's emotional experiences. This will aid in establishing a supportive and receptive environment for communication.
- o **Seek Feedback:** request feedback from your companion on your communication style, and be receptive to suggestions for enhancement. Over time, this can help both parties develop improved communication practices.

- o **Address Obstacles:** Determine and eliminate any obstacles to effective communication in your relationship. This may involve resolving unresolved conflicts, seeking professional assistance, or improving listening skills.

Importance of Trust

Trust is essential to the development of healthy romantic relationships. It enables partners to feel safe, enabling them to be honest and vulnerable with one another. Trust promotes emotional closeness, productive communication, and overall relationship fulfillment. A lack of trust can result in anxiety, tension, and emotional upheaval, all of which are detrimental to mental health (Wieselquist, 2009). Moreover, trustworthy relationships provide a secure environment for personal development and a solid support system during difficult circumstances.

Types of Faith

- o **Emotional trust** is the belief that one's companion will provide emotional support, validation, and comprehension when required. Trust is essential for establishing a profound emotional connection.
- o **Reliability Trust** entails having faith that one's companion will fulfill commitments, promises, and expectations. This form of trust contributes to the relationship's stability and security.
- o **Fidelity Trust:** Believing that your companion will remain emotionally and physically loyal and faithful. This form of trust is necessary to preserve the exclusivity and sanctity of a romantic relationship.

Factors Affecting Trust

- o **Past Experiences:** Previous relationships, family dynamics, and personal experiences can impact an individual's trustworthiness. It is crucial to identify and address any trust issues resulting from past events.
- o **Communication:** Transparency and honesty in communication are essential for establishing trust. When partners are honest about their emotions, intentions, and actions, it is simpler to develop mutual trust.
- o **Consistency:** Demonstrating consistent behavior over time can contribute to the development of trust because it enables partners to rely on each other and develop a sense of predictability in the relationship.

Practical Advice for Establishing Trust

- o **Honesty:** Be frank and honest with your companion, even when discussing challenging topics. Transparency contributes to the development of a sense of safety and fosters trust in a relationship.

- o **Consistency:** Demonstrate your dependability through your actions and honor your promises and commitments. Consistency in behavior fosters a sense of stability and security, which increases confidence.
- o **Emotional Support:** In times of anxiety or ambiguity, provide reassurance and support. Being a dependable source of assistance will increase your partner's trust in you.
- o **Apologize and Forgive:** Accept responsibility for your actions and be willing to sincerely repent when you make a mistake. Also, be willing to forgive your companion if they repent. This will aid in maintaining confidence in the face of difficulties.
- o **Be Patient:** It takes time to build trust, particularly if one or both partners have had trust issues in the past. Be patient and understanding, and permit gradual development of trust.

Emotional Intimacy

Importance of Emotional Intimacy
Emotional intimacy is the proximity and profound connection between companions. It entails feeling understood, valued, and supported by your companion, as well as reciprocating these emotions. Emotional intimacy is essential for overall relationship satisfaction and has been associated with improved mental health and well-being (Feeney & Collins, 2015). When partners feel emotionally connected, they are more likely to overcome obstacles, communicate effectively, and maintain a strong connection.

Influencing Factors of Emotional Intimacy

- o **Trust** plays a crucial role in fostering emotional intimacy because it enables partners to be vulnerable and communicate their most private thoughts and emotions.
- o **Communication:** Open and honest communication is essential for the development of emotional intimacy because it enables partners to comprehend one another's emotions, requirements, and desires.
- o **Empathy:** Building emotional intimacy requires the ability to empathize with your partner's experiences and emotions. It enables partners to feel valued and understood.

Practical Guidelines for Fostering Emotional Closeness

- o **Personal Experience Sharing:** Share your thoughts, emotions, and experiences to create a stronger bond. Share positive and negative emotions, along with aspirations, concerns, and desires. This vulnerability facilitates emotional closeness.

- Empathy: Try to comprehend your partner's feelings and experiences from their point of view. Even if you disagree with their viewpoint, validate their emotions and provide support. This comprehension can strengthen emotional closeness.
- Regular Check-Ins: Schedule regular check-ins to discuss the emotional health of your relationship and address any concerns or issues. These conversations can contribute to the maintenance of emotional closeness and ensure that both partners feel heard and supported.
- Celebrate and Suffer Collectively: Be present for your companion in both happy and difficult circumstances. Commemorate their achievements and provide support during difficult times. This shared emotional experience may strengthen emotional closeness.
- Practice Gratitude: Express gratitude for your companion and acknowledge the positive aspects of your relationship on a regular basis. Gratitude can help maintain a strong emotional bond and remind you of why you value one another.

Conflict Resolution

Importance of Conflict Resolution

In every relationship, conflict is inevitable, but how it is handled can determine the health of the partnership. Unresolved conflicts can contribute to resentment, emotional distress, and dissatisfaction in relationships (Gottman & Silver, 1999). Couples who cultivate healthy conflict resolution skills are better equipped to manage obstacles, maintain emotional intimacy, and nurture a stronger bond.

Conflict Resolution Strategies

- Avoidance: Ignoring conflicts or sweeping problems under the rug constitutes avoidance. This approach may preclude an imminent confrontation, but it can result in unresolved issues and escalating resentment.
- Accommodation: One partner consistently gives in to the demands of the other without addressing their own requirements. This style can lead to an imbalance of power and discontentment.
- Competition: Each companion is more concerned with winning the argument than with resolving the issue. This manner can impair the relationship by fostering feelings of competition and resentment.
- Compromise: Both parties collaborate to discover a solution that meets their respective requirements and preferences. This approach promotes equity and cooperation.
- Collaboration: Both partners actively engage in problem-solving, taking each other's requirements into account and seeking solutions that are mutually beneficial. This style promotes comprehension, development, and relationship satisfaction.

Guidelines for Efficient Conflict Resolution

- o **Select the Right Moment:** When both parties are composed and prepared for a productive conversation, conflicts should be addressed. When emotions are high or when one partner is feeling overwrought or anxious, avoid discussing sensitive topics.
- o **Concentrate on the Issue:** Avoid personal assaults and focus on resolving the issue at hand. Express your sentiments and needs without criticizing or accusing your companion by using "I" statements.
- o **Compromise:** Cooperate to discover a solution that suits the requirements and preferences of both parties. When negotiating, be willing to make concessions and consider your partner's perspective.
- o **Observe active listening:** During a conflict, pay close attention to your partner's concerns, emotions, and requirements. Validate their emotions and make an effort to understand their perspective, even if you disagree with it.
- o **Ensure that communication remains open** and respectful throughout the conflict resolution process. Avoid becoming closed off or defensive, as this can impede the resolution process.

Long-Term Conflict Resolution Strategies

- o **Cultivate Emotional Intelligence:** Cultivating emotional intelligence can assist partners in better comprehending and managing their emotions during conflicts, resulting in healthier resolution strategies.
- o **Consider Consulting a Professional:** If conflicts are persistent and difficult to resolve, consider consulting a professional, such as a therapist or counselor, who can offer guidance and support in developing conflict resolution skills.
- o **Consider Conflict Patterns:** Regularly assess the conflict resolution patterns in your relationship and identify areas for development. This self-awareness can assist you and your companion in developing and strengthening your relationship over time.

Quality Time and Shared Activities

Importance of Quality Time and Shared Activities
Spending quality time together and participating in shared activities is essential for strengthening romantic relationships. Such experiences facilitate the development of emotional intimacy, nurture a sense of companionship, and improve relationship satisfaction (Reis & Gable, 2003). Moreover, engaging in pleasurable activities can reduce tension, improve mental health, and enhance both companions' well-being.

Advantages of Time Spent Together and Shared Activities

- o **Enhanced Communication:** Spending quality time together enables partners to engage in open and honest dialogues, resulting in greater understanding and emotional closeness.
- o **Building Trust:** Shared activities can help partners build trust by offering opportunities to rely on one another and collaborate as a team.
- o **Creating Lasting Memories:** Participating in memorable experiences can help establish a foundation of positive memories, which contributes to the resilience and satisfaction of the relationship.
- o **Personal Growth:** Participation in novel activities or learning experiences can foster personal development and self-discovery for both companions, resulting in a stronger bond.

Incorporating Quality Time and Shared Activities: Useful Suggestions

- o **Prioritize Together Time:** Schedule regular "date nights" or dedicated time for one another, and consider these commitments as non-negotiable.
- o **Explore New Experiences:** Be willing to attempt new activities together, such as taking a class, playing a sport, or traveling to new locations. These experiences can foster personal development and produce enduring memories.
- o **Develop Common Interests:** Find activities or pastimes that both partners appreciate and can savor together. This can foster a sense of community and meaningful connections.
- o **Unplug:** Limit electronic devices and other sources of distraction in order to focus on your companion and be present during your time together. This can contribute to a more intimate and connected environment.
- o **Equilibrate Individual and Group Activities:** While participation in shared activities is essential, maintaining individual interests and pursuits is also crucial. This equilibrium can help one maintain a healthy sense of self and prevent partner dependence.

Couples can strengthen their emotional connection, cultivate trust, and create enduring memories by prioritizing quality time and shared activities. These experiences ultimately promote mental health and well-being by fostering healthier and more gratifying romantic relationships.

Summary & Conclusion

Building robust romantic relationships is essential for overall health because it has a significant impact on mental health, physical health, emotional health, and productivity. By comprehending and focusing on the key factors that contribute to effective relationships, individuals can work to develop satisfying and mutually beneficial relationships.

This chapter has discussed the significance of effective communication, trust, emotional intimacy, conflict resolution, and quality time spent together through shared activities. By implementing the discussed tips and strategies, readers will be able to improve their current relationships and foster healthier ones in the future. These factors not only strengthen the basis of a romantic relationship, but also foster personal development and resiliency.

In conclusion, maintaining healthy romantic relationships is a continuous process that requires fortitude, dedication, and self-awareness. By devoting time and energy to comprehending and addressing these crucial factors, individuals can appreciate the numerous advantages of healthy and fulfilling partnerships. Fostering strong relationships ultimately contributes to enhanced mental health, emotional well-being, and overall life satisfaction, making it a worthwhile endeavor for anyone seeking a fulfilling and supportive romantic relationship.

Chapter 33:
Building Strong Relationships in the Workplace

Introduction:
The Power of Strong Workplace Relationships

Individuals spend a significant component of their lifetimes in a workplace that is both complex and dynamic. In the midst of the difficulties and demands of professional life, the significance of establishing strong relationships with colleagues is frequently overlooked. However, cultivating positive and supportive relationships in the workplace is essential not only for the well-being of individual employees, but also for the organization's overall success.

This chapter will examine the impact of fostering strong workplace relationships on mental health, physical health, emotional well-being, and productivity, as well as their multifaceted benefits. By providing evidence-based explanations, real-life examples, and practical suggestions, the reader will gain a comprehensive understanding of the value of strong workplace relationships and learn strategies for fostering them on a daily basis.

You will discover the power of positive relationships in reducing tension and anxiety, enhancing self-esteem and confidence, bolstering the immune system, and lowering the risk of exhaustion as you read this chapter. In addition, you will understand how these connections contribute to greater job satisfaction, greater resilience in the face of challenges, enhanced cooperation and collaboration, and the promotion of creativity and innovation within teams.

This chapter will provide invaluable insights and practical guidance on how to cultivate strong relationships in the workplace for the benefit of all involved, whether you are an employee seeking to improve your well-being, a manager seeking to create a more supportive work environment, or an organizational leader striving for success.

Mental Health
Reduced Stress and Anxiety
For many individuals, the workplace can be a significant source of stress and anxiety. Strong relationships with colleagues serve as a buffer against these negative feelings by providing social support and fostering a more positive work environment.

- o **Research:** Multiple studies have demonstrated a correlation between robust workplace relationships and reduced levels of tension and anxiety. A study published in the Journal of Occupational Health Psychology, for instance, found that employees who perceived high levels of coworker support had reduced stress levels and greater psychological well-being.
- o **Example:** A technology company's mentorship program partnered new employees with experienced mentors. As a result, new employees felt more supported and confident in their positions, resulting in decreased levels of tension and anxiety throughout the organization.
- o **Practical Tip:** Make an effort to engage in small talk with colleagues, demonstrate empathy, and provide assistance when necessary. This contributes to the development of rapport, nurtures a sense of belonging, and promotes a more supportive work environment.

Increased Self-Respect and Confidence

Positive feedback and encouragement from colleagues play a crucial role in bolstering the self-esteem and confidence of an individual. When employees feel valued and appreciated, their performance is more likely to improve.

- o **Research:** According to research, receiving positive feedback from colleagues is associated with greater self-esteem and confidence. Researchers found in a study published in the Journal of Applied Psychology that employees who regularly received positive feedback had higher self-esteem and were more contented with their jobs.
- o **Example:** Manager in a marketing firm made a concerted effort to frequently commend employees for their accomplishments and efforts. Over time, employees gained confidence in their abilities, resulting in improved performance and a more positive work environment.
- o **Tip:** Offer sincere commendation and acknowledgement to your colleagues for their hard work and achievements. This not only improves their self-esteem and confidence, but also fosters an organization-wide culture of appreciation and support.

Enhanced Emotional Control

Coworkers provide a supportive network for discussing emotions and releasing frustrations, which can contribute to improved emotional regulation.

- o **Research:** According to a study published in the Journal of Managerial Psychology, employees who experienced positive social interactions at work were better able to regulate their emotions and less likely to experience emotional exhaustion.
- o **Example:** A group of nurses in a healthcare organization formed a support group to discuss their emotional experiences and difficulties. This group

became a secure space for them to express their emotions; consequently, they experienced improved emotional regulation and less emotional exhaustion.

- o **Practical Tip:** Promote open communication and establish a secure environment for colleagues to communicate their emotions and feelings. This promotes emotional resilience and a more supportive work environment.

By prioritizing mental health and nurturing strong relationships in the workplace, employees can enjoy numerous benefits, including reduced tension, improved self-esteem, and enhanced emotional regulation. Employees and organizations can contribute to a more positive and mentally healthy work environment by implementing practical guidelines such as engaging in casual conversation, offering commendation, and establishing a secure space for emotional support.

Improved Physical Health
Improved Immune System
It has been demonstrated that social connections and supportive relationships have a positive effect on an individual's immune system. Strong relationships at work can contribute to improved physical health and well-being.

- o **Research:** According to research, individuals with strong social ties have a stronger immune system. A study published in the journal Psychosomatic Medicine, for instance, found that employees with higher levels of social support in the workplace had stronger immune systems and were less susceptible to illness.
- o **Example:** A company that encouraged team-building activities, such as group exercise classes and sporting events, observed a decline in employees' ill days. Increased social connections and physical activity led to enhanced immune function and general health.
- o **Practical Tip:** Participate in team-building activities both inside and outside of the workplace to cultivate relationships and promote physical health. This may involve joining a company sports team, participating in group exercise courses, or coordinating lunchtime group excursions.

Reduced Chance of Burnout
By providing employees with a sense of belonging and a network to discuss their concerns and frustrations, supportive relationships in the workplace can help prevent exhaustion.

- o **Research:** According to a study published in the Journal of Applied Psychology, robust workplace relationships are linked to a reduced risk of exhaustion. Two critical components of burnout, emotional depletion and depersonalization, were less prevalent among employees who reported having supportive relationships with their colleagues.

- o **Example:** A software development company implemented a peer support program that encouraged employees to routinely check in with one another and provide support. As a consequence, employees felt more connected and supported, which contributed to a decline in the organization's disengagement rate.
- o **Practical Tip:** Establish a companion system or peer support network to regularly check in on colleagues, share concerns, and provide support. Employees can feel more supported and be less prone to fatigue by fostering a culture of open communication and empathy.

Superior Sleep Quality

Employees with a supportive work environment are less likely to experience work-related tension and anxiety, which can disrupt sleep.

- o **Research:** According to a study published in the journal Sleep Health, employees with greater social support at work slept better and experienced fewer sleep disturbances.
- o **Example:** A call center implemented team-building activities on a regular basis and encouraged open communication among its employees. As a result, employees reported a reduction in work-related tension and anxiety, resulting in enhanced sleep quality.
- o **Practical Tip:** To create a supportive work environment, encourage open communication and cultivate strong relationships with colleagues. By reducing tension and anxiety at work, employees are more likely to experience improved sleep quality, which contributes to their overall physical health.

By prioritizing physical health and fostering strong relationships at work, employees can experience numerous benefits, including enhanced immune system function, a reduced risk of exhaustion, and improved sleep quality. Employees and organizations can contribute to a healthier and more productive work environment by implementing practical suggestions such as engaging in team-building activities, instituting a companion system, and promoting open communication.

Increased Job Satisfaction

Strong relationships in the workplace contribute to a positive work environment, which in turn increases job satisfaction. When employees feel connected to and supported by their colleagues, they are more likely to experience job engagement and satisfaction.

- o **Research:** Numerous studies have demonstrated that workplace relationships positively affect job satisfaction. For instance, according to a study published in the Journal of Business and Psychology, employees who reported having strong connections with their colleagues reported greater job satisfaction and organizational commitment.

- **Example:** An organization that prioritized relationship building through team-building activities, open communication, and employee recognition experienced a significant increase in employee satisfaction, resulting in reduced turnover rates and increased employee engagement.
- **Practical Tip:** Schedule regular team meals, coffee breaks, and other social events to cultivate relationships between colleagues and create a more positive work environment. This can contribute to increased job satisfaction and a more engaged workforce.

Enhanced Resilience in the Face of Adversity

Supportive workplace relationships are crucial for assisting employees in overcoming obstacles and setbacks. When employees have a strong support network, they are better equipped to deal with adversity and recover from challenging situations.

- **Research:** Studies have demonstrated the significance of healthy relationships in developing resilience. Employees who reported high levels of colleague support were more resilient in the face of work-related challenges, according to a study published in the Journal of Occupational and Organizational Psychology.
- **Example:** A team working on a difficult project encountered setbacks and obstacles, but their strong relationships allowed them to support one another, share ideas, and ultimately surmount the challenges they faced.
- **Practical Tip:** Create a secure environment for colleagues to discuss challenges and provide emotional support. Encourage open communication and collaboration, which can help employees develop resilience and better manage work-related obstacles.

Emotional Intelligence Improvement

Developing emotional intelligence can also be aided by the development of strong relationships in the workplace. As employees interact with and support their colleagues, they acquire essential emotional intelligence skills, including empathy, self-awareness, and emotional regulation.

- **Research:** According to a study published in the Journal of Vocational Behavior, employees who engaged in positive social interactions at work exhibited higher levels of emotional intelligence, which was correlated with improved job performance and greater job satisfaction.
- **Example:** Manager who prioritized relationship building and promoted open communication among team members observed an increase in emotional intelligence among team members. This resulted in enhanced communication, enhanced problem-solving, and a more harmonious workplace.
- **Practical Tip:** Encourage regular discussions and feedback sessions among colleagues to aid in the development of emotional intelligence. Employees can increase their emotional intelligence and contribute to a more emotionally healthy workplace by fostering open communication and empathy.

Employees can increase their job contentment, resiliency, and emotional intelligence by concentrating on their emotional well-being and cultivating strong relationships in the workplace. Employees and organizations can create a more emotionally supportive and fulfilling work environment by implementing practical guidelines such as scheduling regular social events, creating a secure space for discussing challenges, and promoting open communication.

Enhanced Teamwork and Collaboration

Strong relationships in the workplace are crucial for fostering effective cooperation and collaboration. When employees have mutual trust and support, they are more likely to collaborate, share ideas, and achieve common objectives.

- o **Research:** Numerous studies have demonstrated the positive effects of robust workplace relationships on team performance. A study published in the Journal of Management, for instance, found that teams with high levels of trust and social cohesion were more effective at achieving their objectives and had higher levels of overall performance.
- o **Example:** An organization that prioritized relationship-building through team-building activities, open communication, and a supportive work culture saw an increase in employee productivity and collaboration. This resulted in improved problem-solving, increased work quality, and a more successful organization.
- o **Practical Tip:** Schedule regular ideation sessions, team meetings, or seminars to promote collaboration and idea sharing among colleagues. By nurturing strong relationships and trust within the team, employees can work more effectively together and produce superior results.

Increased Originality and Creativity

Additionally, supportive workplace relationships can cultivate innovation and creativity. When employees feel secure sharing their ideas and taking risks, they are more likely to generate innovative solutions and think creatively.

- o **Research:** According to research, there is a correlation between strong workplace relationships and innovative thought. Employees who felt supported by colleagues were more likely to engage in creative problem-solving and generate novel ideas, according to a study published in the Journal of Creative Behavior.
- o **Example:** A creative agency that prioritized relationship-building and open communication among its team members flourished in terms of innovation and creativity. The supportive work environment encouraged employees to share their ideas, resulting in innovative initiatives and a reputation for excellence.
- o **Practical Tip:** Encourage your team to communicate openly and share ideas. Develop a work environment in which employees feel free to take risks and

express their opinions without fear of being judged or criticized. This can contribute to the organization's creativity and innovation.

Increased Employee Retention and Motivation

Strong relationships in the workplace can increase employee retention and engagement. When employees feel connected to and supported by their colleagues, they are more likely to remain loyal to their organization and become more engaged in their work.

- o **Research:** According to a study published in the Journal of Organizational Behavior, employees who report having strong workplace relationships are more likely to remain with their organization and are more engaged at work.
- o **Example:** A company that prioritized developing strong relationships among its employees experienced lower employee attrition and greater employee engagement. This led to decreased hiring and training expenses and a more productive and successful organization overall.
- o **Practical Tip:** Invest in relationship-building initiatives such as mentorship programs, team-building activities, and open communication policies. Organizations can increase employee retention, engagement, and overall productivity by nurturing strong connections between employees.

By focusing on productivity and fostering strong relationships in the workplace, employees can experience improved coordination and collaboration, increased creativity and innovation, and increased employee retention and engagement. Employees and organizations can create a more productive and successful work environment by implementing practical suggestions such as organizing ideation sessions, promoting open communication, and investing in relationship-building efforts.

Summary & Conclusion

This chapter has examined the multifaceted advantages of establishing strong relationships in the workplace, demonstrating their impact on mental health, physical health, emotional well-being, and productivity. Fostering positive relationships between colleagues not only enhances the well-being of individual employees, but also contributes to the organization's overall success and efficiency.

In summary, effective workplace relationships can result in:

- Reduced stress and anxiety
- Enhanced self-esteem and confidence
- Improved emotional regulation
- Better immune system function
- Reduced risk of burnout
- Improved sleep quality
- Increased job satisfaction
- Greater resilience in the face of adversity
- Enhanced emotional intelligence
- More effective teamwork and collaboration
- Greater creativity and innovation
- Greater employee retention and engagement

As we have discussed, various practical tips can be implemented to foster strong relationships in the workplace, such as engaging in small talk, offering praise, creating safe spaces for emotional support, engaging in team-building activities, establishing buddy systems or peer support networks, and encouraging open communication.

In conclusion, the significance of effective workplace relationships cannot be overstated. By prioritizing relationship-building and fostering a supportive work environment, both employees and organizations can realize the many benefits of these connections, which contribute to healthier, happier, and more productive workplaces. As individuals and organizations continue to adapt and evolve in today's swiftly changing world, nurturing strong workplace relationships will continue to play a crucial role in ensuring the success of both individuals and organizations.

Chapter 34:
The Importance of Support in Building Strong Relationships

Introduction:
Why Is It So Important?

Humans are inherently social organisms that flourish on social connections. Relationship building is not only a requirement for survival, but also a prerequisite for attaining personal and professional success and sustaining mental and emotional health. Support from family, friends, and coworkers is crucial for nurturing resiliency, combating stress, anxiety, and depression, and promoting overall happiness and life satisfaction.

In this chapter, we will examine the multifaceted role that support plays in fostering healthy relationships, as well as its impact on various aspects of our lives. We will explore the positive effects of supportive relationships on mental health, physical health, emotional well-being, and productivity. In addition, we will provide real-world examples, scientific research, and practical advice to assist readers in integrating support into their daily lives and cultivating deeper, more meaningful relationships.

By recognizing the significance of support in relationship-building and incorporating these principles into our lives, we can establish a solid foundation for personal development, professional success, and enhanced mental and emotional health. This chapter seeks to equip readers with the knowledge and tools required to leverage the power of support, allowing them to lead more fulfilling, connected, and successful lives.

The Power of Support in Mental Health

Stress Reduction
Supportive relationships provide an essential buffer against stress by allowing individuals to express their emotions, release their frustrations, and seek counsel from dependable sources. Cohen and Wills (1985) found that social support can mitigate the negative effects of stress on mental health, thereby reducing the risk of depression and anxiety. By assisting individuals in navigating challenging circumstances, supportive relationships can cultivate a sense of control and mastery, further reducing tension and promoting mental health.

Developing Resilience

Strong relationships significantly increase resilience, or the ability to overcome adversity. Southwick, Sippel, Krystal, Charney, Mayes, and Pietrzak (2016) found that individuals with supportive networks are more resilient in the face of adversity, resulting in improved mental health outcomes. Individuals are more likely to view setbacks as opportunities for learning and development rather than as insurmountable obstacles when they have supportive relationships. This outlook, in turn, contributes to greater resilience and psychological health.

Social Assistance and Coping Methods

Significant role can be played by supportive relationships in the development of effective coping strategies. Individuals with strong social networks are more likely to employ adaptive coping strategies, such as problem-solving, seeking emotional support, and positive reframing, according to research (Taylor & Stanton, 2007). In contrast, maladaptive coping strategies, such as denial or substance addiction, can worsen psychological distress.

Preventing Social Isolation and Loneliness

Numerous mental health problems, such as melancholy, anxiety, and cognitive decline, have been linked to loneliness and social isolation. By offering companionship, emotional support, and a sense of belonging, supportive relationships can help prevent loneliness and social isolation. According to a study conducted by Cacioppo, Hawkley, and Thisted (2010), individuals with strong social connections experienced reduced levels of loneliness, which contributed to better mental health outcomes.

Practical Tips

- o Engage in regular communication with friends and family, such as phone calls, video chats, or in-person meetings
- o Join clubs or groups to meet like-minded people and expand your social network
- o Practice active listening and empathy when communicating with others to forge stronger bonds
- o Seek professional assistance, such as therapy or counseling, when necessary to address mental health issues.
- o Prioritize self-care and encourage your loved ones to do the same, thereby establishing a supportive environment for mental health.

The Role of Support in Physical Health

Enhanced Immune Function

Positive social relationships have been linked to enhanced immune function, which contributes to better overall health. Supportive relationships can facilitate relaxation and reduce tension, which have a direct effect on the immune system. Uchino,

Cacioppo, and Kiecolt-Glaser (1996) discovered that individuals with strong social networks had a superior immune response to stress, resulting in decreased susceptibility to illness and quicker recovery periods.

Reduced Cardiovascular Disease Risk

Additionally, supportive relationships may reduce the risk of cardiac disease, one of the primary causes of mortality worldwide. Social support is associated with lower blood pressure and less inflammation, both of which are essential for maintaining cardiovascular health, according to research (Holt-Lunstad, Smith, & Layton, 2010). In addition, people with strong social ties may be more likely to engage in health-promoting behaviors, such as regular exercise and a balanced diet, which can further reduce the risk of cardiovascular disease.

Superior Sleep Quality

Supportive relationships can have a positive effect on the quality of slumber, which is crucial for maintaining overall physical health. (Troxel, Robles, Hall, & Buysse, 2007) Research indicates that individuals with strong social connections report improved sleep quality, fewer sleep disturbances, and a lower risk of insomnia. Adequate sleep is necessary for sustaining a robust immune system, cognitive function, and emotional health, highlighting the significance of supportive relationships in promoting physical health.

Reduced Obesity Risk

Social support can contribute to obesity prevention and healthy weight management. Individuals with strong social connections are more likely to engage in regular physical activity and adopt healthier dietary practices, according to research (Christakis & Fowler, 2007). Additionally, supportive relationships can provide motivation and encouragement to maintain a healthy lifestyle, making it simpler for individuals to accomplish and maintain a healthy weight.

Practical Tips

- o   Schedule routine check-ins with loved ones to maintain ties and provide support for physical health objectives
- o   Engage in physical activities with friends or family members, such as walking, hiking, or attending exercise courses together.
- o   Encourage and support one another's health objectives, providing motivation and accountability.
- o   Share nutritious recipes and cookery advice with family and acquaintances to encourage improved nutrition
- o   Establish a network of support for weight management and physical fitness by joining a weight loss group or fitness club, for example.

Emotional Well-Being and the Importance of Support

Enhanced Self-Esteem

By providing positive feedback, encouragement, and validation, supportive relationships enhance self-esteem. This support can cultivate a sense of self-worth and confidence, which are essential for psychological health. Individuals with strong social connections report higher levels of self-esteem and self-worth, according to research (Orth, Robins, & Widaman, 2012). Individuals are better equipped to manage challenges, pursue their objectives, and maintain emotional stability when they cultivate a positive self-image.

Greater Life Contentment

Companionship, shared experiences, and emotional support are all aspects of supportive relationships that increase life satisfaction. Social connection and a sense of belonging can have a significant impact on contentment and overall life satisfaction. Diener and Seligman (2002) found that individuals with robust social networks report higher levels of contentment and life satisfaction. Individuals can create a gratifying, well-rounded existence by cultivating supportive relationships.

Enhanced Emotional Control

Relationships of support can play an essential role in the development of effective emotional regulation skills. Having a support network enables individuals to discuss their emotions, seek guidance, and receive reassurance, which can lead to improved emotional regulation. Studies have shown that individuals with strong social support are better able to manage their emotions and deal with tension, resulting in greater emotional well-being (Gross, 2002).

Promotion of Personal Growth

By offering encouragement, direction, and inspiration, supportive relationships can facilitate personal growth. Supported individuals are more likely to take risks, pursue new opportunities, and embrace change, all of which contribute to their personal development and emotional wellbeing. Individuals who view their relationships as supportive and growth-promoting are more likely to experience psychological well-being and life satisfaction, according to research (Reis, Sheldon, Gable, Roscoe, and Ryan, 2000).

Practical Tips

- Offer words of encouragement to others and accept compliments graciously to foster self-esteem.
- Share achievements and celebrate successes with friends and family, creating a culture of support and appreciation.
- Practice gratitude for the supportive people in your life, recognizing their positive impact on your emotional well-being.

o Seek out friendships and relationships that promote personal growth, challenging you to become your best self.

The Impact of Support on Productivity

Improved Problem-Solving Skills

By offering diverse perspectives, ideas, and resources, supportive relationships can improve problem-solving skills. Possessing the ability to discuss obstacles and generate potential solutions with others can result in improved decision-making and creative thinking. Individuals with strong social support are more likely to approach problems creatively and effectively, according to research (Amabile, Barsade, Mueller, & Staw, 2005). By fostering a collaborative atmosphere, supportive relationships can contribute to increased personal and professional productivity and success.

Enhanced Inspiration and Performance

Positive relationships can increase motivation and performance in both professional and private endeavors. Individuals are more likely to be engaged, productive, and successful in their careers if they feel supported by their coworkers and superiors (Saks, 2006). Moreover, the support of friends and family can provide encouragement and motivation to pursue personal objectives and interests, resulting in a greater sense of accomplishment.

Improved Learning and Skill Growth

Learning and skill development can be significantly facilitated by supportive relationships. Individuals in supportive relationships can help one another develop and improve by providing guidance, mentoring, and constructive feedback. Research demonstrates that individuals who receive encouragement and support from their social networks are more likely to acquire new skills and knowledge, which contributes to their professional and personal development (Ryan, Huta, & Deci, 2008).

Decreased Burnout and Enhancement of Work-Life Balance

By offering emotional support, practical assistance, and a sounding board for addressing challenges, supportive relationships can help mitigate the risk of exhaustion and enhance work-life balance. Studies have shown that individuals with strong social support are less likely to experience fatigue and are better able to maintain a healthy work-life balance (Halbesleben, 2006). Strong relationships can contribute to increased productivity and overall well-being by providing a foundation of support.

Practical Tips

o Collaborate with others to brainstorm solutions to challenges, fostering an environment of creativity and innovation.

- o Seek out mentorship and guidance from experienced individuals in your personal and professional networks.
- o Provide constructive feedback and encouragement to colleagues and friends to promote growth and skill development.
- o Establish boundaries between work and personal life, and encourage your support network to do the same, in order to maintain a healthy work-life balance.

Summary & Conclusion

The significance of support in establishing healthy relationships is a multifaceted and potent force that influences numerous facets of our lives, including our mental health, physical health, emotional well-being, and productivity. By comprehending the extensive benefits of supportive connections, individuals can make informed decisions to nurture and maintain strong relationships, resulting in enhanced well-being and achievement.

In conclusion, supportive relationships can offer the following advantages:

- o Reduced stress and increased resilience for better mental health o Improved immune function, lower risk of cardiovascular disease, better sleep quality, and lower risk of obesity for better physical health.
- o Increased self-esteem, life satisfaction, emotional regulation, and personal growth for greater emotional well-being
- o Enhanced problem-solving abilities, increased motivation and performance, enhanced learning and skill development, and decreased fatigue for increased productivity

To maximize these benefits, individuals should cultivate supportive relationships by maintaining open communication with loved ones, participating in group activities, seeking professional assistance when necessary, practicing gratitude, collaborating with others, and providing feedback.

Individuals can establish a solid foundation for personal and professional success, as well as enhanced mental, emotional, and physical health, by cultivating strong, supportive relationships. This chapter has provided readers with the knowledge and tools required to leverage the power of support and cultivate relationships that contribute to a more fulfilling, connected, and successful existence.

Chapter 35:
Making Building Strong Relationships a Lifelong Habit

Introduction:
Creating a Lifelong Habit

O ur relationships with others are crucial to our well-being as a whole. Strong relationships with family, friends, and coworkers provide emotional support, improve our mental health, and enable us to confront life's challenges with fortitude. It is impossible to exaggerate the significance of cultivating healthy relationships, as they serve as the foundation for a fulfilling and meaningful existence.

In today's fast-paced, technologically-driven society, it can be simple to overlook the relationships that truly matter. Nonetheless, prioritizing relationships and making a concerted effort to cultivate them is essential for experiencing greater pleasure and fulfillment. This chapter examines the myriad ways in which building and maintaining healthy relationships can enrich our lives and provides practical advice for making this a lifelong practice.

We will examine the positive effects of robust relationships on our mental health, physical health, emotional well-being, and productivity, among other aspects of our existence. By recognizing the significance of these relationships and actively striving to strengthen them, we can enhance our quality of life as a whole.

In the following sections, we will examine the research and real-world examples that demonstrate the power of strong relationships, as well as provide suggestions for incorporating relationship-building practices into your daily life. By prioritizing these relationships and cultivating a support network, you can experience enduring improvements to your mental health and well-being.

Mental Health Benefits of Strong Relationships

Reduced Stress and Anxiety
Research indicates that social support is crucial in reducing stress and anxiety levels.
- o **Example:** A study by Cohen and Wills (1985) found that individuals with strong social support networks experienced lower levels of psychological distress during stressful events.

- o **Practical Tip:** Foster a support network by reaching out to friends and family during times of stress. Share your experiences and feelings, and encourage others to do the same.

Enhanced Resilience

Strong relationships help build psychological resilience, enabling us to better cope with adversity.

- o **Example:** A study by Helliwell and Wang (2011) revealed that individuals with stronger social connections experienced faster recovery from negative life events.
- o **Practical Tip:** Regularly engage in social activities and group hobbies to maintain a network of supportive connections. This can include joining clubs, volunteering, or participating in community events.

Improved Mood and Mental Well-being

Positive relationships can enhance our overall mood and contribute to better mental well-being.

- o **Example:** A study by House, Landis, and Umberson (1988) found that individuals with strong social connections reported fewer depressive symptoms and enjoyed better mental health.
- o **Practical Tip:** Schedule regular catch-ups with friends and family, whether it's a phone call, video chat, or meeting in person. This will help to maintain strong connections and improve your overall mood.

Boosted Self-esteem and Confidence

Having strong relationships can contribute to increased self-esteem and confidence.

- o **Example:** A study by Leary, Tambor, Terdal, and Downs (1995) found that individuals with higher self-esteem tend to have stronger, more supportive relationships.
- o **Practical Tip:** Cultivate relationships with people who uplift and encourage you. Surrounding yourself with a supportive network will help boost your self-esteem and confidence.

Enhanced Coping Skills and Emotional Regulation

Nurturing relationships can help us develop better coping skills and emotional regulation during challenging times.

- o **Example:** A study by Lakey and Cronin (2008) revealed that individuals who have supportive relationships are more likely to effectively cope with stressors and regulate their emotions.
- o **Practical Tip:** Practice open communication with your support network to discuss difficult emotions and seek advice on coping strategies. This can lead to better emotional regulation and overall mental health.

By understanding the mental health benefits of strong relationships, we can see the value in prioritizing these connections and fostering a supportive network. Engaging in social activities, nurturing supportive relationships, and maintaining open communication can significantly improve our mental well-being and overall quality of life.

Physical Health Benefits of Strong Relationships

Improved Immune Function

Positive relationships are associated with better immune function and overall health.

- o **Example:** A study by Uchino et al. (1996) found that individuals with strong social networks had lower levels of inflammation and better immune system functioning.
- o **Practical Tip:** Stay connected with loved ones to boost your immune system. Engage in regular social interactions, such as group activities, to maintain strong connections and promote physical health.

Longer Life Expectancy

Research demonstrates that strong relationships can increase life expectancy.

- o **Example:** A meta-analysis by Holt-Lunstad et al. (2010) concluded that individuals with strong social connections have a 50% increased likelihood of survival.
- o **Practical Tip:** Prioritize spending quality time with friends and family to promote longevity. Make a conscious effort to nurture relationships and maintain a strong support network.

Lower Risk of Cardiovascular Disease

Strong social connections can contribute to a reduced risk of cardiovascular disease.

- o **Example:** A study by Orth-Gomér et al. (1993) found that individuals with strong social networks were less likely to develop coronary heart disease.
- o **Practical Tip:** Engage in social activities that promote heart health, such as group exercise classes or outdoor activities with friends and family. This can help maintain strong relationships while also benefiting physical health.

Better Pain Management

Positive relationships can help with the management of chronic pain and improve overall physical health.

- o **Example:** A study by Brown et al. (2003) found that individuals with strong social support reported less pain and disability associated with chronic pain conditions.
- o **Practical Tip:** Reach out to friends and family when experiencing pain and seek their support. Sharing your experiences and receiving emotional support can help improve pain management and overall well-being.

Healthier Lifestyle Choices
Strong relationships can promote healthier lifestyle choices, such as better eating habits and increased physical activity.

- o **Example:** A study by Christakis and Fowler (2007) found that individuals are more likely to adopt healthy habits when they have a strong social network that supports and engages in these behaviors.
- o **Practical Tip:** Collaborate with friends and family to set health goals, share recipes, and participate in physical activities together. By fostering strong relationships, you can motivate each other to make healthier choices.

The physical health benefits of strong relationships are wide-ranging and can significantly impact our overall well-being. By cultivating and maintaining strong social connections, we can experience improved immune function, increased life expectancy, reduced risk of chronic diseases, better pain management, and healthier lifestyle choices. Prioritizing relationships and engaging in social activities can have lasting positive effects on our physical health and quality of life.

Emotional Well-Being Benefits of Strong Relationships

Greater Happiness and Life Satisfaction
Strong relationships contribute significantly to our overall happiness and life satisfaction.

- o **Example:** A study by Diener and Seligman (2002) found that individuals with strong social connections consistently reported higher levels of happiness and life satisfaction.
- o **Practical Tip:** Invest in deepening existing relationships and forming new connections to boost overall well-being. Share positive experiences and celebrate each other's achievements to strengthen bonds and increase happiness.

Improved Emotional Intelligence
Positive relationships help us develop emotional intelligence, empathy, and understanding of others.

- o **Example:** A study by Lopes et al. (2004) found that individuals who are socially skilled are better at managing their own and others' emotions.
- o **Practical Tip:** Practice active listening and empathetic communication with friends and family to enhance emotional intelligence. Seek feedback on your emotional understanding and support skills, and work on improving them.

Sense of Belonging and Social Identity
Strong relationships foster a sense of belonging and a positive social identity, which can lead to increased emotional well-being.

- o **Example:** A study by Baumeister and Leary (1995) found that feeling a sense of belonging and social connectedness is essential for psychological well-being.

- o **Practical Tip:** Engage in activities and communities that share your interests and values. This can help create a sense of belonging and develop meaningful relationships with like-minded individuals.

Emotional Support and Validation

Nurturing relationships provide emotional support and validation, which can help enhance our emotional well-being.

- o **Example:** A study by Thoits (2011) found that social support can buffer the impact of stress on mental health and promote emotional well-being.
- o **Practical Tip:** Offer emotional support and validation to friends and family members in need. Actively listen, empathize, and share your own experiences to create a supportive and validating environment.

Reduced Loneliness and Isolation

Strong relationships can help combat feelings of loneliness and social isolation, leading to improved emotional well-being.

- o **Example:** A study by Cacioppo et al. (2006) found that individuals with strong social connections reported lower levels of loneliness and social isolation.
- o **Practical Tip**: Make an effort to regularly connect with friends, family, and acquaintances, both online and offline. Attend social events and engage in activities that encourage interaction to reduce feelings of loneliness and isolation.

By focusing on the emotional well-being benefits of strong relationships, we can appreciate the importance of cultivating and maintaining these connections throughout our lives. Strong relationships lead to greater happiness, improved emotional intelligence, a sense of belonging, emotional support, and reduced loneliness. By actively nurturing our relationships and engaging in activities that foster connection, we can enhance our emotional well-being and overall life satisfaction.

Productivity Benefits of Strong Relationships

Enhanced Teamwork and Collaboration

Strong relationships at work can lead to increased productivity and better team dynamics.

- o **Example:** A study by Sias (2009) found that individuals who had positive relationships with coworkers experienced higher levels of job satisfaction and productivity.
- o **Practical Tip:** Engage in team-building activities and develop rapport with coworkers to improve workplace relationships. Foster a collaborative environment by openly sharing ideas and encouraging input from others.

Improved Creativity and Innovation

Positive relationships can lead to the exchange of ideas and foster creativity and innovation.

- o **Example:** A study by Perry-Smith and Shalley (2003) revealed that individuals who had diverse social networks were more likely to generate creative ideas.
- o **Practical Tip:** Expand your social circle and engage with people from different backgrounds and fields to spark new ideas and perspectives. Create opportunities for brainstorming sessions with diverse groups of individuals.

Enhanced Problem-solving Abilities

Strong relationships can improve our problem-solving abilities, as we can draw on the support and knowledge of others.

- o **Example:** A study by Anderson and Rodin (1989) found that individuals with strong social connections were more likely to effectively solve problems.
- o **Practical Tip:** Seek input and advice from friends, family, and colleagues when faced with challenges. Approach problems collaboratively to benefit from diverse perspectives and experiences.

Greater Motivation and Goal Achievement

Positive relationships can foster motivation and support in achieving personal and professional goals.

- o **Example:** A study by Locke and Latham (2002) found that individuals who received support from others were more likely to persist in their goals and achieve success.
- o **Practical Tip:** Share your goals with your support network and ask for encouragement, accountability, and feedback. Offer support and motivation to others in return, fostering strong relationships that enable goal achievement.

Reduced Workplace Stress and Burnout

Strong relationships in the workplace can help mitigate stress and prevent burnout, leading to improved productivity and job satisfaction.

- o **Example:** A study by Halbesleben (2006) found that social support from colleagues and supervisors was associated with reduced burnout and increased job satisfaction.
- o **Practical Tip:** Cultivate positive relationships with your coworkers and supervisors by engaging in open communication, offering support, and expressing appreciation. Encourage a culture of mutual support and understanding to minimize workplace stress and burnout.

The productivity benefits of strong relationships are substantial, both personally and professionally. By fostering strong connections with coworkers, friends, and family, we can enhance teamwork, creativity, problem-solving abilities, motivation, and reduce workplace stress. Actively nurturing these relationships and creating a supportive environment can lead to increased productivity and overall success in various aspects of our lives.

Summary & Conclusion: The Lasting Impact of Strong Relationships

In this chapter, we have examined the numerous ways in which establishing and maintaining strong relationships can have a significant impact on our mental health, physical health, emotional well-being, and productivity. By recognizing the significance of these relationships, we can prioritize their maintenance and make relationship-building a lifelong practice.

Strong relationships are beneficial to mental health because they reduce tension and anxiety, increase resilience, temperament, self-esteem, and coping skills. Strong relationships result in enhanced immune function, a longer life expectancy, a reduced risk of cardiovascular disease, enhanced pain management, and healthier lifestyle choices. Emotionally, nurturing relationships contribute to greater contentment, enhanced emotional intelligence, a sense of belonging, emotional support, and a decrease in loneliness. Strong relationships boost productivity by enhancing collaboration, creativity, problem-solving skills, motivation, and lowering workplace tension and exhaustion.

Practical guidelines and strategies, such as engaging in social activities, open communication, providing support, and promoting a collaborative environment, can aid in the development and maintenance of relationships. By prioritizing these relationships, we enhance not only our own quality of life but also that of those around us.

In conclusion, for our success and well-being as a whole, it is essential that we develop a lifelong habit of fostering strong relationships. By recognizing the significance of these relationships and actively cultivating them, we can improve all facets of our lives and create a network of support that benefits both ourselves and others.

Section V. Seeking Professional Help

Chapter 36:
Understanding When it's Time to Seek Professional Help

Introduction:
Seeking Help

The path to maintaining mental health can be difficult and convoluted. Frequently, navigating the ups and downs of daily life requires a delicate balance of self-care, support from friends and family, and the awareness of when additional assistance is required. Although it is common to experience periods of emotional distress or conflict, there are times when seeking professional assistance is not only beneficial, but essential for our well-being as a whole.

In this chapter, we will examine the significance of knowing when to seek the assistance of a mental health professional. By examining the key indicators of the need for professional assistance, we hope to empower individuals to take command of their mental health and make informed decisions regarding their care. Additionally, we will discuss the numerous advantages of seeking professional assistance, such as improved mental and physical health, enhanced emotional well-being, and increased productivity. To further assist readers, we will provide real-world examples and scientific studies that support the value of professional intervention, as well as suggestions for incorporating this information into daily life.

The purpose of this chapter is to equip readers with the tools and knowledge required to recognize when they or a loved one may require professional assistance, and to provide guidance on how to pursue and make the most of such assistance. In doing so, we aim to contribute to a greater comprehension and acceptance of mental health issues and to encourage individuals to make their well-being a priority in all aspects of their lives.

Identifying the Signs
Recognizing when to seek professional assistance is essential for maintaining optimal mental health. In this section, we will elaborate on the main signs that may indicate the need for mental health professional intervention.

Chronic and incapacitating symptoms
It is essential to pay attention to mental and emotional symptoms that interfere with your daily life and are persistent. Possible symptoms include:

- Several weeks or longer of persistent melancholy, hopelessness, or despair
- Persistent anxiety, concern, or fear that impairs your ability to function normally
- Abrupt and severe mood fluctuations or irritability that interfere with your relationships or ability to manage daily stressors.
- Physical symptoms that cannot be attributed to a medical condition, including chronic migraines, stomachaches, and muscle tension.

Difficulty with Daily Activities

When mental health issues begin to interfere with daily life, it is crucial to consider seeking assistance. Some indicators of impaired functioning may include:

- Difficulty performing at work or school, including a decline in performance, attendance, or motivation
- Withdrawal from social activities or relationships, resulting in isolation and loneliness o Loss of interest in pastimes or activities that once provided pleasure and fulfillment
- Alterations in appetite or sleep patterns, including gorging, undereating, insomnia, and oversleeping.

Danger to Oneself or Others

When mental health issues pose a threat to your or others' welfare, it is imperative to seek professional assistance immediately. Among the warning indicators to watch out for are:

- Thoughts of self-harm or suicide, or making a plan to end your life o Engaging in hazardous or impulsive behavior that places you or others at risk, such as irresponsible driving, unprotected sex, or excessive spending
- Substance abuse or addiction, including increased reliance on alcohol or narcotics to manage with emotional distress
- Indications of self- or other-directed aggression, violence, or abuse, including verbal, emotional, or physical abuse

Alterations in Perception or Actuality

Mental health issues can sometimes result in altered perceptions of reality, which may necessitate professional intervention. These symptoms might include:

- Experiencing hallucinations, including hearing voices or seeing nonexistent objects.
- Exhibiting delusional thoughts or beliefs that are not grounded in reality and are resistant to rational persuasion
- Disorganized thinking, speech, or behavior that hinders your ability to communicate or function effectively.

By attentively monitoring your mental health and remaining aware of these indicators, you can make an informed decision regarding when to seek professional assistance. Remember that early intervention is the key to attaining the greatest mental health outcomes attainable.

Benefits to Seeking Professional Help

Recognizing the need for professional assistance and taking the initiative to pursue it can be transformative. In this section, we will discuss the numerous mental health, physical health, emotional well-being, and productivity benefits of engaging with a mental health professional.

Mental Wellness

- **Accurate Diagnosis and Treatment:** A mental health professional can conduct a thorough evaluation that leads to an accurate diagnosis of any underlying mental health disorders. This permits the implementation of individualized treatment plans, which may consist of therapy, medication, or a combination of the two.
- **Improved Coping Skills and Resilience:** Therapy can assist in the development of healthier coping mechanisms to manage stress and adversity, thereby fostering resilience and emotional fortitude.
- **Reduced Stigma:** Seeking professional assistance can normalize conversations about mental health, reducing stigma and encouraging others to prioritize their own health.

Physical Wellness

- **Mind-Body Connection:** Consulting a mental health professional can help you comprehend the relationship between your mental and physical health, allowing you to address both aspects of your wellbeing.
- **Better Sleep and Fewer Physical Symptoms:** As your mental health improves, you may experience better sleep and fewer physical symptoms related to stress or anxiety, such as migraines or gastrointestinal problems.
- **increased Immune System Function:** According to studies, increased mental health can result in a stronger immune system, making you less susceptible to illness and facilitating a quicker recovery if you do become unwell.

Psychological Well-Being

- **Enhanced Self-Awareness**: Therapy can help you acquire a deeper understanding of your emotions, thought patterns, and behaviors, fostering enhanced self-awareness and personal development.

- ○ **Strengthened Relationships and Communication Skills:** Working with a mental health professional can improve your emotional intelligence and communication skills, resulting in more fulfilling and supportive relationships.
- ○ **Greater Sense of Empowerment and Control:** Seeking professional assistance can impart a sense of empowerment and control over your emotions, allowing you to make positive life changes and build a brighter future.

Productivity

- ○ **Increased Focus and Mental Clarity:** As your mental health improves, you may experience increased focus and mental clarity, allowing you to be more productive and successful in your personal and professional lives.
- ○ **Improved Capacity to Manage Stress** Therapy can help you maintain a healthy work-life balance and prevent exhaustion by teaching you effective stress management techniques.
- ○ **Greater Overall Life Satisfaction:** The combination of enhanced mental health, physical health, and emotional well-being can result in a greater sense of overall life satisfaction and fulfillment.

By understanding the numerous advantages of seeking professional assistance, you can make informed decisions regarding your mental health care and seize the opportunity to improve your overall health.

Real-Life Examples and Scientific Studies

The benefits of seeking professional help for mental health concerns are supported by numerous real-life examples and scientific studies. In this section, we will provide a deeper understanding of the effectiveness of therapy and its impact on individuals' lives, as well as the broader implications of mental health on overall well-being.

Real-Life Examples

- ○ **Case Study 1:** A young adult struggling with social anxiety sought professional help after years of avoiding social situations and experiencing severe anxiety during public speaking events. Through cognitive-behavioral therapy (CBT), they learned to identify and challenge irrational thoughts, as well as develop relaxation techniques to manage anxiety. Over time, they reported significant improvements in their confidence and ability to engage in social situations without overwhelming anxiety.
- ○ **Case Study 2:** A middle-aged individual with a history of depression sought professional help after a significant life event triggered a severe depressive episode. Through a combination of therapy and medication, they were able to address the underlying issues contributing to their depression and regain a sense of stability and hope for the future.

- **Case Study 3:** A couple experiencing communication difficulties and escalating conflicts sought couples' therapy to address their issues. Through therapy, they learned effective communication skills, identified negative patterns in their relationship, and worked collaboratively to create a healthier, more supportive partnership.

Scientific Studies

- **Efficacy of Therapy:** A comprehensive review of multiple studies found that therapy, particularly cognitive-behavioral therapy (CBT), is effective in treating a wide range of mental health conditions, including anxiety disorders, depression, and post-traumatic stress disorder (PTSD) (Hofmann, Asnaani, Vonk, Sawyer, & Fang, 2012).
- **Connection Between Mental and Physical Health:** Research has shown that individuals with mental health disorders are more likely to experience physical health problems, such as heart disease, diabetes, and chronic pain (Prince et al., 2007). Conversely, addressing mental health issues through therapy has been shown to improve physical health outcomes (Scott et al., 2016).
- **Workplace Productivity and Mental Health:** A study conducted by the World Health Organization (WHO) estimated that depression and anxiety disorders cost the global economy $1 trillion per year in lost productivity. The study also found that for every $1 invested in scaling up treatment for common mental health disorders, there is a return of $4 in improved health and productivity (Chisholm et al., 2016).

These real-life examples and scientific studies underscore the value of seeking professional help for mental health concerns. By understanding the potential impact of therapy on individuals' lives and overall well-being, you can feel confident in your decision to pursue professional support when needed.

Practical Tips for Incorporating into Your Daily Routine

Recognizing when it's time to seek professional help is just the first step in prioritizing your mental health. In this section, we will provide practical tips and strategies for incorporating this knowledge into your daily routine and making the most of your mental health care journey.

Recognize the Signs
- **Regular Self-Assessment:** Take time to regularly assess your mental health and emotional well-being, paying attention to any changes in mood, behavior, or functioning.
- **Feedback from Loved Ones:** Listen to feedback from friends and family members who may notice signs of distress or changes in your behavior that you may not recognize yourself.

Research Mental Health Professionals
- **Types of Therapy:** Explore different types of therapy and therapeutic approaches, such as cognitive-behavioral therapy, psychodynamic therapy, or acceptance and commitment therapy, to determine which might be the best fit for you.
- **Consult with Your Primary Care Physician:** Your primary care physician can be a valuable resource for referrals to mental health professionals or recommendations for the most appropriate treatment options.

Overcome Barriers to Seeking Help
- **Financial Concerns:** Investigate insurance coverage for mental health services, inquire about sliding scale fees, or explore low-cost therapy options available through community mental health centers.
- **Logistical Issues:** Address scheduling conflicts or transportation challenges by seeking out therapists who offer evening or weekend appointments, or consider the option of teletherapy or online counseling.
- **Confront Stigma and Fear:** Educate yourself about the benefits of therapy and engage in open conversations about mental health to normalize the process of seeking help and dispel any fears or misconceptions.

Establish a Support Network
- **Communicate with Friends and Family:** Share your mental health journey with trusted friends and family members, who can provide encouragement and support throughout the process.
- **Join Support Groups or Online Communities:** Connect with others who share similar experiences by participating in local support groups or joining online mental health forums and communities.

Practice Self-Care and Maintain Mental Health

- ○ **Prioritize Self-Care:** Incorporate self-care practices into your daily routine, such as exercise, healthy eating, and relaxation techniques, to support your mental health and overall well-being.
- ○ **Stay Engaged in Therapy:** Attend therapy sessions consistently and actively participate in the process, applying the skills and insights gained during sessions to your everyday life.
- ○ **Monitor Progress and Adjust as Needed:** Continuously evaluate your progress in therapy and communicate with your mental health professional to adjust your treatment plan as needed, ensuring that you receive the most effective care possible.

By integrating these practical tips into your daily routine, you can take a proactive approach to your mental health, making informed decisions about when to seek professional help and maximizing the benefits of your mental health care journey.

Summary & Conclusion

Understanding when to seek professional aid for mental health issues is crucial for achieving and maintaining optimal health. Individuals can take command of their mental health and make informed decisions about their care by recognizing the signs that indicate the need for professional intervention and the numerous benefits of engaging with a mental health professional.

This chapter has provided an overview of the key signs to look for, the benefits of seeking professional assistance, real-world examples and scientific studies that support the value of therapy, as well as suggestions for incorporating this knowledge into your daily life. You can cultivate greater emotional resilience, improve your overall quality of life, and strengthen your relationships by maintaining awareness of your mental health and proactively pursuing assistance when necessary.

The decision to seek professional assistance is ultimately a personal one that requires self-awareness, candor, and fortitude. By taking this action, you are not only prioritizing your own mental health and well-being, but you are also contributing to a larger culture of mental health awareness, acceptance, and support. Remember that you are not alone on this voyage as you accept the opportunity to pursue the assistance you need.

Chapter 37:
Different Types of Mental Health Professionals and What They Do

Introduction:
Who Are They & How Can They Help?

In recent years, society has become more aware of the influence that mental health has on overall quality of life, resulting in a growing appreciation for the significance of mental health. At various periods in their lives, many individuals may require the assistance of mental health practitioners, whether to manage stress, navigate difficult relationships, or resolve a specific mental health concern. Those seeking assistance may find it difficult to distinguish between the various categories of mental health professionals and their respective functions.

In this chapter, we will elucidate the world of mental health professionals by providing an in-depth overview of their qualifications, responsibilities, and areas of expertise. We will discuss the advantages of seeking professional assistance for mental health issues, including the potential benefits to physical health, emotional well-being, and productivity. In addition, we will provide real-world examples, scientific studies, and practical advice to illustrate how incorporating mental health care into daily routines can lead to a happier, healthier, and more fulfilling existence.

By obtaining a deeper comprehension of the various types of mental health professionals and their roles, readers will be better equipped to make informed decisions regarding their own mental health care and advocate for the support they require. This knowledge can empower individuals to take charge of their health and enhance their quality of life as a whole.

Types of Mental Health Professionals and Their Roles

Understanding the various types of mental health professionals and their roles is essential for those seeking help, as each professional has specific training, qualifications, and expertise. This section will provide a detailed overview of the main types of mental health professionals, highlighting their unique roles and responsibilities in supporting individuals with their mental health concerns.

Psychologists

- **Definition and Qualifications:** Psychologists hold a doctoral degree (Ph.D. or Psy.D.) in psychology and are trained in the assessment, diagnosis, and treatment of mental health disorders. They are often required to complete a supervised internship and pass a licensure exam.
- **Roles and Responsibilities:** Psychologists provide psychotherapy, administer psychological assessments, and conduct research on mental health topics. They work in various settings, including private practice, hospitals, schools, and research institutions.
- **Clinical, Counseling, and Research Psychologists:** Clinical psychologists focus on the assessment and treatment of severe mental health disorders, while counseling psychologists focus on helping individuals with everyday problems and stressors. Research psychologists' study mental health topics and contribute to the development of evidence-based treatments.
- **Evidence-Based Treatments and Therapy Modalities:** Psychologists may use a variety of therapy modalities, such as cognitive-behavioral therapy (CBT), dialectical behavior therapy (DBT), and psychodynamic therapy, depending on their clients' needs.
- **Practical Tip:** When searching for a psychologist, consider their specialization and expertise in relation to your specific needs. For example, if you are struggling with an eating disorder, look for a psychologist with experience in treating eating disorders.

Psychiatrists

- **Definition and Qualifications:** Psychiatrists are medical doctors (M.D. or D.O.) who specialize in psychiatry, the branch of medicine focused on mental health disorders. They complete a medical degree and a residency in psychiatry.
- **Roles and Responsibilities:** Psychiatrists diagnose and treat mental health disorders, often through the use of medications. They may also provide psychotherapy, although their primary focus is on the biological aspects of mental health.
- **Medical Treatments and Medications for Mental Health Disorders:** Psychiatrists prescribe medications such as antidepressants, mood stabilizers, and antipsychotics to help manage symptoms of mental health disorders.
- **Collaboration with other Mental Health Professionals:** Psychiatrists often work in collaboration with other mental health professionals, such as psychologists and therapists, to provide comprehensive care for their clients.
- **Practical Tip:** Consider seeing a psychiatrist if you think medication may be a helpful addition to your mental health treatment plan, or if you have concerns about the biological aspects of your mental health.

Licensed Clinical Social Workers (LCSWs)

- **Definition and Qualifications:** LCSWs hold a master's degree in social work (MSW) and are licensed to provide mental health services. They complete supervised clinical experience and pass a licensure exam.
- **Roles and Responsibilities:** LCSWs provide therapy, case management, and crisis intervention services to individuals and families. They work in various settings, including private practice, hospitals, and community organizations.
- **Support for Individuals and Families in Various Settings:** LCSWs support clients in navigating life challenges and coping with mental health concerns, often with a focus on the social and environmental factors contributing to their clients' well-being.
- **Advocacy and Connecting Clients to Resources:** LCSWs help clients access resources such as housing, financial assistance, and healthcare services, and may advocate for policy changes that support mental health.
- **Practical Tip:** Seek the help of an LCSW if you need assistance navigating complex systems, accessing resources, or addressing social and environmental factors affecting your mental health.

Marriage and Family Therapists (MFTs)

- **Definition and Qualifications:** MFTs hold a master's degree in marriage and family therapy or a related field and are licensed to provide mental health services. They complete supervised clinical experience and pass a licensure exam.
- **Roles and Responsibilities:** MFTs specialize in providing therapy for couples and families, addressing relationship issues and family dynamics that contribute to mental health concerns.
- **Couples and Family Therapy Approaches:** MFTs utilize therapy approaches such as Emotionally Focused Therapy (EFT), Gottman Method, and Structural Family Therapy to help clients improve communication, resolve conflicts, and strengthen their relationships.
- **Addressing Relationship and Family Dynamics:** MFTs work with clients to address underlying relationship issues, such as trust, intimacy, and communication, that may contribute to mental health concerns or impact overall well-being.
- **Practical Tip:** Consider seeking the help of an MFT if you are experiencing relationship difficulties, want to improve family dynamics, or need support in addressing issues affecting your partner or family members.

Licensed Professional Counselors (LPCs)

- **Definition and Qualifications:** LPCs hold a master's degree in counseling or a related field and are licensed to provide mental health services. They complete supervised clinical experience and pass a licensure exam.
- **Roles and Responsibilities:** LPCs provide individual and group counseling services for a wide range of mental health concerns, including stress management, anxiety, depression, and trauma.
- **Areas of Specialization:** LPCs may specialize in specific areas, such as substance abuse counseling, trauma-informed therapy, or career counseling, based on their education, training, and experience.
- **Practical Tip:** When choosing an LPC, consider their areas of specialization and how they align with your specific needs. For example, if you are struggling with substance abuse, seek an LPC with expertise in addiction counseling.

By understanding the distinct roles and expertise of different mental health professionals, you can make informed decisions about the type of support that best meets your needs. This knowledge empowers you to take control of your mental health journey and seek the appropriate help to improve your overall well-being.

Benefits of Seeking Professional Help for Mental Health

Seeking professional help for mental health concerns is an important step towards improving overall well-being. Mental health professionals possess the knowledge and skills necessary to provide support, guidance, and evidence-based treatments tailored to an individual's unique needs. In this section, we will discuss the various benefits of seeking professional help for mental health, including improved mental health, physical health, emotional well-being, and productivity.

Improved Mental Health

- **Reducing Symptoms of Mental Health Disorders:** Mental health professionals can help individuals manage and reduce symptoms of mental health disorders, such as anxiety, depression, and PTSD, through targeted interventions and therapy.
- **Building Resilience and Coping Strategies:** Therapy can help individuals develop effective coping strategies and build resilience, enabling them to better handle stressors and challenges in their lives.
- **Real-Life Example:** Through therapy, a person with social anxiety may learn techniques to manage their anxiety, improve their self-esteem, and gradually increase their comfort in social situations.
- **Scientific Study:** Research has shown that cognitive-behavioral therapy (CBT) is an effective treatment for various mental health conditions, such as anxiety, depression, and obsessive-compulsive disorder (OCD).

Physical Health Benefits

- **Connection Between Mental and Physical Health:** Mental health and physical health are interconnected, with research showing that untreated mental health issues can contribute to the development or worsening of physical health problems.
- **Improved Sleep, Appetite, and Overall Well-Being:** By addressing mental health concerns, individuals may experience improvements in sleep quality, appetite regulation, and overall physical well-being.
- **Real-Life Example:** A person with depression might experience fatigue and loss of appetite, but through therapy and medication, they may see improvements in both their mood and physical health symptoms.
- **Scientific Study:** Research has demonstrated that mental health treatment can lead to positive physical health outcomes, such as reduced inflammation, lower blood pressure, and better immune system functioning.

Emotional Well-Being

- **Increased Self-Awareness and Emotional Intelligence:** Therapy can help individuals increase their self-awareness and emotional intelligence, allowing them to better understand their own emotions and the emotions of others.
- **Improved Relationships and Communication Skills:** By addressing emotional issues and improving communication skills, therapy can lead to healthier, more satisfying relationships with friends, family, and romantic partners.
- **Real-Life Example:** Couples therapy can help partners rebuild trust and intimacy, resulting in a stronger, more fulfilling relationship.
- **Scientific Study:** Studies have shown that therapy can enhance emotional well-being by improving emotional regulation, reducing negative emotions, and increasing positive emotions.

Productivity and Success

- **Overcoming Barriers to Personal and Professional Success:** Therapy can help individuals identify and address barriers to success, such as procrastination, self-doubt, or poor time management.
- **Building Healthy Habits and Routines:** Mental health professionals can assist clients in developing healthy habits and routines that contribute to increased productivity and success in both personal and professional domains.
- **Real-Life Example:** A person struggling with work-related stress may learn stress management techniques in therapy, leading to improved work performance and job satisfaction.
- **Scientific Study:** Research has shown that mental health interventions can have a positive impact on workplace productivity by reducing absenteeism, presenteeism, and job turnover.

By seeking professional help for mental health concerns, individuals can experience a wide range of benefits that extend beyond the alleviation of symptoms. Improved mental health, physical health, emotional well-being, and productivity are all potential outcomes of engaging in therapy or other mental health services. These benefits highlight the importance of addressing mental health concerns and taking proactive steps to improve overall well-being.

Incorporating Mental Health Care into Daily Life

Taking care of one's mental health is an essential component of maintaining overall well-being. Incorporating mental health care into daily life can be a proactive approach to addressing concerns before they become more significant problems. In this section, we will discuss various strategies for recognizing the need for help, finding the right mental health professional, and balancing mental health care with daily responsibilities.

Recognizing the Need for Help

- **Identifying Signs of Mental Health Concerns:** Be aware of changes in mood, behavior, or functioning that may indicate a need for professional support. This can include persistent feelings of sadness or anxiety, withdrawal from activities or relationships, or difficulties with concentration or decision-making.
- **Overcoming Stigma and Seeking Help Early:** It is essential to challenge the stigma surrounding mental health and recognize that seeking help is a sign of strength and self-awareness. Early intervention can lead to better outcomes and prevent more severe issues from developing.
- **Practical Tip:** Utilize self-assessment tools and resources available online or through mental health organizations to better understand your mental health needs and recognize when professional help may be beneficial.

Finding the Right Mental Health Professional

- **Researching Different Types of Professionals:** Understanding the various types of mental health professionals and their roles can help you determine which professional is best suited to address your specific needs and concerns.
- **Asking for Recommendations and Reading Reviews:** Seek recommendations from friends, family, or healthcare providers, and read reviews or testimonials to gain insight into a mental health professional's expertise and approach.
- **Practical Tip:** Interview potential therapists by asking about their experience, areas of specialization, and treatment approach to ensure a good fit for your needs and preferences.

Balancing Mental Health Care with Daily Life

- o **Scheduling Appointments and Prioritizing Self-Care:** Make mental health care a priority by scheduling appointments during times that work best for you, and try to maintain consistency in attending sessions.
- o **Building a Support Network and Using Resources: In** addition to seeking professional help, establish a support network of friends, family, and community resources that can provide additional guidance and encouragement in your mental health journey.
- o **Practical Tip:** Utilize teletherapy and digital mental health tools to access care more conveniently, especially if you have a busy schedule or limited access to in-person services. Many mental health professionals offer virtual appointments, and there are numerous apps and online resources available to support mental health and well-being.

Incorporating mental health care into your daily life is an ongoing process that requires commitment and self-awareness. By recognizing the need for help, finding the right mental health professional, and balancing mental health care with other responsibilities, you can take control of your mental health and make lasting improvements in your overall well-being.

Summary & Conclusion

Understanding the various categories of mental health professionals and their respective functions is a crucial first step in seeking assistance and support for mental health issues. By learning about the credentials and areas of expertise of psychologists, psychiatrists, licensed clinical social workers, marriage and family therapists, and licensed professional counselors, individuals can make well-informed decisions regarding the type of assistance that will best suit their individual requirements.

There are numerous advantages to seeking professional assistance for mental health issues, including improved mental and physical health, enhanced emotional well-being, and increased productivity and success. Individuals can take proactive measures to improve their well-being by recognizing the need for assistance, locating the appropriate mental health professional, and incorporating mental health care into daily life.

This chapter has provided an overview of various mental health professionals, the advantages of seeking professional assistance, and suggestions for incorporating mental health care into daily life. By obtaining a greater comprehension of these topics, readers will be better able to advocate for their own mental health needs and make informed decisions regarding their care. Individuals can experience long-lasting improvements in their overall well-being and quality of life if they receive the appropriate support and resources on their voyage toward enhanced mental health.

Chapter 38:
How to Find and Work with a Mental Health Professional

Introduction:
Finding Your Professional

Mental health is an essential component of our well-being, influencing numerous facets of our lives, such as our relationships, work performance, and physical health. Although society has made significant advances in reducing the stigma associated with mental health, many individuals are still reluctant to seek assistance for mental health issues. This reluctance may originate from a lack of comprehension about the therapeutic process, a dread of being judged, or a lack of clarity regarding how to locate the appropriate mental health professional. Regardless of the reason, it is essential to comprehend the significance of seeking assistance when necessary and how to navigate the process.

The purpose of this chapter is to provide exhaustive advice on locating the appropriate mental health professional and collaborating with them to achieve your desired outcomes. We will discuss the various categories of mental health professionals, their areas of expertise, and how to select the most appropriate professional for your specific requirements. In addition, we will discuss the practical aspects of therapy, including costs, insurance coverage, and scheduling.

To better illustrate the significance of mental health care, we will examine the advantages of therapy in terms of mental health, physical health, emotional well-being, and productivity. These benefits will be supported by real-world examples, scientific studies, and practical advice for incorporating therapy into your daily life.

Our mission is to equip you with the knowledge and resources you need to confidently embark on your therapeutic journey and attain a healthier, more fulfilling existence. By comprehending the process of locating and collaborating with a mental health professional, you can be an active participant in your mental health care and experience the transformative effects of therapy.

Identifying Your Needs and Mental Health Concerns

Understanding your needs and mental health concerns is the first step in finding the right mental health professional to guide you on your journey to wellness. This section will help you identify your symptoms, determine the urgency of your needs, and consider your preferences in therapy styles and treatment goals.

Self-Assessment

Reflect on your emotions, thoughts, and behaviors: Pay attention to any patterns, recurring thoughts, or emotional states that are causing distress or impacting your daily functioning. Journaling or talking to someone you trust can be helpful in exploring your feelings and concerns.

- **Recognize Your Mental Health Symptoms and Concerns:** Familiarize yourself with common mental health disorders and their symptoms. If you notice that your experiences align with a specific disorder, such as depression or anxiety, make a note of it to discuss with a professional.
- **Determine the Urgency of Your Needs:** Evaluate the severity and duration of your symptoms. Are they causing significant distress or impairing your ability to function in daily life? If so, seeking help sooner rather than later is essential.

Consider Your Preferences

- **Therapy Styles:** Different mental health professionals may utilize various therapy approaches, such as cognitive-behavioral therapy (CBT) or psychodynamic therapy. Research the different styles to determine which one resonates with you and aligns with your needs.
- **Treatment Goals:** Consider what you hope to achieve through therapy. Do you want to develop better coping skills, improve your relationships, or overcome specific fears or phobias? Having a clear idea of your goals will help you find a professional who can tailor their approach to meet your objectives.

Types of Mental Health Professionals

- **Psychiatrists:** Medical doctors who specialize in the diagnosis, treatment, and prevention of mental health disorders. They can prescribe medication, provide psychotherapy, and offer other treatments.
- **Psychologists:** Professionals with a doctoral degree in psychology who diagnose and treat mental health disorders through various forms of psychotherapy, psychological testing, and research.
- **Counselors:** Professionals with a master's degree in counseling or a related field who provide counseling and psychotherapy services to help clients cope with mental health issues, relationship problems, or other life challenges.

- o **Social Workers:** Professionals with a master's degree in social work (MSW) who provide therapy, case management, and other services to help individuals, families, and communities cope with mental health and social issues.
- o **Marriage and Family Therapists:** Professionals with a master's degree in marriage and family therapy who specialize in helping couples and families address relationship issues and improve communication.

Specializations

In addition to understanding the different types of mental health professionals, it is essential to consider their areas of specialization. Some common specializations include:

- o **Cognitive-Behavioral Therapy (CBT):** An evidence-based approach that focuses on identifying and changing negative thought patterns and behaviors to improve mental health.
- o **Dialectical Behavior Therapy (DBT):** A form of CBT that helps clients develop skills in mindfulness, emotion regulation, distress tolerance, and interpersonal effectiveness, often used for individuals with borderline personality disorder or suicidal tendencies.
- o **Psychodynamic Therapy:** An approach that explores how unconscious thoughts and feelings rooted in past experiences influence current behavior and relationships.
- o **Humanistic Therapy:** A client-centered approach that emphasizes empathy, unconditional positive regard, and personal growth to help clients reach their full potential.
- o **Couples and Family Therapy:** A therapeutic approach that addresses relationship issues, communication, and family dynamics to improve overall functioning and satisfaction.

By considering your needs, preferences, and the various types of mental health professionals and their specializations, you can make an informed decision about who to work with on your mental health journey.

Finding a Mental Health Professional

Once you have identified your needs and mental health concerns, the next step is to find a mental health professional who can provide the appropriate support and treatment. In this section, we will discuss the process of finding a mental health professional, including seeking referrals and recommendations, navigating insurance coverage and costs, and evaluating potential therapists.

Referrals and Recommendations

- **Friends, Family, and Colleagues:** Reach out to people in your social network who have experience with therapy. They may be able to provide personal recommendations for mental health professionals they have found helpful.
- **Primary Care Physician:** Your primary care doctor can be an excellent resource for referrals, as they often work with mental health professionals and can recommend those who have expertise in your specific area of concern.
- **Local Mental Health Clinics:** Community mental health clinics may offer therapy services or maintain a referral network of mental health professionals in your area.
- **Online Directories and Databases**: Websites such as Psychology Today and the American Psychological Association provide searchable databases of mental health professionals. These directories often include profiles with information on each professional's credentials, specializations, and treatment approaches.

Insurance Coverage and Costs

- **Determine What Your Insurance Covers:** Contact your insurance provider to inquire about your mental health coverage. Ask about in-network providers, the number of covered therapy sessions, and any required co-payments.
- **Estimate Out-Of-Pocket Expenses:** If your insurance does not cover mental health services or you choose to see an out-of-network provider, inquire about their fees and payment options. Some professionals may offer a sliding scale fee structure based on your income.
- **Consider Sliding-Scale Options for Affordability:** If the cost of therapy is a barrier, search for mental health professionals or clinics that offer sliding scale fees, which are adjusted based on your financial situation.

Evaluating Potential Therapists

- **Credentials, Experience, and Specialization:** Review the potential therapist's educational background, licensure, and years of experience. Ensure that they specialize in the area of mental health relevant to your needs and have experience treating clients with similar concerns.
- **Compatibility and Communication Style:** Schedule an initial consultation or phone call with potential therapists to discuss your needs and determine if their therapeutic approach aligns with your preferences. Consider whether you feel comfortable and at ease when talking to the therapist, as the therapeutic relationship plays a significant role in the success of therapy.
- **Location, Availability, and Scheduling:** Consider the practical aspects of attending therapy sessions, such as the therapist's location, office hours, and appointment availability. Choose a mental health professional whose schedule

and location are compatible with your daily routine to facilitate consistent attendance and commitment to therapy.

By following these steps, you can find a mental health professional who is well-suited to address your unique needs and concerns, setting the stage for a successful therapeutic experience.

Establishing a Therapeutic Relationship

A strong therapeutic relationship is essential for successful therapy outcomes. This section will provide guidance on establishing a therapeutic relationship, including the initial consultation, setting boundaries, and goal setting and progress monitoring.

Initial Consultation

- **Discuss Your Mental Health Concerns and Goals:** Be open and honest about your mental health concerns, symptoms, and history during your first session. This information will help your therapist understand your needs and tailor their approach accordingly.
- **Ask About the Therapist's Experience and Approach:** Inquire about the therapist's experience in treating clients with similar concerns, their therapeutic approach, and their perspective on the therapeutic process. This conversation will help you determine if their approach aligns with your needs and preferences.
- **Evaluate Your Comfort and Rapport with the Therapist:** Reflect on your feelings during the initial consultation. Did you feel heard and understood? Did you feel comfortable discussing your concerns? Trust your instincts and choose a therapist with whom you feel a strong connection and sense of trust.

Setting Boundaries

- **Establish Clear Expectations and Boundaries**: Discuss your expectations for therapy, including session frequency, duration, and communication methods. Establish clear boundaries with your therapist to ensure that your time together is focused on your needs and concerns.
- **Communicate Openly About Any Concerns or Issues:** If you encounter any problems or concerns during the course of therapy, bring them up with your therapist. Open communication is crucial for addressing any misunderstandings or difficulties and maintaining a healthy therapeutic relationship.
- **Address and Respect Confidentiality and Privacy:** Discuss the therapist's confidentiality policies and any exceptions, such as mandated reporting for child abuse or imminent danger to yourself or others. Ensure that you feel comfortable with these policies and that your privacy is respected.

Goal Setting and Progress Monitoring

- **Develop Specific, Achievable Goals with Your Therapist:** Work together with your therapist to identify specific, measurable, achievable, relevant, and time-bound (SMART) goals for therapy. These goals should be tailored to your unique needs and concerns, providing a clear roadmap for your therapeutic journey.
- **Monitor Progress Regularly and Adjust Goals as Needed:** Regularly assess your progress towards your therapy goals with your therapist. Celebrate successes, acknowledge challenges, and adjust goals as necessary to ensure that your therapeutic journey remains relevant and effective.
- **Discuss Any Challenges or Setbacks Openly:** Be open with your therapist about any challenges, setbacks, or difficulties you encounter during therapy. This honesty will help your therapist adjust their approach or provide additional support to help you overcome these obstacles and continue making progress.

By establishing a strong therapeutic relationship, you can create a supportive and collaborative environment in which to work towards your mental health goals. This foundation will be instrumental in ensuring that therapy is a positive, transformative experience.

Benefits of Therapy for Mental & Physical Health and Emotional Well-Being

Engaging in therapy can have far-reaching benefits that extend beyond mental health improvements. In this section, we will explore the advantages of therapy as they relate to mental health, physical health, emotional well-being, and productivity. We will support these benefits with real-life examples, scientific studies, and practical tips.

Mental Health Benefits

- **Reduced Symptoms of Depression, Anxiety, and Other Mental Health Disorders:** Therapy can help individuals manage and reduce symptoms associated with various mental health conditions, leading to improved daily functioning and overall well-being. Research has demonstrated the effectiveness of therapy, particularly cognitive-behavioral therapy (CBT), in reducing symptoms of depression and anxiety (Hofmann, Asnaani, Vonk, Sawyer, & Fang, 2012).
- **Improved Coping Mechanisms and Resilience:** Therapy can equip individuals with effective coping strategies to manage stress, adversity, and emotional challenges. Developing these skills can lead to increased resilience and the ability to bounce back from difficult situations.
- **Enhanced Self-Awareness and Understanding**: Therapy can promote self-reflection and self-awareness, enabling individuals to better understand their

emotions, thoughts, and behaviors. This increased understanding can foster personal growth and help individuals make more informed choices in their lives.

Physical Health Benefits

- o **Reduced Stress and Its Related Physical Symptoms:** Therapy can help individuals manage stress more effectively, leading to a reduction in stress-related physical symptoms such as headaches, muscle tension, and digestive issues. A study by Schneiderman, Ironson, and Siegel (2005) demonstrated the negative impact of stress on physical health and the potential for therapy to mitigate these effects.
- o **Improved Sleep Quality:** Therapy, particularly CBT, has been shown to be effective in treating insomnia and improving sleep quality (Trauer, Qian, Doyle, Rajaratnam, & Cunnington, 2015). Better sleep quality can lead to improved overall physical health and well-being.
- o **Enhanced Overall Well-Being:** By addressing mental health concerns and improving coping mechanisms, therapy can contribute to better overall physical health and well-being. This improvement may manifest as increased energy levels, a stronger immune system, and a reduced risk of developing stress-related health issues.

Emotional Well-Being Benefits

- o **Increased Emotional Regulation and Stability:** Therapy can help individuals develop skills in managing and regulating their emotions, leading to increased emotional stability and reduced mood fluctuations.
- o **Enhanced Interpersonal Relationships:** Through therapy, individuals can gain insight into their communication patterns and relationship dynamics, enabling them to build healthier and more satisfying relationships with friends, family, and romantic partners.
- o **Boosted Self-Esteem and Self-Compassion:** Therapy can support individuals in cultivating a more positive self-image and greater self-compassion, leading to increased confidence and self-worth.

Productivity Benefits

- o **Improved Focus and Concentration:** By addressing mental health concerns that may interfere with cognitive functioning, therapy can help individuals improve their focus and concentration, leading to increased productivity at work or in school.
- o **Enhanced Decision-Making Skills:** Therapy can help individuals develop better problem-solving and decision-making skills by fostering increased self-awareness, emotional regulation, and critical thinking.

- o **Increased Motivation and Goal Achievement:** Therapy can help individuals set and work towards personal and professional goals, leading to increased motivation, goal achievement, and overall satisfaction with life.

By engaging in therapy and addressing mental health concerns, individuals can experience a wide range of benefits that improve their mental health, physical health, emotional well-being, and productivity. These benefits underscore the importance of seeking professional help and incorporating therapy into one's self-care routine.

Practical Tips for Incorporating Therapy into Your Daily Routine

To experience the full benefits of therapy, it is essential to integrate it into your daily routine and make a commitment to the therapeutic process. This section will provide practical tips for incorporating therapy into your life and maximizing its impact on your mental health and overall well-being.

Scheduling and Consistency

- o **Prioritize Therapy Appointments:** Schedule therapy appointments at a consistent time and day each week to establish a routine. Treat therapy as an essential commitment by avoiding cancellations or rescheduling unless absolutely necessary.
- o **Set Reminders for Appointments:** Use a calendar, planner, or digital reminders to ensure that you remember your appointments and allocate sufficient time for them in your schedule.
- o **Plan for Transportation and Logistics:** Choose a therapist whose location is convenient for you, and plan your transportation to and from appointments. Taking care of these logistical details can help reduce stress and ensure consistent attendance.

Goal Setting and Accountability

- o **Set Achievable Therapy Goals:** Work with your therapist to establish clear, specific goals for your therapeutic journey. These goals should be tailored to your unique needs and concerns and should provide a clear roadmap for your progress.
- o **Review and Adjust Goals Regularly:** Periodically assess your progress towards your therapy goals and make adjustments as necessary. This ongoing evaluation will help ensure that your therapeutic journey remains relevant and effective.
- o **Share Your Goals With Someone You Trust**: Sharing your therapy goals with a supportive friend or family member can provide additional accountability and motivation to stay committed to the therapeutic process.

Integrating Therapy Skills into Daily Life

- o **Practice Skills and Techniques Learned in Therapy:** Work on applying the skills and techniques you learn in therapy to your everyday life. This practice can help reinforce your progress and support long-term change.
- o **Create a Self-Care Routine:** Develop a daily self-care routine that includes activities to support your mental, emotional, and physical well-being. This routine can complement your therapy sessions and help maintain progress between appointments.
- o **Use a Journal to Track Progress and Reflect on Experiences:** Journaling can be a helpful tool for documenting your therapy journey, tracking your progress, and reflecting on your thoughts and emotions. Regular journaling can provide insights into your growth and development throughout the therapeutic process.

Open Communication with Your Therapist

- o **Be Honest and Open with Your Therapist:** Share your thoughts, feelings, and experiences openly and honestly during therapy sessions. This transparency will help your therapist better understand your needs and tailor their approach accordingly.
- o **Provide Feedback and Address Concerns:** If you encounter any challenges or concerns during therapy, communicate them with your therapist. Open communication is essential for maintaining a healthy therapeutic relationship and ensuring that your needs are met.

By incorporating therapy into your daily routine and making a commitment to the therapeutic process, you can experience the full benefits of therapy and make lasting improvements to your mental health and overall well-being.

Summary & Conclusion

Finding and collaborating with a mental health professional can be a life-changing experience, with far-reaching benefits for mental health, physical health, emotional well-being, and productivity. This chapter has covered the stages involved in identifying your mental health concerns, locating an appropriate mental health professional, establishing a strong therapeutic relationship, and incorporating therapy into your daily life.

By recognizing your unique needs and seeking professional assistance, you can embark on a therapeutic journey that fosters self-awareness, personal development, and enduring enhancements to your well-being. This chapter will assist you in traversing the process of finding a therapist, setting attainable objectives, and maintaining your commitment to the therapeutic process through the use of practical advice.

Remember that therapy is an ongoing process that requires fortitude, effort, and commitment as you embark on this voyage. Be receptive to change, accept challenges and opportunities for growth, and celebrate your progress along the way. By doing so, you can maximize the therapeutic benefits and improve your mental health, emotional well-being, and quality of life overall.

Chapter 39:
The Importance of Finding the Right Mental Health Professional

Introduction:
Launching Point is Key

Finding the appropriate mental health professional is frequently the first step on the path to enhanced mental health. This is a crucial choice, as the right professional can facilitate your development, empower you to surmount obstacles, and guide you toward improved emotional health. In an era where mental health issues are becoming increasingly prevalent, it is crucial to choose the right mental health professional. The purpose of this chapter is to explain the significance of this decision by discussing its positive effects on mental health, physical health, emotional well-being, and productivity. Thus, we aim to equip readers with the knowledge and resources necessary to make informed decisions regarding their mental health care.

This chapter will examine in detail the various ways in which the proper mental health professional can positively affect one's existence. We will investigate the significance of personalized treatment, early intervention, and crisis support in the enhancement of mental health. In addition, we will discuss how the proper mental health professional can improve physical health by addressing the mind-body connection and promoting healthy sleep and nutrition practices.

The chapter will also explore the benefits for emotional health, such as improved emotional regulation and enhanced relationships. In addition, we will investigate the effect of the proper mental health professional on productivity by discussing how increased motivation and concentration, as well as reduced workplace tension, can contribute to improved job performance and satisfaction.

To illustrate these points, we will provide real-world examples, empirical studies, and practical advice that readers can use in their daily lives. By the end of the chapter, readers should have a thorough comprehension of the significance of finding the appropriate mental health professional and feel empowered to take the necessary measures to improve their mental health and well-being.

Personalized Treatment

Professionals in mental health are able to tailor treatment to the specific requirements and preferences of each client, ensuring that they receive the most effective interventions for their particular difficulties.

Individualization of evidence-based approaches (e.g., cognitive behavioral therapy, psychodynamic therapy, dialectical behavior therapy) improves the treatment experience and outcomes for each client.

The appropriate mental health professional will continuously evaluate and modify the treatment plan as required, adjusting to the client's changing circumstances and progress.

Intervention and Preventive Measures

Appropriate professional assistance can detect early signs of mental health problems and promptly treat them, thereby preventing the escalation of symptoms and reducing the risk of long-term complications.

- By providing clients with coping strategies and resources to effectively manage their mental health, early intervention can prevent the development of more severe issues, such as chronic depression, anxiety disorders, and substance misuse problems.
- he appropriate mental health professional will also assist clients in identifying and addressing potential triggers, thereby preventing future relapses or crises.

Help in Times of Crisis

Mental health practitioners can provide invaluable assistance during challenging times by providing clients with a secure environment in which to articulate their emotions, process their experiences, and develop coping mechanisms.

- Crisis intervention can result in enhanced functioning and resiliency as clients learn to navigate obstacles with the assistance of a mental health professional.
- The appropriate mental health professional will also assist clients in developing a crisis plan, thereby preparing them for future emergencies and providing a sense of security and control during uncertain times.

Increased Self-Awareness and Personal Development

The proper mental health professional can assist clients in gaining insight into their thought patterns, emotions, and behaviors, thereby fostering greater self-awareness and personal development.

- By comprehending the fundamental factors that contribute to their mental health issues, clients can take proactive measures to resolve these issues and develop healthier behaviors and thoughts.

- o Enhanced self-awareness can result in improved decision-making, self-compassion, and mental health and well-being in general.

Reduction of Stigma and Promotion of Assistance Seeking

By providing accurate information, empathy, and support, mental health professionals play a crucial role in reducing the stigma associated with mental health issues.

- o Consulting the appropriate mental health professional can encourage clients to seek assistance for themselves and others, thereby fostering a culture of mental health awareness and support.
- o The positive experience of finding the appropriate mental health professional can contribute to breaking down barriers to seeking assistance, allowing individuals to access the care they require without fear of discrimination or judgment.

Mind-Body Connection

According to research, mental and physical health are intricately intertwined, with mental health problems frequently manifesting as physical symptoms and vice versa. Mental health practitioners can assist in the treatment of psychosomatic conditions such as stress-induced discomfort, gastrointestinal issues, and tension migraines by examining the emotional and psychological factors at play.

By working with the appropriate mental health professional, clients can learn to more effectively manage stress, thereby reducing the physical effects of mental health issues on their bodies.

Enhanced Rest and Nutrition

Professionals in mental health can aid in the development of healthful sleeping and dietary patterns, which are fundamental to physical health and well-being.

- o A balanced lifestyle contributes to improved overall health, as sufficient sleep and appropriate nutrition can strengthen the immune system, enhance cognitive function, and boost mood.
- o The appropriate mental health professional can assist clients in identifying and overcoming obstacles to healthy sleep and nutrition, such as emotional eating, insomnia, and irregular sleep patterns, and provide guidance for implementing long-term changes.

Enhanced Physical Exercise

Physical activity has been shown to have numerous physical and mental health benefits, and mental health professionals can assist clients in incorporating it into their daily routines.

- o Regular physical activity can enhance cardiovascular health, increase energy levels, and reduce the risk of chronic diseases like diabetes and obesity.
- o The appropriate mental health professional can assist clients in setting reasonable objectives for physical activity and provide strategies for overcoming obstacles, such as motivation or time management issues.

Substance Abuse Rehabilitation and Prevention

Mental health professionals can play a vital role in assisting clients through the substance misuse recovery process by addressing both the physical and psychological aspects of addiction.

- o The appropriate mental health professional can assist clients in identifying substance-use triggers, developing coping strategies, and establishing a support network to maintain sobriety.
- o In addition, mental health practitioners can contribute to the prevention of substance misuse by providing early intervention and education and by assisting clients in the development of healthy coping mechanisms and resilience.

Improved Immune System Performance

Chronic stress and mental illness can have a negative effect on the immune system, making individuals more susceptible to illness and infection.

- o By addressing mental health issues and enhancing emotional well-being, the proper mental health professional can indirectly promote a stronger immune system and improved physical health overall.
- o Mental health practitioners can teach techniques such as stress management, relaxation, and mindfulness to help clients maintain a balanced state of mind, thereby enhancing their immune function.

Enhanced Emotional Regulation

Mental health practitioners can teach clients effective emotional management skills, allowing them to face life's challenges with greater resilience and stability.

- o Individuals who are better able to manage with stressors, convey their emotions in healthy ways, and maintain a positive outlook on life experience greater life satisfaction as a result of enhanced emotional regulation.
- o The appropriate mental health professional can assist clients in recognizing unhelpful emotional patterns, provide guidance on modifying maladaptive behaviors, and instruct techniques for enhancing emotional intelligence and resiliency.

Improved Relationships

Therapy can assist clients in developing healthier communication and conflict resolution skills, resulting in ultimately more satisfying and supportive relationships.

- o Positive relationships contribute to an individual's overall emotional health by providing a sense of belonging, affection, and social support.
- o The appropriate mental health professional can assist clients in examining relationship patterns, establishing boundaries, and learning to navigate interpersonal dynamics more effectively, thereby nurturing stronger relationships with others.

Enhanced Self-Worth and Confidence

Mental health professionals can assist clients in developing self-esteem and confidence by identifying and challenging negative self-beliefs and promoting self-compassion.

- o Individuals who feel more capable of pursuing their goals, asserting their needs, and honoring their authentic selves may experience greater emotional well-being as a result of higher self-esteem and confidence.
- o The proper mental health professional can guide clients in developing a positive self-image and cultivating self-compassion, allowing them to feel more empowered and fulfilled in their lives.

Enhanced Adaptability and Resilience

A variety of coping skills, such as problem-solving, relaxation techniques, and mindfulness practices, can be taught by mental health practitioners to clients in order to improve their emotional health.

- o Individuals who develop resilience are better able to recover from setbacks and acclimate to change, resulting in greater emotional stability and life satisfaction.
- o The appropriate mental health professional can assist clients in developing personal resilience by assisting them in identifying their strengths, cultivating a growth mindset, and cultivating a supportive social network.

Enhanced Sense of Purpose and Significance

Professionals in mental health can assist clients in exploring their values, passions, and objectives, ultimately guiding them toward a greater sense of purpose and meaning in life.

- o Living with a sense of direction, motivation, and fulfillment can contribute to psychological health.
- o The appropriate mental health professional can facilitate clients' investigation of their life purpose by assisting them in setting meaningful objectives,

aligning their actions with their values, and nurturing a sense of personal agency.

Increased Motivation and Focus

Mental health practitioners can assist clients in overcoming obstacles to productivity, such as procrastination, self-doubt, and disorganization, by identifying the underlying causes and devising individualized improvement strategies.

- o Better mental health can result in increased motivation and concentration at work or in personal pursuits, as individuals feel more capable, invigorated, and engaged in their endeavors.
- o The proper mental health professional can offer advice on goal-setting, time management, and maintaining a healthy work-life balance, ultimately leading to increased productivity and personal satisfaction.

Reduced Workplace Stress

Therapy can assist clients in more effectively managing workplace stressors, thereby fostering a healthier and more productive work environment.

- o Reduced tension can improve overall job performance and job satisfaction, as employees feel more capable of navigating challenges and interpersonal dynamics at work.
- o The proper mental health professional can assist clients in developing stress management techniques, assertiveness skills, and other coping mechanisms in order to maintain a positive outlook on their professional lives.

Superior Creativity and Problem-Solving Capabilities

By addressing mental blocks, nurturing self-awareness, and promoting a growth mindset, mental health professionals can help clients access their creativity and enhance their problem-solving skills.

- o Enhanced creativity and problem-solving skills can contribute to increased productivity, as individuals are better able to generate innovative ideas, surmount obstacles, and acclimate to change.
- o The correct mental health professional can offer advice on fostering creativity and enhancing critical thinking, enabling clients to excel in their personal and professional lives.

Enhanced Determination and Prioritization

Mental health practitioners can assist clients in refining their decision-making and prioritization skills, allowing them to make more informed decisions, effectively manage their time, and accomplish their objectives.

- o Enhanced decision-making and prioritization skills can result in increased productivity, as individuals are able to concentrate on high-impact tasks and avoid becoming inundated by contending demands.
- o The appropriate mental health professional can teach clients techniques for elucidating their values, establishing priorities, and making decisions that are consistent with their long-term goals.

Enhancing Work-Life Balance

Professionals in mental health can assist clients in establishing a healthy work-life balance, allowing them to maintain high levels of productivity without sacrificing their own well-being.

- o A balanced lifestyle can increase productivity because individuals feel more energized, engaged, and fulfilled in their personal and professional lives.
- o The proper mental health professional can offer advice on setting boundaries, managing stress, and incorporating self-care practices into daily routines, thereby contributing to a healthier and more sustainable approach to productivity.

Summary & Conclusion

Finding the correct mental health professional is of paramount significance. This chapter has outlined the numerous advantages of hiring the right professional for your specific requirements, including improvements in mental health, physical health, emotional well-being, and productivity. The appropriate mental health professional can provide individualized treatment, early intervention, and crisis support, as well as contribute to a strengthened mind-body connection, improved sleep and nutrition, and increased physical activity. In addition, they can foster emotional regulation, improved relationships, a higher sense of self-worth, and a stronger sense of life's purpose, ultimately resulting in increased productivity through motivation, stress management, creativity, decision-making, and work-life balance.

Including the proper mental health professional in one's daily routine can be transformative. As demonstrated through real-world examples, scientific studies, and practical advice, selecting the appropriate mental health professional is a crucial step toward enhanced mental health and well-being as a whole. We encourage readers to consider these insights and make an informed decision when selecting a mental health professional, as this choice can have a significant impact on their personal development, contentment, and success. Individuals can pave the way for a more fulfilling, balanced, and fruitful existence by prioritizing mental health and pursuing appropriate professional support.

Chapter 40:
Overcoming Stigma & Barriers to Seeking Professional Help

Introduction:
What Causes These to Occur?

Mental health is an essential component of overall health and a major determinant of our quality of life. There are still a significant amount of stigma and barriers that prevent individuals from seeking professional assistance, despite the growing awareness of mental health and the increase in related discourse. Not only do these obstacles impede timely intervention and treatment, but they also perpetuate myths and stereotypes about mental health issues. As a result, many people continue to suffer in silence, with the potential for their mental health issues to worsen and negatively impact multiple aspects of their lives.

This chapter examines the significance of confronting the stigma and barriers associated with obtaining professional assistance for mental health issues. We will begin by analyzing the origins of stigma and the barriers that may prevent individuals from gaining access to needed resources. Following this, we will examine the numerous advantages to mental health, physical health, emotional well-being, and productivity that overcoming these obstacles can bring. To provide a comprehensive comprehension, this chapter will integrate pertinent research, real-world examples, and expert advice.

Finally, we will provide recommendations and strategies for successfully navigating the process of seeking professional assistance. In addition to empowering individuals to take charge of their mental health journey, these strategies will also contribute to a societal transition toward a greater understanding and acceptance of mental health issues. At the conclusion of this chapter, readers will have gained valuable insights and tools to assist them in overcoming stigma and obstacles and moving forward on the path to better mental health and well-being.

Understanding the Stigma and Barriers to Seeking Help

The Stigma of Mental Health
The stigma surrounding mental health can be a significant obstacle for individuals seeking professional help. Stigma arises from various sources, including societal

misconceptions, stereotypes, and media portrayals. Understanding these sources can help us challenge and dismantle them effectively.

a) Societal Misconceptions and Stereotypes: Many people still hold misconceptions about mental health issues, often fueled by a lack of education and awareness. Common stereotypes include the belief that mental health problems are a sign of weakness or that people with mental health issues are dangerous or unpredictable. These stereotypes can make individuals reluctant to disclose their struggles or seek help, for fear of being judged or discriminated against.

b) Media Portrayal: The media can sometimes perpetuate stigmatizing beliefs about mental health through inaccurate or sensationalized portrayals of mental illness. These portrayals can reinforce negative stereotypes and contribute to the stigmatization of those experiencing mental health issues.

c) Self-Stigmatization: Unfortunately, the stigma surrounding mental health can lead individuals to internalize these negative beliefs and stereotypes. Self-stigmatization can result in feelings of shame, guilt, and worthlessness, further discouraging individuals from seeking help.

Barriers to Seeking Help
In addition to stigma, several barriers may hinder individuals from seeking professional help for their mental health concerns. Recognizing these barriers is the first step towards addressing them.

a) Financial Constraints: The cost of mental health care can be prohibitive for many people, especially those without insurance coverage or with limited financial resources. This can lead to individuals delaying or forgoing treatment altogether.

b) Limited Access to Professionals: In some areas, access to mental health professionals is limited due to a shortage of providers or long waiting lists. In rural or remote locations, the availability of mental health services can be particularly scarce, making it challenging for individuals to find the help they need.

c) Cultural and Language Barriers: Cultural differences and language barriers can make it difficult for some individuals to access mental health services or feel comfortable discussing their concerns with a mental health professional. These barriers can be particularly pronounced for immigrants, refugees, and members of minority communities.

d) Fear of Judgment: Many people may be hesitant to seek professional help due to concerns about how they will be perceived by others. This fear of judgment can stem from the stigma surrounding mental health, as well as the worry that disclosing their struggles may negatively impact their personal or professional relationships.

By identifying and understanding the sources of stigma and the barriers to seeking help, we can begin to develop strategies for overcoming these obstacles and ensuring that individuals have access to the support they need for their mental health and well-being.

The Benefits of Overcoming Stigma and Barriers

Successfully addressing the stigma and barriers to seeking professional help for mental health concerns can yield a wide range of benefits, spanning from improved mental health to enhanced emotional well-being and productivity. In this section, we will explore these benefits in greater detail.

Improved Mental Health
Overcoming stigma and barriers to seeking professional help can significantly improve mental health outcomes by facilitating early intervention and promoting access to effective treatment.

a) Early Intervention: Timely diagnosis and treatment are essential for managing mental health issues. Early intervention can help prevent the exacerbation of symptoms and reduce the likelihood of long-term negative consequences.

b) Effective Treatment: Access to professional help can connect individuals with evidence-based therapies and interventions tailored to their specific needs. These treatments can lead to a reduction in symptoms and an overall improvement in mental health.

c) Improved Quality of Life: As mental health symptoms decrease and coping skills improve, individuals often experience an enhanced quality of life. This can manifest as stronger relationships, increased satisfaction in personal and professional pursuits, and a greater sense of well-being.

d) Case Study: Cognitive Behavioral Therapy (CBT) has been shown to be highly effective in treating a wide range of mental health issues, including depression and anxiety. By challenging negative thought patterns and promoting healthier behaviors, CBT can lead to lasting improvements in mental health.

Enhanced Physical Health
Mental and physical health are deeply interconnected, and addressing mental health concerns can lead to significant improvements in physical well-being.

a) The Mind-Body Connection: Poor mental health can contribute to the development or worsening of physical health issues. Conversely, improving mental health can result in better physical health outcomes.

b) Improved Sleep and Nutrition: Seeking professional help for mental health concerns can lead to improvements in sleep quality and dietary habits, both of which are crucial for maintaining overall health.

c) Reduced Risk of Chronic Diseases: Addressing mental health issues can reduce the risk of developing chronic diseases such as heart disease, diabetes, and obesity, as well as alleviate the symptoms of existing conditions.

d) Research: Numerous studies have demonstrated a strong relationship between mental health and physical health, underscoring the importance of addressing mental health concerns to promote overall well-being.

Emotional Well-being
Seeking professional help for mental health issues can lead to enhanced emotional well-being by fostering increased self-awareness, emotional intelligence, and effective stress management.

a) Increased Self-Awareness: Engaging in therapy or counseling can help individuals gain a deeper understanding of their emotions, thoughts, and behaviors, leading to greater self-awareness and personal growth.

b) Enhanced Emotional Intelligence: Professional help can equip individuals with the tools and skills necessary to effectively navigate their emotions and develop healthy coping mechanisms.

c) Better Stress Management: Through professional support, individuals can learn to identify and manage
stressors in their lives, leading to improved emotional resilience and well-being.

d) Example: Mindfulness-based interventions have been shown to be effective in promoting emotional regulation and well-being. By cultivating present-moment awareness, individuals can develop a greater understanding of their emotions and learn to respond to them more adaptively.

Greater Productivity
Improved mental health can have a positive impact on work performance, leading to increased productivity and professional success.

a) The Impact of Mental Health on Work Performance: Mental health issues can result in reduced focus, motivation, and decision-making abilities, all of which can hinder work performance.

b) Reduced Absenteeism and Presenteeism: Addressing mental health concerns can lead to decreased absenteeism (missing work due to illness) and presenteeism (working while unwell), resulting in increased productivity and reduced financial strain for both employees and employers.

c) Improved Relationships with Colleagues: As individuals address their mental health concerns, they are better equipped to communicate effectively and empathetically with colleagues, leading to stronger professional relationships and a more positive work environment.

d) Research: Studies have shown that promoting mental health in the workplace can result in significant economic benefits, including increased productivity, reduced healthcare costs, and decreased employee turnover.

By overcoming the stigma and barriers to seeking professional help, individuals can experience a multitude of benefits that extend to various aspects of their lives, including improved mental and physical health, enhanced emotional well-being, and greater productivity. These benefits underscore the importance of addressing mental health concerns and breaking down the obstacles that prevent individuals from accessing the support they need.

Practical Tips for Overcoming Stigma and Barriers

To overcome stigma and barriers to seeking professional help for mental health concerns, it is essential to adopt proactive strategies that empower individuals to access the support they need. In this section, we will outline practical tips and recommendations for addressing these challenges.

Educate Yourself and Others

Knowledge is power, and understanding the facts about mental health can help combat stigma and misconceptions.

a) Understand the Facts: Educate yourself about mental health conditions, their prevalence, and the effectiveness of various treatments. This knowledge can help dispel myths and challenge stereotypes.

b) Challenge Misconceptions: Be prepared to confront misconceptions and stereotypes when you encounter them, whether in conversations with friends, family, or colleagues, or in the media.

c) Share Your Knowledge and Experiences: By openly discussing mental health and sharing your experiences, you can help normalize conversations about mental health, break down stigmas, and encourage others to seek help.

Seek Support from Trusted Individuals

Building a support network can make the process of seeking professional help less daunting and provide valuable encouragement.

a) Reach Out to Friends and Family: Share your concerns and feelings with trusted friends or family members. They can provide emotional support, encouragement, and practical assistance.

b) Connect with Support Groups: Many communities offer support groups for individuals facing mental health challenges. These groups can provide a safe space for sharing experiences, discussing coping strategies, and building connections with others who understand your struggles.

c) Leverage Online Communities and Resources: There are numerous online forums, blogs, and resources dedicated to mental health. These platforms can offer valuable information, support, and connections with others who share similar experiences.

Be Proactive in Finding Professional Help

Taking an active role in seeking professional help can empower you to find the support that best meets your needs.

a) Research Available Mental Health Services: Investigate local mental health services, including therapists, psychologists, psychiatrists, and counseling centers, to determine which providers and treatments may be most suitable for your needs.

b) Consider Teletherapy and Online Counseling: If access to mental health professionals is limited in your area, explore teletherapy and online counseling options. These remote services can provide a more accessible and convenient means of obtaining professional support.

c) Advocate for Workplace Mental Health Programs: Encourage your employer to implement mental health initiatives in the workplace, such as Employee Assistance Programs (EAPs), mental health training for staff, and supportive policies for employees seeking mental health support.

Develop a Self-Care Routine
Maintaining a self-care routine can help support your mental health and emotional well-being while you work towards overcoming stigma and barriers.

a) Incorporate Physical Activity: Engage in regular physical activity, as exercise has been shown to improve mental health by reducing stress, anxiety, and depression.

b) Practice Mindfulness and Relaxation Techniques: Incorporate mindfulness practices, such as meditation and deep breathing exercises, into your daily routine to help manage stress and promote emotional well-being.

c) Maintain a Healthy Diet and Sleep Schedule: Prioritize a balanced diet and consistent sleep schedule, as both are essential for supporting mental health and overall well-being.

d) Engage in Hobbies and Social Activities: Pursue hobbies and interests that bring you joy and satisfaction, and cultivate connections with others through social activities and events.

By implementing these practical tips and strategies, individuals can effectively overcome the stigma and barriers to seeking professional help, paving the way for improved mental health and well-being.

Summary & Conclusion

Vital to the promotion of overall well-being and quality of life is overcoming stigma and barriers to seeking professional assistance for mental health issues. By addressing these obstacles, individuals can gain access to the necessary resources for enhancing their mental health, physical health, emotional well-being, and productivity. This chapter has examined the origins of stigma and the various impediments to seeking assistance, as well as the numerous benefits that can result from overcoming these obstacles.

In addition, we have provided guidelines and recommendations for overcoming stigma and barriers, such as educating oneself and others about mental health, requesting support from trusted individuals, being proactive in locating professional assistance, and developing self-care practices. Individuals can take charge of their mental health journey and contribute to a societal transition toward a greater understanding and acceptance of mental health issues by implementing these strategies.

In conclusion, addressing stigma and barriers to professional assistance is essential for promoting a more compassionate and supportive society in which individuals can discuss mental health openly and access the resources they need to flourish. By embracing these principles, we can create a world in which mental health is acknowledged, supported, and celebrated as a fundamental component of overall well-being.

Chapter 41:
Making Seeking Professional Help a Priority

Introduction:
First and Foremost

In today's fast-paced society, it is crucial to prioritize mental health and wellbeing. The stigma associated with mental health issues has diminished substantially over the years, and society has become more accepting of discussing these issues. Despite these advancements, many individuals continue to be hesitant to seek professional assistance, frequently due to a lack of knowledge regarding the significance and benefits of mental health care. In this chapter, we will examine why seeking professional assistance should be a top priority for overall health and happiness.

We will examine the various advantages of collaborating with mental health professionals, including how seeking assistance can positively affect an individual's mental health, physical health, emotional well-being, and productivity. In addition, we will discuss real-world examples of people who have benefited from professional assistance, citing pertinent scientific studies to support the importance of mental health care. Finally, we will provide readers with ideas and recommendations for incorporating professional assistance into their daily lives, encouraging them to take the necessary steps to improve their mental health and quality of life as a whole.

At the conclusion of this chapter, readers will have a comprehensive comprehension of the importance of making professional assistance a priority and will be endowed with the knowledge and tools necessary to take charge of their mental health and well-being.

Early Detection and Treatment

Seeking professional assistance at the onset of mental health problems enables early diagnosis and treatment, which can significantly improve prognosis. According to a study by Wang et al. (2005), early intervention in mental health care is essential for minimizing the detrimental long-term consequences of mental illnesses. By addressing mental health issues early, individuals can prevent the worsening of their symptoms and increase their likelihood of recovery.

Avoiding Relapse

Regular sessions with a mental health professional can aid in symptom management and relapse prevention. A 2014 study published in JAMA Psychiatry found that those who received ongoing professional care had a substantially reduced risk of relapse compared to those who did not. This ongoing support enables individuals to track their progress and modify their treatment plans as necessary, ensuring that they remain on the road to recovery.

Reducing the Effect on Everyday Life

Untreated mental health issues can have a significant impact on a person's daily life, making it difficult to sustain relationships, work, and participate in pastimes. Seeking professional assistance can mitigate these difficulties by providing guidance, coping strategies, and support, thereby enabling individuals to lead a more fulfilling and balanced existence.

Developing Effective Coping Strategies

Professionals in mental health can assist individuals in developing healthy coping mechanisms for tension, anxiety, and other emotional difficulties. Among these coping mechanisms are relaxation techniques, mindfulness practices, and cognitive restructuring. By learning and employing these coping mechanisms, individuals can more effectively manage their mental health and navigate difficult situations.

Practical Tip: Consider contacting a mental health professional for an evaluation if you observe any changes in your disposition, thoughts, or behavior. Early intervention and ongoing support can substantially enhance mental health outcomes and quality of life overall.

Improved Sleep and Nutrition

According to research, mental health issues can negatively influence sleep quality and dietary decisions. By addressing these issues with a mental health professional, individuals can improve their sleeping patterns and dietary habits, resulting in improved physical health overall. According to a study by Baglioni et al. (2011), addressing mental health issues, specifically insomnia and depression, improved sleep quality. Similarly, Daubenmier et al. (2016) found that addressing emotional eating through mindfulness-based interventions resulted in healthier dietary selections and weight loss.

Reduced Chance of Chronic Disease

Numerous studies have found a correlation between untreated mental health issues and an increased risk of chronic diseases like heart disease and diabetes. For instance, Whooley et al. (2008) found that depression is associated with an increased risk of cardiovascular disease. By enhancing mental health and encouraging healthier lifestyle choices, professional assistance can reduce the risk of developing these conditions.

Strengthened Immune System

A developing body of evidence suggests a close relationship between mental health and immune system function. Chronic stress and mental health issues can impair an individual's immune system, making them more susceptible to infections and diseases. By seeking professional assistance to manage mental health issues, individuals can reduce tension and boost their immune system, resulting in improved overall health. According to a study by Marsland et al. (2017), psychological interventions designed to reduce stress improved immune system function.

Enhanced Pain Treatment

Chronic pain and mental health problems frequently coexist, with each aggravating the other. By addressing mental health concerns with a professional, individuals can learn more effective pain coping strategies and potentially experience less pain. Ehde et al. (2014) found cognitive-behavioral interventions for chronic pain to be effective at reducing pain intensity and enhancing overall functioning.

Practical Tip: To prioritize your physical health, ensure you discuss mental health concerns with a professional and adhere to their treatment recommendations. Incorporating techniques for stress reduction, such as mindfulness or meditation, can also contribute to better physical health outcomes.

Building Emotional Resilience

Individuals can develop emotional resilience, or the capacity to deal with stress and adversity, by collaborating with a mental health professional. This skill is essential for maintaining emotional health and can be fostered through a variety of therapeutic techniques, including cognitive-behavioral therapy (CBT), dialectical behavior therapy (DBT), and mindfulness-based stress reduction (MBSR). According to a study by Galante et al. (2018), mindfulness-based interventions are effective for enhancing emotional resilience and decreasing psychological distress.

Enhanced Connections

Professional assistance can enhance a person's ability to communicate and empathize with others, resulting in healthier relationships with family, friends, and coworkers. Better emotional health can also lead to enhanced conflict resolution and emotional intimacy skills. According to a study by Baucom et al. (2015), couples' therapy, which frequently incorporates communication skills training, is effective for increasing relationship satisfaction and decreasing relationship distress.

Self-Esteem and Self-Compassion Improvements

Professionals in mental health can assist individuals in cultivating healthier self-esteem and self-compassion, resulting in a more positive self-image and a greater sense of self-worth. Individuals can learn to embrace and appreciate themselves more completely if they address negative self-talk and self-defeating behaviors. According to a study conducted by Neff and Germer (2013), self-compassion interventions are effective at enhancing self-esteem and decreasing feelings of humiliation and self-criticism.

A higher level of emotional intelligence

Working with a mental health professional can also aid in the development of emotional intelligence, which involves the ability to recognize, comprehend, and manage one's own emotions and the emotions of others. Emotional intelligence is necessary for maintaining emotional health because it enables individuals to navigate complex social situations and respond appropriately to their own emotions. According to a study by Gilar-Corbi et al. (2019), emotional intelligence training is effective for enhancing emotional well-being and decreasing emotional distress.

Practical Tip: Consider joining a support group or attending group therapy sessions, where you can learn from others experiencing similar challenges, to improve your emotional health. Engaging in self-care practices such as journaling, meditation, and exercise can also contribute to enhanced emotional health.

Improved Focus and Concentration

Biochemistry Focus and concentration can be negatively impacted by mental health issues, making it difficult to complete tasks efficiently and effectively. By seeking professional assistance, individuals can learn techniques to manage their symptoms and surmount these obstacles, resulting in increased work or school productivity. Greeson et al. (2014) found that mindfulness-based interventions were effective at enhancing focus and attention in individuals with anxiety and depression.

Increased Job Contentment

Individuals who are better suited to manage work-related stressors and maintain a healthy work-life balance are more likely to enjoy their jobs. Lamers et al. (2012) discovered a significant positive correlation between mental health and job satisfaction. Individuals can develop coping strategies and stress management techniques that contribute to a more gratifying and rewarding work experience by pursuing professional assistance.

Increased Originality and Problem-Solving

Good mental health is frequently associated with enhanced creativity and problem-solving abilities. Individuals can surmount cognitive barriers and unlock their creative potential by addressing mental health concerns with a professional. According to a study by Forgeard and Elstein (2014), engaging in creative activities can improve psychological health and boost overall productivity.

Absenteeism and Presenteeism are Decreased

Untreated mental health issues can increase absenteeism and presenteeism, resulting in decreased productivity. Individuals can improve their overall job performance and attendance by seeking professional assistance and addressing mental health issues. According to a study by Dewa et al. (2014), absenteeism and presenteeism of employees who received mental health care decreased significantly.

Practical Tip: Implement strategies recommended by a mental health professional, such as scheduling regular breaks, practicing mindfulness, and setting attainable objectives, in order to increase productivity and job satisfaction. In addition, consider discussing your mental health requirements with your employer in order to investigate potential accommodations or adjustments that can further enhance your productivity and well-being at work.

Summary & Conclusion

In conclusion, it is crucial to make seeking professional assistance a top priority for promoting overall well-being and enhancing multiple aspects of life, including mental health, physical health, emotional well-being, and productivity. By addressing mental health issues early and engaging in regular sessions with a mental health professional, individuals can substantially improve their prognosis, prevent relapse, and manage their daily lives more effectively.

Prioritizing professional assistance can also improve physical health by promoting better sleep, nutrition, and immune system function, and by reducing the risk of developing chronic diseases. Through the development of emotional resilience, improved relationships, self-esteem, self-compassion, and emotional intelligence, emotional well-being is enhanced. Improved concentration, increased job satisfaction, enhanced creativity, and decreased absenteeism and presenteeism are also productivity benefits of seeking professional assistance.

To completely realize the benefits of seeking professional assistance, it is essential to recognize the signs of mental health problems and to seek assistance when necessary. Individuals can take charge of their mental health and well-being in this manner, resulting to a healthier, more fulfilling existence. In addition, employing practical guidelines and self-care practices in conjunction with professional guidance can assist individuals in establishing a solid foundation for their mental health and well-being.

Chapter 42:
Supporting Others in Seeking Professional Help

Introduction:
When It's Time to Support Others

Mental health is a crucial component of an individual's well-being, effecting not only their emotional state but also their physical health and productivity. In today's fast-paced world, mental health issues are on the rise, and it has become increasingly essential to obtain professional assistance. However, the stigma associated with mental health issues and the reluctance to seek assistance frequently serve as obstacles to treatment. Here, the assistance of friends, family, and coworkers can make a significant difference. By recognizing when a person we care about requires professional assistance and providing them with encouragement and support, we can assist them on the road to recovery.

This chapter will explore the significance of encouraging others to seek professional assistance by examining the benefits to mental health, physical health, emotional well-being, and productivity. We will use real-world examples and scientific research to illustrate the importance of this topic. In addition, we will provide suggestions for incorporating this information into your daily life, allowing you to better support your loved ones and foster a more compassionate and psychologically healthy environment.

In the following sections, we will discuss how to recognize the need for professional assistance by recognizing the symptoms and promoting open dialogue. Then, we will examine the advantages of seeking professional assistance for mental health, physical health, emotional well-being, and productivity, with a focus on the role of support networks in facilitating these positive outcomes. Finally, we will provide suggestions and recommendations on how readers can incorporate these factors into their lives to enhance their mental health.

Recognizing the Need for Professional Help

Understanding the Signs and Symptoms
It is crucial to be aware of the signs and symptoms of mental health issues in order to recognize when a loved one may require professional assistance. Depending on the

specific mental health condition, these signs can vary, but some common red flags include:

- ○ Persistent sadness or irritability
- ○ Alterations in sleep patterns (insomnia or oversleeping)
- ○ Alterations in appetite or weight o Withdrawal from social activities and hobbies
- ○ Decreased energy or constant fatigue
- ○ Difficulty concentrating or making decisions
- ○ Feelings of worthlessness or excessive guilt
- ○ Increased anxiety or constant worrying
- ○ Unexplained physical symptoms (headaches, stomachaches, etc.)

It is essential to keep in mind that early intervention can substantially improve the outcomes for people with mental health issues. By recognizing and proactively addressing these indicators, you can help your loved ones obtain the necessary support before their condition worsens.

Promoting Open Discussions

The key to encouraging frank conversations about mental health is to provide a safe and supportive environment. It enables individuals to express their thoughts and emotions without fear of stigma or judgment. Here are some techniques for facilitating frank discussions:

- ○ **Be Nonjudgmental:** Listen to the person's experiences and emotions without passing judgment. Validate their emotions by recognizing their suffering and displaying empathy.
- ○ **Ask Open-Ended Questions:** Encourage the individual to share more about their experiences by asking open-ended inquiries such as "How have you been feeling lately?" or "What has been troubling you?"
- ○ **Be Patient:** Allow the individual time to articulate their thoughts and emotions. Do not hurry them or attempt to promptly "fix" their problems. Simply being present and attentive can have a significant impact.
- ○ **Share Your Own Experiences:** If you feel secure, discuss your own experiences with mental health issues or seeking professional assistance. This can help normalize the conversation and reduce the person's sense of isolation.

It is essential to eliminate the stigma encircling mental health in order to encourage individuals to seek assistance. By creating an environment that encourages open and honest communication, you can assist your loved ones in breaking down these barriers and taking the initial steps toward recovery.

Timely Access to Treatment and Resources

Seeking professional assistance for mental health issues can result in prompt access to the most suitable treatment options and resources. Mental health professionals, such as therapists, psychologists, and psychiatrists, are trained to use evidence-based practices to assess, diagnose, and treat a variety of mental health conditions. Typical therapeutic options include:

- **Psychotherapy**, also known as talk therapy, entails discussing thoughts, emotions, and behaviors with a mental health professional in order to obtain insight, develop coping strategies, and promote personal development.
- **Medication:** In certain instances, medication may be prescribed to alleviate symptoms and enhance functioning. Medications can help modulate brain chemistry and enhance, among other things, mood, anxiety, and sleep.
- **Support Groups:** Many individuals benefit from participation in support groups, where they can share their experiences and learn from others confronting similar challenges.

By encouraging your loved ones to seek professional assistance, you enable them to gain access to individualized treatments and resources that can significantly improve their mental health outcomes.

Increasing Social Support

One of the most important advantages of pursuing professional assistance is the enhancement of social support networks. Social support is essential for promoting mental health because it helps people feel understood, valued, and connected. When friends and family members encourage their loved ones to seek assistance, they actively contribute to the expansion of their support network. This can result in:

- **Improved Relationships:** By comprehending and empathizing with the individual's mental health struggles, family and friends can strengthen their connections and create a more supportive environment for recovery.
- **Decreased Isolation and Loneliness:** Mental health problems frequently result in social withdrawal and feelings of isolation. When individuals seek professional assistance and have the support of loved ones, they are more likely to reengage in social activities and feel less isolated.
- **Enhanced Coping Mechanisms**: Mental health professionals frequently collaborate with patients to develop coping mechanisms that can be shared with friends and family. This collaborative approach facilitates the development of a strong support network capable of effectively addressing mental health challenges.

By encouraging others to seek professional assistance, you can contribute to the growth of a strong social support network, which is essential for enhancing mental health and fostering resilience.

Addressing Physical Symptoms

As the mind and body are interconnected, mental health problems frequently have a substantial impact on physical health. The physical manifestations of stress, anxiety, melancholy, and other mental health conditions include migraines, digestive issues, and chronic discomfort. Individuals who seek professional assistance for mental health issues can address these physical symptoms by:

- o **Identifying Underlying Mental Health Issues:** Mental health professionals can assist individuals in recognizing the relationship between their physical symptoms and mental health conditions, resulting in a more comprehensive understanding of their overall health.
- o **Providing Appropriate Treatment:** Once the link between physical and mental health has been established, mental health professionals can recommend interventions that address both aspects. For instance, cognitive-behavioral therapy (CBT) can aid in the management of both anxiety and chronic pain.
- o **Promoting Self-Care:** Mental health professionals frequently emphasize the significance of self-care and can offer advice on incorporating healthy practices, such as exercise, balanced nutrition, and relaxation techniques, into daily routines.

By encouraging your loved ones to seek professional assistance for their mental health, you can also aid in the improvement of their physical health and well-being.

Promoting Healthy Lifestyle Selections
Mental health professionals play a crucial role in promoting healthful lifestyle choices that lead to improved physical health. By seeking professional assistance, individuals can learn to make healthier decisions and form practices that are beneficial to their overall health. The following are examples of ways mental health professionals can encourage healthful lifestyle choices:

- o **Stress Management:** Mental health professionals can instruct individuals in a variety of stress management techniques, such as mindfulness, deep breathing exercises, and progressive muscle relaxation, in order to reduce the negative effects of stress on the body.
- o **Sleep Hygiene:** Insomnia and sleep disturbances are prevalent among those with mental health issues. Professionals in mental health can offer advice on developing healthy sleep hygiene practices, such as maintaining a consistent sleep schedule, establishing a soothing twilight routine, and optimizing the sleep environment.
- o **Exercise and Nutrition:** Mental health professionals can educate individuals on the mental and physical health benefits of regular physical activity and

balanced nutrition. They can assist in the development of individualized strategies for incorporating these healthful behaviors into daily routines.

By encouraging others to seek professional assistance, you can improve their overall physical health by promoting healthy lifestyle choices and cultivating long-term wellbeing.

Developing Emotional Resilience

Seeking professional assistance for mental health issues can substantially improve an individual's emotional health by fostering emotional resilience. Emotional resilience is the capacity to adapt to adversity, duress, or trauma and recover. Mental health professionals can assist with the development of emotional resiliency by:

- o **Teaching Coping Strategies**: Mental health professionals can help individuals develop an arsenal of coping strategies to manage stressors and challenges more effectively by utilizing a variety of therapeutic approaches.
- o **Improving Self-Awareness:** Professional assistance can assist individuals in gaining a deeper comprehension of their emotions and triggers, enabling them to recognize when they require additional support or coping mechanisms.
- o **Building Self-Esteem and Self-Compassion:** Therapy can assist individuals in developing a healthier self-image and cultivating self-compassion, enabling them to navigate emotional challenges with greater resilience and confidence.

By encouraging your loved ones to seek professional assistance, you can contribute to their emotional well-being by equipping them with the skills and resources necessary to navigate the ups and downs of life.

Developing Good Emotions

Possessing the capacity to experience and cultivate positive emotions is a crucial element of emotional health. Seeking professional assistance can enhance a person's general disposition and emotional state, allowing them to cultivate contentment and life satisfaction. Mental health practitioners can assist people in cultivating positive emotions by:

- o **Promoting Positive Thinking:** Using cognitive restructuring techniques, mental health professionals can assist individuals in identifying and challenging negative thought patterns, enabling them to adopt a more optimistic outlook on life.
- o **Promoting Gratitude**: Mental health professionals may encourage individuals to practice gratitude by reflecting on the positive aspects of their lives, which can lead to a greater sense of contentment and well-being.

- **Facilitating Personal Development**: Therapy can serve as a catalyst for personal development and self-discovery, assisting individuals in recognizing their strengths and developing a sense of purpose and meaning in their lives.

Supporting others in obtaining professional assistance can have a significant impact on their emotional health by enabling them to develop emotional resilience and cultivate positive emotions, leading to a more fulfilling and gratifying existence.

Improving Work Performance

Mental health issues can have a significant impact on an individual's work performance and productivity. Untreated mental health conditions can result in difficulties with concentration, decision-making, and motivation, all of which can inhibit a person's ability to perform at his or her best. By obtaining professional assistance, individuals can address these issues and enhance their efficacy at work:

- **Improved Cognitive Function:** Mental health interventions, such as psychotherapy and medication, can improve cognitive functioning by addressing underlying issues, such as anxiety or depression, that may be contributing to concentration and decision-making difficulties.
- **Reduced Absenteeism and Presenteeism:** When individuals receive adequate mental health support, they are less likely to leave work due to mental health issues and more likely to be fully present and engaged at work.
- **Increased Job Satisfaction and Engagement:** Mental health support can assist individuals in achieving a healthier work-life balance, enhancing their capacity to manage with work-related stress, and ultimately increasing their job satisfaction and engagement.

By encouraging your loved ones to seek professional assistance, you can contribute to their overall productivity and assist them in reaching their complete professional potential.

Advancing the work-life balance
Achieving a healthy work-life balance is crucial to one's overall health and productivity. Mental health practitioners can assist individuals in harmonizing their professional and personal lives by addressing issues such as exhaustion and stress management.

- **Identifying Sources of Imbalance**: Mental health practitioners can assist individuals in identifying areas of their lives where an imbalance may exist, such as excessive work demands or insufficient self-care.
- **Developing Coping Strategies**: Therapy can help individuals develop coping strategies to manage work-related stress and prevent exhaustion, such as setting boundaries, delegating tasks, and exercising relaxation techniques.

- o **Fostering a Culture of Well-Being in the Workplace:** Mental health professionals can provide guidance on how to create a supportive work environment that promotes mental health and well-being, such as by encouraging open communication about mental health, providing access to resources, and promoting flexible work arrangements.

By encouraging others to seek professional assistance, you can assist them in achieving a healthier work-life balance, thereby enhancing their overall productivity and well-being.

Summary & Conclusion

Friends, family members, and coworkers have an important obligation to encourage others to seek professional assistance for mental health issues. By acknowledging the need for professional assistance and promoting open dialogue, we can foster a more compassionate and supportive environment for those battling mental health issues. This chapter has discussed the numerous advantages of seeking professional assistance, including improvements in mental health, physical health, emotional well-being, and productivity.

In summation, encouraging others to obtain professional assistance:

- o Facilitates prompt access to suitable treatment options and resources
- o Strengthens social support networks, promoting recovery and resiliency
- o Treats physical symptoms and promotes healthy lifestyle choices o Builds emotional resilience and promotes positive emotions
- o Boosts work performance and encourages a healthy work-life balance

You can make a significant difference in the lives of those around you by incorporating the knowledge and practical advice from this chapter into your daily activities. Encouraging loved ones to seek professional assistance not only empowers them on their path to improved mental health, but also contributes to a more supportive and understanding society in which mental health issues are acknowledged, accepted, and addressed with care and compassion.

Section VI.
Mind over Matter: Conclusion and Next Steps

Chapter 43:
Recap of Key Takeaways from This Book

As we conclude our voyage through the various facets of mental health and well-being, it is crucial to reflect on the book's key insights. You can take charge of your mental health and work towards a more balanced, fulfilling existence by comprehending and implementing the valuable insights and practical suggestions discussed throughout the chapters. In this chapter, we will enumerate the next actions you can take to prioritize your mental health and well-being and review the book's key principles.

Key Takeaways

- o **Understanding Mental Health:** Mental health incorporates our emotional, psychological, and social wellbeing. Understanding and addressing the complex interplay of factors, including genetics, environment, and lifestyle, is necessary for achieving good mental health.
- o **Recognizing Mental Health Conditions:** Awareness of prevalent mental health conditions, their symptoms, and available treatments is essential for early intervention and effective management.
- o **The Role of Genetics and Environment:** Both genetic and environmental factors contribute to our mental health; comprehending this relationship can assist us in making well-informed decisions regarding our mental health.
- o **Lifestyle and Mental Health:** Adopting a healthy lifestyle that includes regular exercise, a balanced diet, sufficient sleep, and stress management techniques can have a significant effect on our mental health and well-being as a whole.
- o **The Connection between Physical and Mental Health:** The Relationship Between Physical and Psychological Health: Physical and mental health are inextricably intertwined, and taking care of one frequently benefits the other.
- o **The Importance of Self-Care:** Self-care entails engaging in activities and routines that promote physical, emotional, and mental health. It is an essential component of maintaining mental health.
- o **Mindfulness and Meditation:** Mindfulness and meditation are potent instruments for reducing tension and anxiety and enhancing mental health as a whole. Developing a routine can have long-lasting positive effects on health.
- o **Managing Stress and Anxiety:** Effectively managing stress and anxiety is crucial for mental health, and various coping strategies can assist you in navigating difficult situations.
- o **Building Strong Relationships:** Healthy relationships are an essential element of mental health, and acquiring effective communication and conflict resolution skills can assist you in establishing and sustaining strong connections with others.

- ○ **Seeking Professional Assistance:** Understanding when to seek professional assistance and the different categories of mental health professionals available can have a significant impact on your mental health journey.

Next Steps

Consider the following measures to prioritize your mental health and well-being as you move forward:

- ○ **Evaluate Your Current Mental Health**: Evaluate your current mental health status and identify areas that may require improvement or additional care.
- ○ **Establish Realistic Objectives:** Establish specific, attainable objectives to address problem areas and better your mental health.
- ○ **Create a Personalized Plan**: Create a personalized plan that incorporates the strategies and practices discussed in this book, based on your specific requirements and preferences.
- ○ **Track Your Progression:** Regularly assess your progress and make any necessary adjustments to your plan to ensure continued growth and improvement.
- ○ **Seek Support:** Engage with friends, family, and support groups in order to share your experiences, gain insight from others, and receive encouragement.
- ○ **Remain Informed:** Continue to educate yourself on mental health and well-being by gaining access to additional resources and keeping abreast of the latest research and developments.

By comprehending this book's key insights and proactively prioritizing your mental health, you can achieve a more balanced, fulfilling existence. Remember that maintaining mental health is a journey that requires consistent effort, self-awareness, and social support. Embrace the power of mind over matter to effect positive, long-lasting change in your life.

Chapter 44:
Stay Encouraged

Closing and Final Thoughts

As this voyage comes to a close, it is important to reflect on the main insights garnered throughout this book and the vital role mental health plays in our lives. Our mental health is equally as important as our physical health, and together they form the basis for a satisfying, balanced life.

This book has examined various strategies, techniques, and practices to support and enhance mental health, including self-care, mindfulness, stress management, relationship-building, and obtaining professional assistance. Each of us is responsible for prioritizing our mental health, which is a lifelong endeavor requiring consistent effort, self-awareness, and flexibility.

It is crucial to keep in mind that the path to mental health is not a linear one. There will be ups and downs, successes and failures, but the key is to remain persistent, resilient, and kind to ourselves. Celebrate your progress, regardless of its size, and learn from your obstacles. When necessary, reach out to your support network and do not hesitate to seek professional assistance.

Remember that you are not alone as you proceed down this path. The pursuit of mental health and wellbeing is supported by a community of individuals, professionals, and resources. Continue to be receptive to learning, development, and self-improvement, and accept that your mental health is an ongoing priority.

It may be intimidating to incorporate the practices discussed in this book into your daily routine, but it's essential to start modest and build progressively. Developing new routines and behaviors requires time, persistence, and tolerance. Remember that enduring change is the result of consistent effort, and that it is never too late to prioritize your mental health.

To maintain motivation, establish attainable objectives and monitor your progress. Remember that self-care is a necessity, not a luxury. Maintain an open mind and experiment with numerous strategies and techniques to determine which ones work best for you. The journey towards improved mental health is ultimately profoundly personal and unique to each individual.

In conclusion, we encourage you to incorporate the insights and tools provided in this book into your daily existence. Prioritize your mental health and wellbeing, and equip yourself to live a balanced, happy, and fulfilling existence. The journey may be difficult, but the payoff is immeasurable. Remember that every step towards improved mental health is a step toward a better, more fulfilling existence. Embrace this voyage with optimism, courage, and the knowledge that putting your mental health first is one of the best investments you can make in your future.

Chapter 45:
How to Access Additional Resources and Support from Mentally Healthy

Connect with Us

In this final chapter, we will guide you on how to access additional resources and support from MentallyHealthy, an organization dedicated to promoting mental health awareness and providing valuable information and tools for individuals seeking to improve their mental well-being. One of the most accessible resources is the MentallyHealthy YouTube channel, which offers a wealth of educational content, practical tips, and inspiring stories to assist you on your mental health journey.

MentallyHealthy YouTube Channel

The MentallyHealthy YouTube channel (https://www.youtube.com/c/MentallyHealthy IPP) is an excellent resource for individuals seeking to deepen their understanding of mental health and well-being. The channel features a wide range of content designed to educate, inspire, and empower viewers, with playlists organized by topic for easy navigation. Here are some of the key playlists and resources available on the channel:

- **Mental Health Explained:** This playlist offers a series of informative videos that delve into various aspects of mental health, including understanding different mental health conditions, coping strategies, and tips for maintaining mental well-being.
- **Mindfulness and Meditation:** This collection of videos focuses on the practice of mindfulness and meditation, providing guided sessions, techniques, and insights into the benefits of these practices for mental health.
- **Self-Care and Well-Being:** This playlist is dedicated to self-care strategies and practices that can help you cultivate a balanced, healthy lifestyle. Videos cover topics such as sleep, nutrition, exercise, and stress management.
- **Building Strong Relationships:** In this playlist, you will find content on developing and maintaining healthy relationships, with tips on communication, conflict resolution, and empathy.
- **Personal Stories and Interviews:** This collection features inspiring personal stories and interviews with mental health professionals, advocates, and individuals who have overcome mental health challenges.

- ○ **Expert Series:** The Expert Series playlist offers in-depth discussions and presentations from mental health professionals, providing valuable insights into various aspects of mental health and well-being.
- ○ **Webinars and Workshops:** In this playlist, you'll find recorded webinars and workshops conducted by mental health professionals and experts, covering a variety of mental health topics and offering practical strategies to apply in your daily life.

To make the most of these resources, we recommend subscribing to the MentallyHealthy YouTube channel and enabling notifications to stay updated on new content. Additionally, you can engage with the community by leaving comments, asking questions, and sharing your experiences.

Other MentallyHealthy Resources

Besides the YouTube channel, MentallyHealthy also provides various resources and support through their website and social media platforms.

- o **Website:** Visit the MentallyHealthy Facebook Page (via Innovative Products | Portal) to access articles, blog posts, and links to additional resources on mental health topics. You can also find information on events, workshops, and support groups offered by MentallyHealthy.
- o **Newsletter:** Sign up for the MentallyHealthy newsletter to receive updates, event information, and exclusive content directly to your inbox. This is an excellent way to stay informed and motivated on your mental health journey. This is available to MH Club Members – visit the YouTube channel for more information.
- o **Social Media:** Stay connected with MentallyHealthy through their social media channels, such as Facebook, Instagram, and Twitter, to receive daily inspiration, tips, and news on mental health. Additionally, these platforms offer opportunities to engage with the MentallyHealthy community, share your experiences, and learn from others.
- o **Online Courses and Workshops:** MentallyHealthy will be offering online courses and workshops in the future that will provide in-depth guidance on specific. These courses and workshops will be offered and led by mental health professionals, experts, and experienced educators, ensuring that the content is reliable and effective. Stay connected to us for more information on this!
- o **Online Support Groups and Forums:** MentallyHealthy also hosts from time to time online support groups and forums, where individuals can connect with others facing similar mental health challenges. These groups provide a safe space to share experiences, seek advice, and receive encouragement from a supportive community. Visit our YouTube "Community Tab" for more information on this.
- o **Resource Library:** The MentallyHealthy is planning to offer a resource library that will contains a variety of downloadable resources, such as worksheets, guides, and checklists, that can help you implement the strategies and practices discussed throughout the book and in their other resources.
- o **Local Events and Workshops:** Keep an eye out for local events and workshops organized by MentallyHealthy or affiliated organizations. Attending these events can be an excellent opportunity to connect with others, learn new strategies, and deepen your understanding of mental health.

Continue Your Journey and Help Us Grow

As you continue on your journey towards improved mental health and well-being, remember that support and resources are available to help you navigate this path. The MentallyHealthy YouTube channel, community, and social media platforms offer valuable information, practical tips, and a supportive arena to encourage and inspire you along the way. Make the most of these resources, stay committed to your mental health journey, and remember that you are not alone in this pursuit of a healthier, more balanced life. We ask, in return, if this book did help you in some way, we'd love to hear from you about it. Honest reviews help readers find the right book for their needs. Thanks again for reading and supporting us at "MentallyHealthy!!"

As we always say, *"If You're Ready, Let's Get Started!"*

Section VII. INDEX

Printed in the USA
CPSIA information can be obtained
at www.ICGtesting.com
LVHW082040151023
761155LV00008B/600

9 798218 195953